SYNTHESIS AND ENGINEERING OF NANOSTRUCTURES BY ENERGETIC IONS

NANOTECHNOLOGY SCIENCE AND TECHNOLOGY

Additional books in this series can be found on Nova's website
under the Series tab.

Additional E-books in this series can be found on Nova's website
under the E-book tab.

SYNTHESIS AND ENGINEERING OF NANOSTRUCTURES BY ENERGETIC IONS

DEVESH KUMAR AVASTHI

AND

JEAN CLAUDE PIVIN

EDITORS

Nova Science Publishers, Inc.

New York

For permission to use material from this book please contact us:
Telephone 631-231-7269; Fax 631-231-8175
Web Site: http://www.novapublishers.com

NOTICE TO THE READER

Additional color graphics may be available in the e-book version of this book.

LIBRARY OF CONGRESS CATALOGING-IN-PUBLICATION DATA

Synthesis and engineering of nanostructures by energetic ions / editors,
Devesh Kumar Avasthi, Jean Cladude Pivin.
    p. cm.
 Includes bibliographical references and index.
 ISBN 978-1-62100-261-1 (softcover)
 1. Nanostructured materials--Design and construction. 2.
Nanostructures--Design and construction. 3. Ion bombardment--Industrial
applications. I. Avasthi, Devesh Kumar. II. Pivin, Jean Cladude.
 TA418.9.N35S969 2010
 620'.5--dc22
                                                            2010016725

Published by Nova Science Publishers, Inc. † New York

CONTENTS

PREFACE

Materials with nanometric dimensions such as nanodots, nanowire, nanotubes, functional structures, multi-layers of low dimensions, have unique properties, which can be tuned by varying their size. Therefore they have tremendous potentials for applications in various fields. The understanding of the properties of these low dimension systems is equally interesting and challenging. Ion irradiation is a powerful means for modifying the structure of thin films because of the out of equilibrium process of interaction and low dimension of the perturbed volume (irrespective of the slowing down mechanism: collision cascades at low energies or electronic excitations at high energies). The atomic disordering or extreme conditions of temperature and pressure generated during very short times may lead to the synthesis of materials with new properties. In addition, the induced modifications of structure may be adjusted via the nuclear or electronic energy loss of each ion and the ion fluence. Within the low energy regime, the generation of buried nanodots by ion implantation has become a standard tool. Ions of still lower energies (up to a few keV, available in plasma) are now commonly used to promote the nucleation of nano-particles or the texturing of thin films during their growth by physical vapor deposition. On the other hand, the columnar defects of nanometric size generated by swift heavy ions (which undergo only electronic stopping along their straight path) have high potential for the synthesis of nanowires. Membranes with pores of controlled size have been achieved by chemical etching of their tracks in polymers. An Indo French conference (sponsored by Indo French Centre for Promotion of Advanced Research, IFCPAR New Delhi) was organized under the theme of 'Nanostructuring by ion beams' where researchers with expertize in this focused area of research presented their work. It was realized that it would be a good idea to collect all the ideas of speakers and researchers in the form of a book with focus on the following topics.

(a) Ion beam synthesis of nanoparticles with low energy ions
(b) Generation of nanostructures by swift heavy ions
(c) Self-organization of surfaces and thin films by sputtering and diffusion processes
(d) Nanostructures synthesis by plasma assisted or sputtering deposition techniques
(e) Applications in biological and interdisciplinary areas

We sincerely hope that this collection of the articles in the book will be beneficial to those working in the field of nanomaterials, nanostructures, nanocomposite thin films etc., especially with ion beams. To our knowledge it is first collection of articles in the form of a book dealing with possible applications of ion beam in the field of nanotechnology. The transmission electron microscopy and surface microscopy being two most important tools for characterization of nanostructures are also discussed in the chapters Dr. P.V. Satyam and Dr. A. Tripathi. Some of the chapters deal with possible applications and theoretical modeling of the consequences of ion energy deposition in materials.

We are thankful to all the authors for their efforts and cooperation to bring out the research work and ideas in the form of articles. We acknowledge with thanks the help extended by Dr. Anjana Trivedi, Associate Professor, Head, department of English, Kanpur Vidya Mandir Post Graduate College, for language review at a glance. We must not forget to mention generous cooperation by Dr. D.C. Agarwal and Mr. R. Singhal for their help at different stages.

We express our heartfelt gratitude to Dr. Amit Roy, Director, IUAC Delhi for his ever encouraging attitude and support for research in materials science with emphasis on nanostructures with ion beams at IUAC Delhi. We take this opportunity to appreciate and thank Prof. Mehta (former Director of Nuclear Science Centre) for his vision to initiate research work in the field of materials science with ion beams at IUAC Delhi.

We extend our sincere thanks to various publishers (American Institute of Physics, Institute of Physics, Elsevier, American Physical Society, Springer, Ceramic Society of Japan, Springer, Royal Society Publishing, Trans Tech Publications, Indian Academy of Sciences) for granting permissions to authors for using their published figures and diagrams in their journals.

At last but not the least, we thank Nova Science publisher for cooperation in bringing out this book.

D.K. Avasthi

Inter University Accelerator Centre
Post Box 10502
New Delhi-110067
India

J.C. Pivin

CSNSM Orsay
France

A. SYNTHESIS OF NANOCOMPOSITE THIN FILM AND NANOSTRUCTURES AT SURFACE BY LOW ENERGY ION BEAMS

ISBN 978-1-62100-261-1
© 2012 Nova Science Publishers, Inc

Chapter 1

ENERGETIC ION BEAMS IN NANOSTRUCTURING: AN OVERVIEW

D.K. Avasthi

Inter University Accelerator Centre, Post Box 10502, New Delhi-110067, India

Energetic ions, depending on their mass and energy, have different roles in nanostructuring of materials. Broadly, the areas of research activities using ion beams in nanostructuring are: (i) synthesis of nanostructures and (ii) study of the modifications of existing buried nanoparticles in a matrix so as to explore the possibility of engineering the size and shape of the nanostructures. IUAC has the facilities to provide (i) 1-1.5 keV wide atom beam (2 inch diameter), used for synthesis of metal or semiconductor nanoparticles embedded in dielectric matrix and synthesis of nanostructures at the surface (ii) typically tens of keV to 1 MeV ions suitable for synthesis of buried nanoparticles and (iii) swift heavy ions (ions of energies from 50 MeV to 200 MeV, of mass up to ~200), used for synthesis and engineering the size and shape of the buried nanostructures. The ion beams in different energy regimes at IUAC, have been used in synthesis of metal-silica nanocomposites, ripples at surface and engineering the size and shape of nanoparticles embedded in silica matrix. The chapter gives an overview of different possible roles of ion beams in synthesis and engineering of nanostructures.

1. INTRODUCTION:

Nanotechnology is one of the fastest growing branches of science and technology for the last ten years or so, due to immense possibilities of applications in diversified areas. Huge funds are made available for this particular branch of science and technology by fund giving agencies all over the world. Nanoscience deals with small dimensions typically from 1 nm to 100 nm. The size dependent properties (physical as well as chemical) of nanomaterials make them attractive for applications as well as for the underlying physics. Technologists as well as Research and Development teams in industries/institutes are hunting for applications in various walks of life, whereas physicists look at the nanomaterials to fulfill their quest for basic understanding. Two basic challenges in nanotechnology are (i) to engineer the size and shape of nanoparticles and (ii) to control (preferably narrow down) the size distribution of nanoparticles. There are several methods to achieve the controlled synthesis of nanomaterials and nanostructures. Ion beams offer one of the possibilities with its unique features in synthesis and engineering of nanostructures. This chapter gives an overview of all possible routes of ion beams ranging in energy from a few hundred eV to a few hundred MeV in engineering the nanostructures.

Ion beams have special features which can be judiciously utilized in creating as well as modifying the materials of low dimension (nanomaterials). The specific feature of energetic ions is that they deposit a large energy density in a small volume. The ion beam processes have high degree of spatial selectivity. The energy of ions provides depth vise selectivity also, which means that the elements can be buried in a substrate at a desired depth, tunable by ion energy. The low energy ions typically up to a few MeV undergo elastic collisions (with rather small probability of inelastic collisions), while traversing the material. The elastic collisions result in recoils and point defects. If the incident ion mass and energy is high, the recoils have sufficient energy to produce subsequent recoils, which too can produce further recoils and thus a single ion can cause collision cascade. The elastic collisions near surface region can cause ejection/removal of an atom from the lattice and is referred to as sputtering. High energy (typically 1MeV/u or higher) ions, dominantly undergo inelastic collisions leading to excitation or ionization of atoms, and have low probability of elastic collisions. Such high energy heavy ion is called as swift heavy ion (SHI) and the velocity of SHI is comparable or more than the Bohr electron velocity. The energy lost in elastic collisions is referred to as nuclear energy loss, whereas the energy lost in inelastic collisions is referred to as electronic energy loss. Figures 1 and 2 give an idea of nuclear and electronic energy loss variation with ion energy and the corresponding ion trajectories.

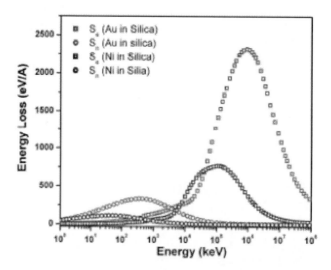

Figure 1. The variation of the nuclear energy loss (S_n) and the electronic energy loss (S_e) is plotted against ion energy for Au and Ni ions in silica. It shows that nuclear as well as electronic energy loss can be controlled by ion mass and energy.

a)

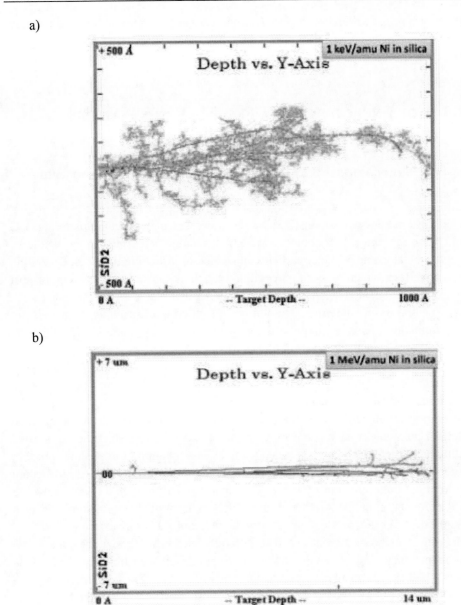

b)

Figure 2. SRIM simulations of six Ni ion impacts on silica are shown, indicating that (a) the trajectories of ions (of energy 1 keV/amu, i.e. 58 keV), are zig zag due to elastic collisions and subsequent collision cascade in nuclear slowing down regime, whereas (b) the swift Ni ions (of energy 1 MeV/amu, i.e. 58 MeV), undergo inelastic collisions and the ion paths are straight except at the end of range. It is to be noted that ion path is exactly straight near the surface region up to a few micrometers.

At low energies, the ion trajectories deviate from the straight path due to elastic collisions, while at high energies the ion trajectories are straight except at the end of ion range where the elastic collisions dominate. The consequence of ion traversal and their energy deposition is the determining factor for materials modification by ion beams. Low energy ions where nuclear energy loss dominates, produce defects due to recoils and collision cascade. SHI is capable of creating ion track, a narrow cylindrical zone typically of a few nm to 10 nm which is different from its surrounding region, (beyond certain threshold of electronic energy loss), in insulators, some semiconductors and metals. With this background, the role of ions in nanostructuring is discussed in order of increasing energy, with suitable examples.

2. ION OF ENERGIES UPTO A FEW MEV IN SYNTHESIS OF NANOSTRUCTURES

2.1. Synthesis of Nanocomposite Thin Films by Atom Beam Co-Sputtering

The ejection of atoms near surface region under ion impingement, known as sputtering [1], is exploited in thin film deposition [2,3] by the processes of ion beam sputtering, DC sputtering and RF sputtering. The noble metal and insulating material can be sputtered together to get the metal atoms or metal particles embedded in insulating matrices, depending on the metal volume fraction and deposition conditions such as substrate temperature or post deposition annealing treatment. The sputtering of insulating material is either possible by RF sputtering or by neutral beam sputtering. The ion beam sputtering of insulating matrix is not feasible due to formation of space charge at the surface of insulating material, repelling the subsequent incident ions. A neutral beam (atom beam) sputtering set up, as shown in figure 3, is designed and assembled at IUAC Delhi [4]. The atom beam source is preferred to the ion source, as the neutral beams produced by atom source do not produce the space charge at the insulating matrix and therefore the insulator target can be sputtered without any problem. The atom beam sputtering set up consists of an atom source in a vacuum chamber, a combination of turbo molecular pump and rotary pump for creation of vacuum, a substrate holder located below the sputtering target which can be rotated using an in-vacuum motor, at slow speed, to get uniform deposition. The voltage (0.5 to 2 kV) is given to the source through a vacuum feed through from the bottom of the chamber. The Ar gas is fed through a needle valve, to atom source for production of the Ar atom beam. The geometry of the atom source is such that it delivers the neutral beam as the ion produced, are neutralized before extraction.

The atom beam sputtering set up has been successfully used to synthesize the noble metal nanoparticles, semiconducting nanoparticles and magnetic nanoparticles embedded in insulating matrix [5-12]. The insulating matrices taken were silica, ZnO, polymer, etc. The noble metal nanoparticles have been characterized by absorption spectroscopy for surface plasmon resonance (SPR) and transmission electron microscopy for particle size determination. The Ag polymer (Ag-Polyethylene tetraphelate) nanocomposite thin films have been shown [6] to have optical properties suitable for application as UV filter, as shown in figure 4. The TEM picture of a thin Ag-PET nanocomposite thin film is shown in figure 5. Metal nanoparticles in silica matrix by coevaporation and by atom beam co-sputtering have been synthesized and studied. It has been shown that the nanocomposite thin film synthesized by atom beam co-sputtering is superior in terms of uniformity of metal contents [13]. In atom beam sputtering, the noble metal nanocomposite thin films grow without any subsequent annealing, whereas the thermal co-evaporation requires subsequent annealing for nucleation and growth of nanoparticles in silica matrix. The basic difference in the two methods is that the metal atoms arrive at the substrate with energy of a few eV in the case of atom beam sputtering, whereas in the thermal evaporation process the atoms arrive at the substrate with energies of about 0.1 eV.

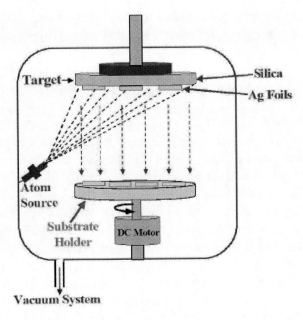

Figure 3. Schematic sketch shows an atom beam sputtering set up [from Ref. 4 copyright (2006) by Elsevier].

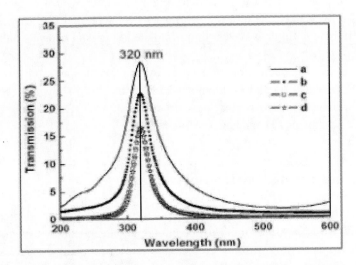

Figure 4. The optical transmission spectra of Ag-PET nanocomposites showing the UV filter characteristics of the nanocomposite thin film [Reprinted from Avasthi, D. K.; Mishra, Y. K.; Kabiraj, D.; Lalla, N. P.; and Pivin, J. C. *Nanotechnology* 2007, *18*, 125604., Copyright (2007) with permission from IOP Publishing Ltd.].

The atoms having higher energy arriving at the substrate in the case of atom beam sputtering enhance the surface and bulk diffusion resulting in the nucleation and growth of metal particles. When two metal atoms come in contact due to surface diffusion process, it forms a nucleation site (due to minimization of total free energy), which grows into a nanoparticle.

A chapter by S. Mohapatra [14] is devoted to the atom beam sputtering. The ion beam sputtering and RF sputtering processes are discussed in two separate chapters for applications in hard coatings and sensors by J.P. Riviere[15] and F. Alves [16] respectively.

2.2. Creation of Nanoripples at Surface by KeV Ion Beams

The basic interests in nanodots and nano ripples at surface is that (i) it can further act as a template for growing nanostructures (ii) the nanodots and the nanoripples can be engineered by the ion beam parameters [17-20] and (iii) the understanding of the creation such surface nanostructures and their correlation with the growth of thin films. The ion energies from a few hundred eV to a few hundred keV have been very effective for creation of such nano-dots and nano-ripples at the surface. The evolution of surface morphology leading to the nanostructures at surface, is a complex phenomenon [17], resulting from roughening and smoothing processes. The final surface morphology is determined by these two competing processes. Cuerno et al [18] gave a stochastic model to explain the structures induced by ion sputtering, where the surface morphology was suggested to be governed by the two simultaneous processes of surface diffusion and surface erosion.

An Ar atom beam of 1.5 keV has been used to create nano dots and nano ripples at the surface of Si and InP wafers [20], at IUAC Delhi. The dependence of the ripple wavelength on fluence and the incident angle were studied. Figure 6 shows typical ripples at the surface of InP bombarded by 1.5 keV Ar atoms performed by Sulania et al [20]. It was observed by Kulriya et al [20] that the ripple wavelength in irradiated Si crystal depends on the orientation of Si surface.

Detailed discussions on creation of ripples by ion beam sputtering are given in the chapters by P. Karmakar [21] and O. Plantevin [22]. It has been shown in recent years that swift heavy ion irradiation, too can cause nanostructures at the surface, which is dealt with, in chapters by D.C. Agarawal [23] and and T. Mohanty [24].

2.3. Buried Nanostructures by Ion Implantation

Ion implantation is the most versatile way to introduce a foreign element in the near surface region [25, 26] of a solid. High fluence implantation can lead to a supersaturated solid solution, which on annealing results in precipitation of implanted species resulting in formation of nanoparticles buried in the matrix. Nanoparticles of implanted species can be formed buried in the host matrix, if the two are immiscible. A compound may form, if the implanted atoms and the host matrix are miscible. The implanted samples may have to be annealed for the formation of nanoparticles of implanted species in the host matrix. The implantation at higher temperatures or the high beam current density can be used to achieve the dynamic annealing of the defects and growth of nanoparticles by radiation enhanced diffusion.

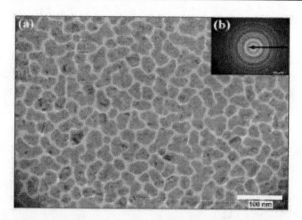

Figure 5. TEM micrographs of Ag - PET nanocomposite with 71 at. % Ag is shown. The corresponding diffraction rings are shown in the inset. Dark region represents the metal and the bright region represents the polymer [Reprinted from Avasthi, D. K.; Mishra, Y. K.; Kabiraj, D.; Lalla, N. P.; and Pivin, J. C. *Nanotechnology* 2007, *18*, 125604., Copyright (2007) with permission from IOP Publishing Ltd.].

Figure 6. AFM images showing nano ripples on InP (100) single crystal irradiated with 1.5 keV Ar atom at different fluences; the result from Sulania et al. Ref [20]. Z scale represents height of the nano features.

Since the depth profile of implanted species is Gaussian with high concentration in the centre of profile with low concentration at both the sides of the maxima, the size distribution and the inter particle separation varies with depth. The surface Plasmon resonance (SPR) of such metal nanocomposite system is broader because of the variation in the particle size with depth and the interaction between particles and mutual polarization effects.

The synthesis of nanoparticles by ion implantation has certain problems associated with sputtering. If the implantation is at low energies, the implanted species are near the surface and they can be sputtered during implantation. Therefore the maximum concentration of the implanted element becomes limited. To overcome this problem, one may opt for implantation at higher energies. However this will result in broadening of implanted species profile due to straggling and therefore the concentration of the implanted species decreases. An optimum choice has to be made for the energy of ion implantation. Implantation at several energies is also, a way to get broader but uniform depth profile of implanted species.

Details on the aspects of ion implantation for synthesis of buried nanostructures are given in chapters by H. Bernas [26], A. Claverie [27], E. Oliviero [28] and S. Ghosh [29]. Especially the chapter by H. Bernas deals with important issues on the control of size and size distribution by ion beams and the role of thermodynamics and chemistry. The chapter by E. Oliviero deals with the nanometric size Kr bubble formation in SiO_2, a novel approach for achieving low k dielectric materials.

2.4. Buried Nanostructures by Ion Beam Mixing

Ion beam mixing is a phenomenon where the elements across an interface in a bilayer are mixed together under the influence of the incident ion beam. The mechanism behind the low energy ion beam mixing is collision cascade, recoil implantation and radiation enhanced diffusion. The metal layer sandwiched between two layers of insulating matrix can be transformed to metal insulator nanocomposite thin films by ion irradiation up to a few MeV energy. The energy needs to be tuned in such a way that S_n is maximum at the interface. Details of this particular approach to get nanoparticles embedded in the matrix are in references [30, 31].

2.5. Precipitation Resulting from Electronic Energy Deposited by Ions

Ion irradiation induces selective release of H from H containing molecules and polymers, followed by a cross linking of the bonds. This leads to collapse of the molecular structure into an amorphous network of a-C:H, similar to diamond like carbon. The ion irradiation induced reduction process can lead to the formation of C nanoclusters. In the case of inorganic polymers and gels, consisting of metal-oxygen or metal-carbon chains with organic side groups, ion irradiation induces the segregation of C to form C nanodots. The size of C nanodots grows with ion fluence. It has been shown that the atomic collisions play no role in these transformations (H release, crosslinking and C segregation) and the electronic energy deposition is responsible for the segregation of C atoms (due to reduction process) to form C clusters [32].

Figure 7. TEM image shows C nanodots synthesized by 3 MeV Au ion irradiation of Si based gel [from Ref. 32 copyright (2005) by Elsevier].

Figure 7 shows the energy filtered TEM image indicating the C nano dots formed by irradiation of a gel with composition [Si(CH$_3$)(H)-0-]$_n$ [32] by 3 MeV Au ions. The C clusters are randomly distributed in the film because the ions experienced both the elastic and inelastic collisions. The S$_e$ induced reduction process leads to the formation of C clusters whereas the collision cascades due to S$_n$, caused the random and scattered distribution of these C clusters. If the energy is so high that the ion tracks are formed and S$_n$ is insignificant, the C nanodots precipitate along the in path in the track, resembling a nanowire, which is discussed in section 3.1. Further details on this aspect can be found in chapter by J.C. Pivin [33].

3. HIGH ENERGY (SWIFT HEAVY IONS) IN SYNTHESIS OF THE NANOSTRUCTURES

SHI can produce ion tracks in most of the insulators, some semiconductors and metals beyond certain threshold of electronic energy loss, S$_{eth}$, as discussed in the introduction. This specific feature is utilized (i) to synthesize nanostructures and (ii) to modify the existing nanoparticles into specific shapes. Figure 8 gives a schematic sketch about how the density of defects increases with S$_e$ and finally a track is formed [34] at a threshold S$_{eth}$. This unique feature of SHI of creating ion track is effectively exploited in creation of nanostructures as discussed below:

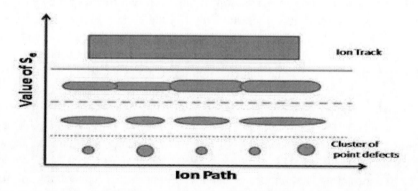

Figure 8. Schematic of ion track formation. Y-axis represents the value of S$_e$ and X-axis shows the ion path. A is the effective cross section of track [concept from Ref. 34].

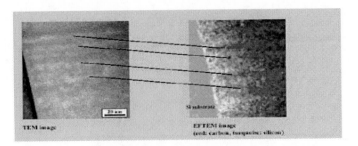

Figure 9. Cross sectional TEM picture shows the formation of C nanowire in Allylhydridopolycarbosilane thin film irradiated by 100 MeV Au ions. [Reprinted from Avasthi, Srivastava, S.K.; Avasthi, D.K.; Pippel, E.; Nanotechnology 2006, 17, 2518., Copyright (2006) with permission from IOP Publishing Ltd.].

3.1. Creation of Carbon Nanowire in Si Based Gels

It has been seen in section 2.5 that creation of nanodots of carbon occurs when the Si based gel are subjected to a large value of electronic and nuclear energy loss. The same system, in the case of irradiation with swift ions (S_n is negligible and S_e is more than S_{eth}), having a straight path in the material, results in the clusters aligned in strings along the tracks [35-37]. Several experiments on different Si based gels exhibited the formation of C clusters along the ion track. The C clusters have almost similar sizes for a given local density of transferred energy $S_e\phi$ (where S_e is the stopping power and ϕ is the ion fluence). The irradiated films exhibit a red luminescence, shifting from 2.1 to 1.7 eV as the clusters grow with fluence with maximum intensity of luminescence when the local deposited energy density is of the order of 30 eV per target atom. The C clusters seem to form almost continuous wires [37] as seen in figure 9 for 100 MeV Au ion irradiated thin film of Allylhydridopolycarbosilane.

3.2. Creation of Carbon Nanowires in Fullerene

Fullerenes are very sensitive to irradiation. It has been reported that the conductivity of the ion irradiated fullerene film increases suddenly beyond certain fluence, corresponding to the percolation of the ion tracks within the film plane [38, 39]. Each ion tack, due to damage of fullerene has amorphous and diamond like carbon which is more conducting than the fullerene film. It is therefore expected that each ion track across the film plane will have high conductivity. Since the conductivity in ion track region (due to amorphous carbon) is higher than the surrounding region of fullerene, it is like a conducting carbon nanowire. To observe these conducting nanowires, the irradiation needs to be done at lower fluence, far below the fluence required for track overlap. Figure 10 gives a conducting AFM image showing the conducting paths observed [40, 41] in fullerene film irradiated with 120 MeV Au ions at a fluence of 6×10^{10} ions/cm^2. The number of conducting nanowires (conducting ion tracks) is less than the ion fluence. The threshold voltage for recording an electrical conductivity (in conducting AFM) decreases with the increasing ion mass and stopping power and their diameter increases [42]. In principle, the diameter of the conducting nanowire can be tuned.

Formation of C nanowire like structures by low fluence swift heavy ion irradiation and their field emission studies are discussed in chapter by A. Tripathi [43].

3.3. Si and Ge Nanoparticles by SHI Irradiation of Si and Ge Suboxide

Thin films of SiO_x (silicon rich silicon oxide) were irradiated with swift heavy ions [44], resulting in the formation of Si nanocrystals. The ion irradiation causes evolution of oxygen from the film [45] and the possible reaction due to SHI was formation of Si nanocrystal within SiO_2 accompanied by release of oxygen. It is an interesting example of phase separation of Si and silica under dense electronic excitation due to reduction process. In the similar fashion, the formation of Ge nanocrystals by SHI irradiation of Ge rich germanium oxide thin film [46, 47] has also been observed. Figure 11 shows the X-ray diffraction (XRD) of ion irradiated (100 MeV Ag) of Ge rich germanium oxide (GeO_x), indicating the formation of nanoparticles as evident by the full width at half maximum (fwhm) of XRD peaks.

Synthesis of Si nanocrystals in silica by irradiation of Si rich silica is dealt in chapter by S.V. Bhoraskar [48].

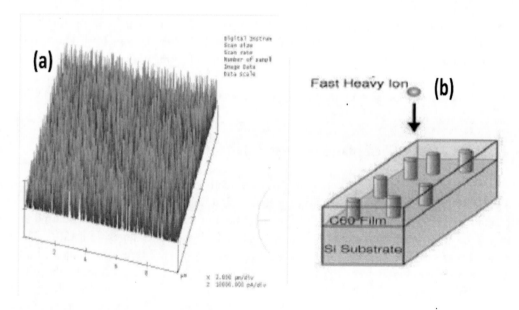

Figure 10. (a) CAFM image of C nanowire synthesized by SHI irradiation of thin fullerene film is shown [Reprinted with permission from, Kumar, A. et al, Journal of Applied Physics 2007, 101, 014308. Copyright [2007], American Institute of Physics', Ref 41]. The irradiation was by 120 MeV Au ions at fluence lower than required for overlapping of ion tracks. (b) It shows schematic of the formation of ion tracks in thin fullerene film at the places where the ion is passed through [from Ref. 40 copyright (2006) by Elsevier].

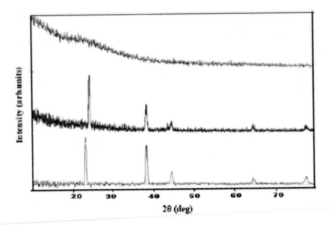

Figure 11. XRD shows the precipitation of Ge in silica matrix. [from Ref. 46 copyright (2007) by Elsevier].

3.4. Reduction of Copper Oxide Nanoparticles by SHI

The copper oxide nano particles having (both the phases CuO and Cu_2O) were subjected to large electronic excitation (24 keV/nm) generated by the 120 MeV Ag ions [49]. The X-ray diffraction of the irradiated samples revealed only Cu_2O, indicating that ion beam induced reduction occurred for the formation of Cu_2O. It is similar to the results of section 3.3, showing the reduction processes induced by electronic energy loss.

3.5. Latent Tracks as Templates for Nanostructures

The ion tracks especially in polymers can be chemically etched out preferentially and one can achieve nanopores with the density same as that of ion fluence. The diameter of nanopore can be controlled by the etching time. These etched nano or submicron pores can be used as templates to grow nanostructures of desired materials by electro-deposition [50]. The submicron pores can also be used in controlled drug delivery [51]. There have been various efforts to use the submicron pores in different possible ways [52-54]. Applications related to this concept are in chapter by J.C. Pivin [33].

3.6. Ion Tracks in Polymers for Grafting Functional Monomers

The functional monomers are often difficult to attach on the polymer surface. The ion tacks in polymers are used for grafting the functional monomers to the polymers. The modified region within the ion track has dangling bonds which on exposure to air forms bonds with oxygen of the air. The functional monomer can get attached to these modified chemical species in the track region [55, 56]. The attachment of functional monomer is verified by the contact angle measurements.

Details of ion beam irradiated polymers for grafting are in chapter by J.C. Pivin [33].

4. HIGH ENERGY (SWIFT HEAVY IONS) IN MODIFYING THE NANOSTRUCTURES

Metal nanoparticles embedded in silica matrix, (metal-silica nanocomposites) have attracted wide attention of researchers in recent years due to their unique properties, useful for diverse applications. The size, shape and inter particle separation of the nanoparticles in a matrix are the key parameters for the properties of the nanocomposite thin film. These parameters are mainly governed by the metal volume fraction. The particle size and shape are difficult to control for a given volume fraction, by deposition parameters. The swift heavy ion (SHI) beam provides unique possibility to engineer the size and shape of the nanoparticles in the metal dielectric matrix. A large number of experiments on Au-silica and Ag-silica nanocomposite thin films have been performed at IUAC Delhi and the results have similar trends in both the cases. Here the results of SHI irradiation of Au-silica nanocomposite thin films are briefed.

4.1. Engineering the Size of Buried Nanostructures

Two sets of Au silica NC thin films (A and B) were used for SHI irradiation. The films A were prepared by thermal co-evaporation and subsequent annealing at 900 C. The films B were prepared by atom beam co-sputtering [4]. The ion beams (90 MeV Ni and 100 MeV Ag) were used for irradiation at fluences ranging from from 10^{12} ions/cm^2 to 10^{14} ions/cm^2. Rutherford backscattering was performed to determine the metal to silica ratio in the films. The samples (pristine and irradiated films) were characterized by UV-Vis absorption spectroscopy, transmission electron microscopy (TEM) and X-ray diffraction. Depending on the particle size and inter particle separation, the reduction and growth of particle size were observed. These are discussed as follows:

The Au-silica NC thin films with metal fraction of 5 at. % (films A) was irradiated with 100 MeV Ag ions. The TEM pictures of the pristine and irradiated (at a fluence of 10^{13} ions/cm^2) samples on TEM grids showed that the particle size reduced from 11 nm to about 5nm, as shown in figure 12..The absorption spectra too revealed [57] the decrease in particle size, which was evident by increase in full width at half maximum (FWHM), shown in figure 13.

The Au-silica NC thin films B (synthesized by atom beam co-sputtering) with metal fraction of about 19.6 at. %) were irradiated with 90 MeV Ni ions, up to a fluence of 10^{14} ions/cm^2 and in-situ XRD [58] was performed at different fluences [59] as shown in figure 14. The decrease in the FWHM of the diffraction peak with fluence was observed, which is signature of the growth of average particle size. This was further confirmed by the cross sectional TEM of the pristine and irradiated sample. The growth of Au nanoparticles from an average size of 4 nm to 9 nm was observed.

An estimate of average inter particle separation is made, considering the metal fraction, Au packing fraction in unit cell and the average particle size. For the cases A and B, the average inter particle separations (from surface to surface) are 14.2 nm and 2.1 nm respectively. It is noticed that the increase or decrease in size of Au nanoparticles with ion irradiation, depend on the inter particle separation which is determined by the metal fraction, deposition conditions and post deposition treatments. When the inter particle separation is large, decrease in particle size is observed as evident from TEM in figure 12. The corresponding UV-Vis spectra are shown in figure 13, supporting the decrease in particle size with ion irradiation. On the other hand, when the inter particle separation is small, an increase in size of Au nanoparticles is observed, as evident by the figure 14. The growth/reduction in particle size in the metal-silica nanocomposite thin film can be explained as follows.

The passage of ion through silica creates a molten cylindrical zone for a typically ps time, according to thermal spike model [60, 61]. It can be recalled that although the melting point of Au is 1337 K (lower than the melting point 1800 K of silica), still the bulk Au remains unaffected by the SHI irradiation, due to very high thermal conductivity. However the Au in nanodimensions has lower melting point [62]. For example the melting point of Au nanoparticle of 6 nm diameter is around 900 K. It is therefore expected that Au particle will also in the transiently molten ion track of silica, which results in its dissolution. During this process of dissolution, the Au atoms from Au nanoparticles diffuse out to silica matrix and become a solid solution in silica as shown in schematic in figure 15. If the separation among the particle is large, the Au atoms do not find another particle nearby and remain in silica as solid solution. However if the separation between the nanoparticle is small, the diffusing Au atoms precipitate on nearby Au nanoparticle, which results in growth of particle as shown in schematic in figure 16. Thus large size Au nanoparticles grow at the expense of small size particles.

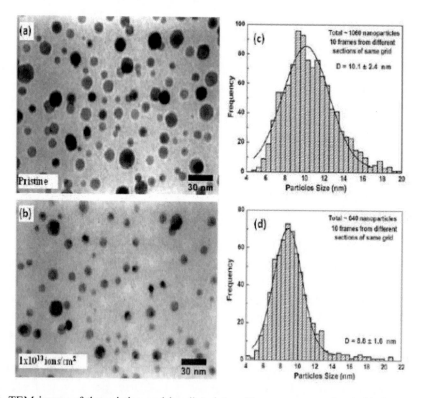

Figure 12. TEM image of the pristine and irradiated Au-silica nanocomposite (with low Au content), indicating reduction of Au particles under SHI (Ag ions at two fluences) irradiation [from Ref. 63 copyright (2010) by Elsevier].

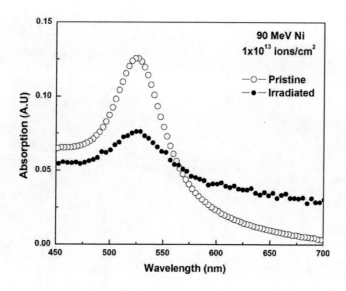

Figure 13. The absorption spectrum of the pristine and irradiated film is shown, indicating the dissolution and reduction in size of Au nanoparticles by SHI irradiation. The particle size reduction is evident by increase in the fwhm of absorption peak [from the results of Ref 57].

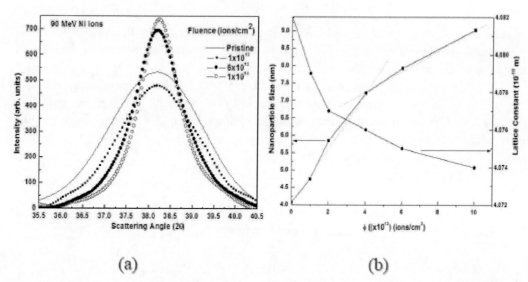

(a)   (b)

Figure 14. Figure shows the ripening of Au particles in silica matrix by 90 MeV Ni irradiation as observed by in-situ XRD. The film had 19.6 at. % Au ['Reprinted with permission from, Mishra, Y. K. et al., *Appl. Phys. Lett.* 2007,*90,* 73110., Copyright [2007], American Institute of Physics', Ref.60].

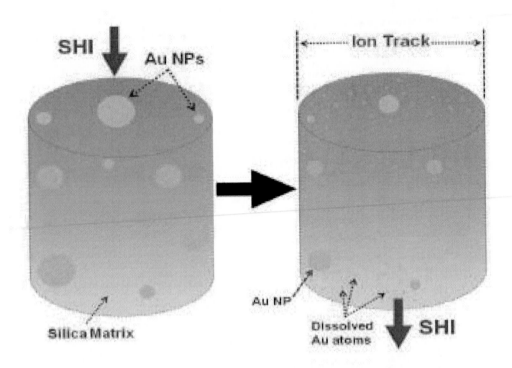

Figure 15. Schematic shows the dissolution of Au nanoparticles leading to the reduction in size of nanoparticles [from Ref. 63 copyright (2010) by Elsevier].

The increase or decrease in particle size, observed by us, is due to diffusion of Au atoms in transiently molten silica created by ion beam. This explanation of increase or decrease of nanoparticle size by ion irradiation, can be tested quantitatively as follow:

The diffusivity of Au atoms in silica ion track can be determined using the experimental data of change in particle size, ion fluence along with theoretically estimated ion track size and duration of transiently molten silica by the following relation [63]. The values of last two quantities are determined by calculations of thermal spike model.

$$D = \Delta (d^2) / 2 \times t_d$$

where $\Delta (d^2)$ is the difference of square of the initial (pristine) and final diameter (at fluence Φ) of nanoparticle, t_d is the diffusion time and is given by

$$t_d = (\Phi/\Phi_c) \times t_s$$

Φ_c is the fluence where overlap of ion tracks occur and t_s is the duration of temperature spike (or molten phase of silica). The value of Φ_c is estimated using the ion track diameter in silica as (πr^2), where r is the ion track radius. Using the experimental results, the value of D is found to be 10^{-6} to 10^{-8} m^{2}s^{-1}, which is in agreement with the liquid state diffusivity. Therefore the hypothesis of the correlation of the change (reduction or growth) of Au nanoparticles with the diffusion of Au atoms in transiently melt silica, is justified.

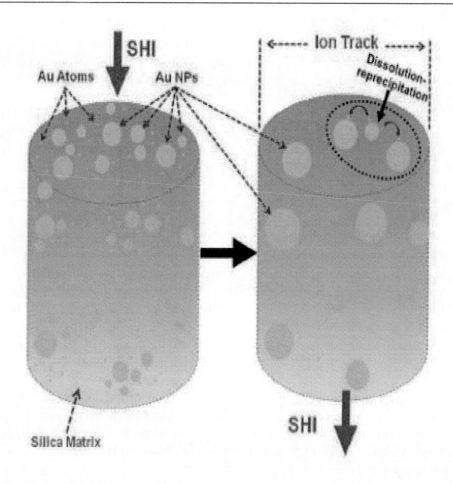

Figure 16. Schematic shows growth of Au nanoparticle when the interparticle separation is rather small [from Ref. 63 copyright (2010) by Elsevier].

4.2. Engineering the Shape of Nanoparticles Embedded in Silica

The importance of elongated, non spherical particles is due to occurrence of the longitudinal and transverse plasmon oscillations, depending on the direction of electric vector of the electromagnetic wave. The plasmon frequency differs for transverse and longitudinal modes and hence the absorption peak, whereas in case of spherical particles, the plasmon frequency remains the same because of spherical symmetry and is independent of the direction of electric vector of electromagnetic wave.

The Au-silica NC thin film, with metal fraction of 15 at.% (synthesized by RF co-sputtering and subsequent annealing), were irradiated with 120 MeV Au ions at a fluence of 3×10^{13} ions/cm^2. The cross sectional TEM of the pristine and irradiated samples (figure 17) shows the elongation of Au nanoparticles along the beam direction [64]. Since it is observed that the small size particles remain spherical, it can be stated that the elongation in nanoparticles occurs when the diameter is quite large as compared to track size. The observation of elongation in Au nanoparticles under SHI irradiation has also been observed by several other groups: Awazu et al [65], Rizza et. al. [66], Dawi et al. [67] and Roorda et al. [68]. The summary of the results on elongation of Au nanoparticles, from our group along with synthesis details are shown in figure 18, giving a summary of the aspect ratios plotted against the product of S_e and the fluence. Here a clear distinction is made among various types of nanostructures. The core shell system consists of an Au spherical core and a shell of silica surrounding it. A two and three dimensional nanocomposite thin films are (i) single layer of nanoparticles in two dimensions, buried in silica thin film, made by sequential thin film deposition of thin metal layer and silica on silica substrate and subsequent annealing and (ii) several random layers of Au nanoparticles embedded in silica matrix which could be synthesized by ion implantation of Au in silica or by co-sputtering of Au and silica respectively. It is noticed that SHI irradiation induces highest aspect ratio in the core shell particles followed by three dimensional and the two dimensional nanocomposite thin films.

The ion beam induced elongation of Au nanoparticles can be explained in different ways. One of them was proposed by Roorda et al [68] to explain the shape deformation of Au-silica core-shell nanoparticles by swift heavy ion irradiation. It was suggested that the silica under swift heavy ion bombardment, gets compressed in the beam direction and gets expanded in plane perpendicular to the ion beam, which is a consequence of hammering effect [69]. The pressure exerted by silica results in compression of the Au nanoparticle causing shape transformation from spherical to elliptical with major axis along the beam direction. However, if we consider this mechanism, then the elongation should take place, irrespective of nanoparticle size, except for very big size particles, where the pressure is not enough to cause any deformation. Since we observed in our experiments that the small size particles remain spherical, therefore this particular mechanism is not favorable to explain the ion beam induced elongation in Au silica nanocomposite thin film.

The second possibility is that the growth of the particle occurs, only in that part of nanoparticle, which is in contact with transiently molten silica as shown in figure 19. At a fluence of $3x10^{13}$ ions/cm^2, the nanocomposite thin film has about thirty overlaps of ion tracks. For Au nanoparticles smaller or comparable to the ion track diameter in silica, there is isotropic growth or reduction in particle size depending on the inter particle separation and there is no shape change.

Third possible explanation considers the volume expansion coefficient of Au and silica in molten state. It is known that the volume expansion of Au in transformation from solid to molten state, is more than that for silica under similar transformation. Therefore the elongation of Au nanoparticle (larger than the ion track size) along ion track is expected. Recent MD simulations [70] reveal low density region in the ion track of silica and this too, favors the elongation of Au nanoparticle along the ion track.

Swift heavy ion induced changes in of Ag and other metal nanoparticles in silica have been thoroughly studied [71, 72, 73] along with the possible mechanism.

The explanation of the dissolution, growth and elongation of Au particles under SHI bombardment is discussed under thermal spike model in a chapter by J.P. Stoquert [74]. The change of size and shape as well as matrix by ion irradiation has effect on the optical properties of the metal dielectric nanocomposite thin films.

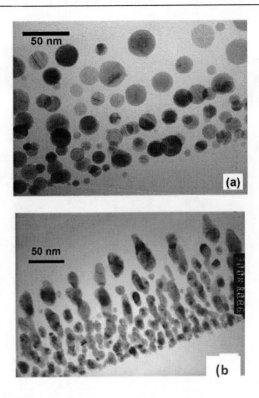

Figure 17. (a) Elongation of Au nanoparticles embedded in silica by SHI irradiation is clearly evident by cross sectional TEM image. (b) The cross sectional TEM image of the pristine Au-silica thin film ['Reprinted with permission from, Mishra, Y. K. et al., Appl. Phys. Lett. 2007, *91*, 63103, Copyright [2007], American Institute of Physics', Ref. 65].

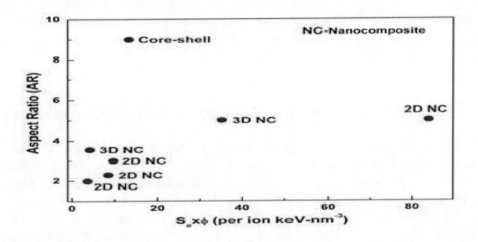

Figure 18. Summary of the results by different groups on the elongation of Au nanoparticles by SHI irradiation is shown [from Ref. 68 copyright (2010) by Elsevier].

22   D. K. Avasthi

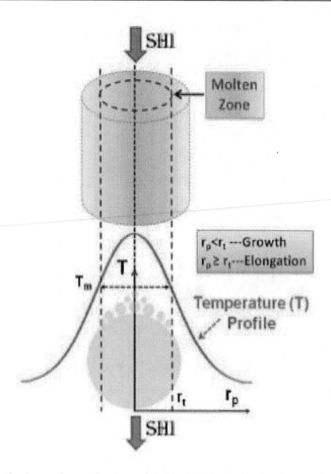

Figure 19. Schematic shows the mechanism of shape transformation in the transiently melt silica ion track [from Ref. 63 copyright (2010) by Elsevier]. The diameter of the Au nanoparticle is larger than the track diameter.

The aspects related with modification in optical properties of noble metal-Carbon nanocomposite thin films in the SHI irradiation are discussed as tuning of surface plasmon resonance by Singhal and Avasthi [75].

4.3. Influence of SHI on Magnetic Nanoparticles of Fe Embedded in Silica

There are applications such as magnetic recording where the plane of magnetization is preferred to be perpendicular to the film plane. It has been shown in recent SHI irradiation experiments that the plane of magnetization can be tilted from in plane to out of plane (perpendicular to the film plane) in the silica film containing the Fe particles at a moderate fluence of 10^{13} ions/cm^2 [76, 77]. The TEM investigations did not reveal elongation of alignment of particles. It is believed that the stress on the particles due to the hammering effect [69] must have been the cause of the tilt of magnetization plane. Figure 20 gives the ESR measurements showing the tilt of the plane of magnetization plane.

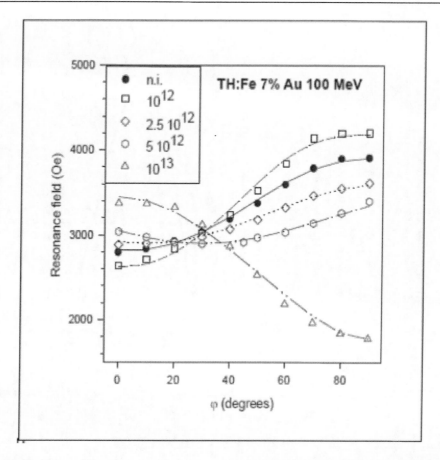

Figure 20. Variation of the electron spin resonance (ESR) field as a function of the angle between the field and the surface in silica containing 7 at% Fe irradiated with 100 MeV Au ions, at different fluences in the frame (n.i. is for non irradiated). Since the minimum field indicates the easy axis, the irradiated sample shows the out of plane magnetization, indicating the tilt of easy magnetization axis ['Reprinted with permission from Pivin,J.C. et al., J. Appl. Phys. 2005, 98, 023908; Copyright [2007], American Institute of Physics', Ref. 76].

5. FOCUSED ION BEAMS FOR NANO STRUCTURES

The current state of art is the focused ion beams of diameter down to 5 nm. Theory as well as details of micro and nano machining are discussed in reviews and books [78-81]. The focused ion beams due to their nanometric spatial dimension are excellent tools for creating desired nanostructures at small scales for research and fundamental goals. A few focused ion beam facilities have been set up in India and one such set up at Indian Institute of Kanpur is discussed in a chapter by V.N. Kulkarni [82].

The other topics in the book, are basics of TEM and surface microscopy, citing suitable samples, by P.V. Satyam [83] and A. Tripathi [43] respectively, effect of ion radiation on biomaterials by S.N. Kalkura [84] and MD simulations by S. Mookherjee [85].

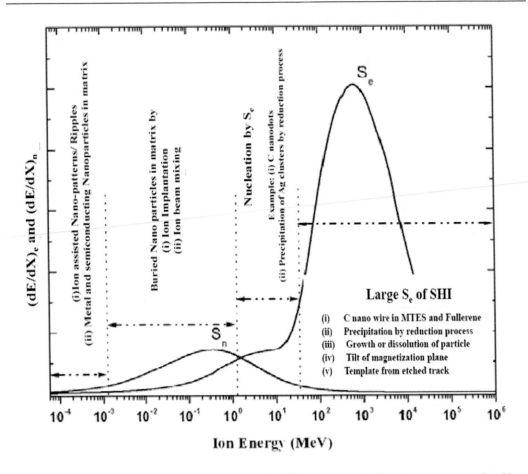

Figure 21. Sketch indicating the role of ion beams in different energy regimes in nanostructuring [from Ref. 86]. The regions are divided as guideline only. There are no sharp demarcations from one region to another region.

CONCLUSION

Various possibilities and aspects of synthesis and engineering of nanostructures by energetic ions are summarized [86] in figure 21 and are discussed in various sections. Low energies of a few keV are useful in creating nanostructures at surface and nanocomposite thin films. Ion energies of a few hundred keV and a few MeV have been tools for creating embedded nanostructures by ion implantation and ion beam mixing. Ion beam induced reduction process is effective in synthesizing nanostructures. Swift heavy ions are capable of producing controlled nanowires and can engineer the size and shape of embedded nanostructures. The focused ion beam is unique tool for creating nanostructures of any shape. The nano dimensional ion beam will also play a crucial role in characterization of nanoparticles, where the composition and structure can be probed at nano scale.

ACKNOWLEDGMENTS

I am thankful to the Indo French Centre for Promotion of Advanced Research (IFCPAR), New Delhi for its financial support to the project 'Nano phase generation by energetic ion beams' and to the Department of Science and Technology (DST) for providing a financial support to the project 'Intensifying research in high priority areas' IRHPA and project titled 'Nanostructuring by energetic ions', a Nano Mission project. I owe special thanks to J.C. Pivin for his suggestions and excellent collaborative work with him. I am thankful to all my collaborators D. Kabiraj, A. Tripathi, F. Singh, S.A. Khan, P. Kulriya, I. Sulania, S. Ghosh, S.K. Srivastava, S. Mohapatra, A. Kumar, Y.K. Mishra, D.C. Agarwal, R. Singhal and U. Singh who actively contributed to this fascinating field of research. I am grateful to A. Roy, Director, IUAC for his encouragement to excel in research.

REFERENCES

[1]   Ziegler, Z.F.; Biersack, J. P. [www.srim.org].

[2]   Krishnaswamy, S.V.; Rieger, J.H.; Doyle, N.J.; Francomve, M. H.; *J. Va. Sci. Tecnol.* 1987, *A5*, 2106.

[3]   Preparation of thin films by George, J; Marcel Dekker Inc., New York 1992.

[4]   Kabiraj, D.; Abhilash, S. R.; Vanmarcke, L.; Cinausero, N.; Pivin, J. C.; and Avasthi, D. K. *Nucl. Instr. and Meth. B* 2006, *244*, 100-104.

[5]   Mishra, Y. K.; Mohapatra, S.; Kabiraj, D.; Mohanta, B.; Lalla, N. P.; Pivin, J. C.; and Avasthi, D. K. *Scripta Mater.* 2007, *56*, 629-632.

[6]   Avasthi, D. K.; Mishra, Y. K.; Kabiraj, D.; Lalla, N. P.; and Pivin, J. C. *Nanotechnology* 2007, *18*, 125604.

[7]   Mishra, Y. K.; Mohapatra, S.; Singhal, R.; Avasthi, D. K.; Agarwal, D. C.; and Ogale, S. B. *Appl. Phys. Lett.* 2008, *92*, 043107.

[8]   Mohapatra, S.; Mishra, Y. K.; Kabiraj, D.; Avasthi, D. K.; Ghatak, J.; and Verma, S. *Appl. Phys. Lett.* 2008, *92*, 103105.

[9]   Mohapatra, S.; Mishra, Y. K.; Avasthi, D.K.; and Kabiraj, D.; Ghatak, J.; and Verma, S. *J. Phys. D: Appl. Phys.* 2007, *40*, 7063-7068.

[10] Mohapatra, S; Mishra, Y.K.; Ghatak, J.; Kabiraj, D.; and Avasthi, D.K. *J. Nanosci. and Nanotech.* 2008, *8*, 4285-4289.

[11] Agarwal, D.C.; Singh, F.; Kabiraj, D.; Sen, S.; Kulriya, P.K.; Sulania, I.; Nozaki, S; Chauhan, R.S.; and Avasthi, D.K. *J. Phys. D: Appl. Phys.* 2008, *41*, 045305.

[12] Mishra, Y. K.; Mohapatra, S.; Avasthi, D. K.; Kabiraj, D.; Lalla, N. P.; Pivin, J. C.; Sharma, H.; Kar, R.; and Singh, N. *Nanotechnology* 2007, *18*, 345606.

[13] Warang, T. N.; Kabiraj, D.; Avasthi, D.K.; Jain, K.P.; Joshi, K.U.; Narsale, A.M.; Kothari, D.C. *Surf. and Coatings Tech.* 2009, *203*, 2506-2509.

[14] Mohapatra, S; Kabiraj, D.; and Avasthi, D.K. Chapter in this book

[15] Rivier, J.P.; Akbari, A.; Templier, C. Chapter in this book

[16] Alves, F.; AbiRached, L.; Le Bihan, Y.; Moulin, J.; Gergam, E.D.; Schwebel, C.; Gupta, A.; Reddy, V.R. Chapter in this book

[17] Rusponi, S.; Costantini, G.; Boragno, C.; and Valbusa U. *Phys. Rev. Lett.* 1998, *81*, 2735. and Rusponi, S.; Costantini, G.; Boragno, C.; and Valbusa, U. *Phys. Rev. Lett.* 1997, *78*, 2795.

[18] Paramanik, D.; and Verma, S. *Nucl. Instr. and Meth.* B 2006, *244*, 69 and Karmakar, P; and Ghose D.; *Surface Sci.* 2004, *554*, L101. Karmakar, P.; Mollick, S.A.; Ghose, D.; and Chakrabarti, A. *Appl. Phys. Lett.* 2008, *93*, 103102.

[19] Cuerno, R.; Makse, H. A.; Tomassone, S.; Harrington, S. T.; and Stanley, H. E. *Phys. Rev. Lett.* 1995, *75*, 4464.

[20] Sulania, I.; Tripathi, A.; Kabiraj,D.; Verma, S.; Avasthi, D.K. Int. J. Nanoscience and Nanotechnology 2008, *8*, 4163-4167 and Kulriya, P.; Tripathi, A.; Kabiraj, D.; Khan, S.A.; and Avasthi, D.K. *Nucl. Instr. and Meth. B* 2006, *244*, 95.

[21] Karmakar, P. Chaper in this book

[22] Plantevin, O.; Gago R.; Vázquez, L.; Biermanns, A.; Carbone, D.; and Metzger, T.H. Chapter in this book

[23] Agarwal, D.C.; Chauhan, R.S. Chapter in this book

[24] Mohanty, T. Chapter in this book

[25] Use of ion beams to produce or modify nanostructures in materials, Pivin, J.C.; in "Nanomaterials: New Research", ed. B.M. Caruta (Nova Science Publishers, Inc, 2005), chapter 2, pp 81-113. and Pivin, J.C.; Singh, F.; Kumar, A.; Patel, M.K.; Avasthi, D.K.; Dimova-Malinovska, D.; in "Nanostructured Materials for Advanced Technological Applications", NATO Science Series B: Physics and Biophysics, ed. J.P. Reithmaier, P. Petkov, W. Kullisch, C. Popov, Springer Dordrecht Netherland 2009, p145 .

[26] Bernas, H. and Lamaëstre, R.E. de chapter in this book,

[27] Claverie, A.; Bonafos, C; Carles, R.; Schamm, S.; Arbouet, A.; Vincent Paillard, V.; Benassayag, G. chapter in this book

[28] Oliviero, E.; Décamps, B; Ruault, M.O.; Kaitasov, O. and Ntsoenzok, E. Chapter in this book

[29] Ghosh, S. Chapter in this book

[30] Pivin, J.C.; Garcia,M.A.; Hofmeister, H.; Martucci,A.; Sendova Vassileva M.; Nikolaeva, M.; Kaitasov,O. ; Llopis, J. *Euro. Phys. Journal* D 2002, *20*, 251.

[31] Pivin, J.C. *Mat. Sci. Engineer* A 2000, *293*, and Pivin, J. C.; García, M. A.; Hofmeister, H.; Martucci, A.; Vassileva, M. S.; Nikolaeva, M.; Kaitasov O.; Lopis, J. *Eur. Phys. J.* D 2002, *20*, 251.

[32] Pivin, J. C.; Pippel, E.; Woltersdorf, J.; Avasthi, D. K.; Srivastava, S. K.; Zeitschrift fur Metallkunde 2001, *92*, 7. and Pivin, J. C.; Avasthi, D. K.; Singh, F.; Kumar, A.; Pippel, E.; and Sagon, G.; *Nucl. Instr. and Meth.* B 2005, *236, 73*.

[33] Pivin, J. C. and Chlochord, M.C. Chapter in this book

[34] Toulemonde, M.; Nucl. Instr. And Meth. B 1999,156, 1.

[35] Kumar, A.; Singh, F.; Pivin, J. C.; Avasthi, D.K. *Journal of Applied Physics* D 2007, *40*, 2083.

[36] Seki, S.; Maeda, K.; Tagawa, S.; Kudoh, H.; Sugimoto, M.; Morita, Y.; and Shibata, H.; *Adv. Mater.* 2001, *13*, 1663. and Pivin, J.C.; Vincent, E.; Esnouf, S.; Dubus, M. *E. Phys. J.* B. 2004, *37*, 329.

[37] Srivastava, S.K.; Avasthi, D.K.; Pippel, E.; Nanotechnology 2006, 17, 2518.

[38] Bajwa, N.; Dharamvir, K.; Jindal, V. K.; Ingale, A.; Avasthi, D. K.; Kumar, R.; Tripathi, A. *J. Appl. Physics* 2003, *94*, 326. and Bajwa, N.; Ingale, A.; Avasthi, D. K.;

Kumar, R.; Tripathi, A.; Dharamvir, K.; Jindal, V. K.; *J. Appl. Physics* 2008, *104*, 054306.

[39] Singhal, R.; Kumar, A.; Mishra, Y. K.; Mohapatra, S.; Pivin, J. C.; Avasthi, D. K. *Nucl. Instr. And Meth. in Phys. Res.* B 2008, *266*, 3257. and Singhal, R.; Singh, F.; Tripathi, A.; Avashti, D. K.; *Radiation Effects and Defects in Solids* 2009,*166*, 38.

[40] Tripathi, A.; Kumar, A.; Singh, F.; Kabiraj, D.; Avasthi, D. K.; and Pivin, J.C. *Nucl. Instr. and Meth.* B 2005, *236*,186. and Tripathi, A.; Kumar, A.; Kabiraj, D.; v, S.A.; Baranwal, V.; and Avasthi, D. K. *Nucl. Instr. and Meth.* B 2006, *244*, 15.

[41] Kumar, A.; Avasthi, D.K.; Tripathi, A.; Kabiraj, D.; Singh, F.; Pivin, J. C. *Journal of Applied Physics* 2007, *101*, 014308.

[42] Kumar, A.; Avasthi, D. K.; Tripathi, A.; Filip, L. D.; Carey, J. D.; Pivin, J. C. *J. Appl. Phys.* 2007, *102*, 044305.

[43] Tripathi, A. Chapter in this book

[44] Chaudhari, P. S.; Bhave, T. M.; Kanjilal, D.; and Bhoraskar, S. *J. Appl. Phys.* 2003, *93*, 3486.

[45] Arnold, W.M.; Zeijlmans, V.E.; and Habraken, F.H.P.M.; Phys. Rev. Lett. 2005, 94, 245504.

[46] Rath, S.; et al. *Nucl. Instr. and Meth. in Phys. Res.* B 2007, *263*, 419.

[47] Batra, Y.; Mohanty, T.; Kanjilal, D. *Nucl. Instr. and Meth. in Phys. Res.* B 2008, *266*, 3107. and Rao, N. S.; Dhamodaran, S.; Pathak, A. P.; Kulriya, P. K.; Mishra, Y. K.; Singh, F.; Kabiraj, D.; Pivin, J. C.; Avasthi, D. K. *Nucl. Instr. and Meth. in Phys. Res.* B 2007, *264*, 249.

[48] Bhraskar, S. V.; et al Chapter in this book

[49] Balamurugan, B.; Mehta, B. R.; Avasthi, D. K.; Singh, F.; Arora, A. K.; Rajalakshmi, M.; Raghvan, G.; Tyagi, A. K.; and Shivaprasad, S. M. *J. Appl. Phys.* 2002, *92*, 3304.

[50] Martin, C.R. *Adv. Mater.* 1991, *3*, 457.

[51] Rao, V.V.; Amar, J.V.; Avasthi, D. K.; Charulu, R. N. *Radiation Measurements* 2003, *36*,585.

[52] Wade, T. L.; and Wegrowe, J. E. *European Physical Journal – Applied Physics* 2005, *29*, 3-22.

[53] Kulshrestra, V.; Acharya, N.K.; Awasthi,K.; Singh, M.; Avasthi, D.K.; Vijay, Y.K. International Jl. Oh Hydragen Energy (in press)

[54] *Ohgai, T.; Hoffer, X.; Gravier, L.; Wegrowe, J. E.; and Ansermet, J. P.; Nanotechnology 2003,14 , 978.*

[55] Chawla, S.; et al. *J. Appl. Polym. Sci.* 2007,*105*, 3578.

[56] Ferain, E.; and Legras, R. *Nuclear Instruments and Methods in Physics Research B* 2003, *208*,115.

[57] Mishra, Y. K.; Kabiraj, D.; Avasthi, D. K.; Pivin, J. C. *Radiation Effects and Defects in Solids* 2007,*162*, 207.

[58] Kulriya, P. K.; Singh, F.; Tripathi, A.; Ahuja, R.; Kothari, A.; Dutt, R. N.; Mishra, Y. K.; Kumar, A.; Avasthi, D. K. *Rev. Sci. Instr.* 2007, *78*, 113901.

[59] Mishra, Y. K.; Avasthi, D. K.; Kulriya, P. K.; Singh, F.; Kabiraj, D.; Tripathi, A.; Pivin, J. C.; Bayer, I. S.; Biswas, A. *Appl. Phys. Lett.* 2007,*90*, 73110.

[60] Wang, Z. G.; Dufour, Ch.; Paumier, E.; and Toulemonde, M. *J. Phys. Condens. Matter* 1994, *6*, 6733; ibid. 1995,*7*, 2525.

[61] Wang, Z. G.; Dufour, Ch.; Paumier, E.; and Toulemonde, M. *J. Phys. Condens. Matter* 1995,*7*, 2525.

[62] Cortie, M. B.; and Lingen, E. van der *Mat. Forum* 2002, *26, 1*.

[63] Avasthi, D. K.; *Invited talk at International conference on Radiation Efeects in Insulators*, 2009 Aug. 30th to Sept. 4th, Padova. In Nucl. Ionstr. And Meth. B 2010, 268, 3027.

[64] Mishra, Y. K.; Singh, F.; Avasthi, D. K.; Pivin, J. C.; Malinovska, D.; Pippel, E. *Appl. Phys. Lett.* 2007,*91*, 63103.

[65] Awazu, K.; Wang, X.; Fujimaki, M.; Tominaga , J.; Aiba, H.; and Ohki, Y.; Komatsubara, T. *Phys. Rev.* B 2008, *78*, 054102.

[66] Rizza, G.; Dawi, E. A.; Vredenberg, A. M.; Monnet, I. *Appl. Phys. Lett.* 2009, *95*, 43105.

[67] Dawi, E. A.; Rizza, G.; Mink, M. P.; Vredenberg, A. M.; Habraken, F. H. P. M. *J. Appl. Phys.* 2009,*105*, 074305.

[68] Roorda, S.; Dillen, T. V.; Polman, A.; Graf, C.; Blaaderen, A. V. and Kooi, B. J. Adv. Mater. 2004, 16, 235.

[69] Klaumünzer, S.; Li,C.L. ; Löffler, S.; Rammensee, M.; Schumacher, G.; and Neitzer, H.C. ; Rad. Eff. and Def. in Sol. 1989,108, 131.

[70] Kluth, P.; et al, Phys. Rev. Lett. 2008,101, 175503.

[71] Singh, F.; Ph.D. Thesis, Orsay university 2007.

[72] Singh, F.; Mohapatra, S; Stoquert, J.P.; Pivin, J.C.; Avasthi, D.K. ; Nucl. Instr. And Meth. B 2009, 267, 936.

[73] Pivin, J.C.; Singh, F.; Mishra, Y.K.; Avasthi, D.K.; Stoquert, J.P.; Surface and Coating Technology 2009, 203,2432.

[74] Stoquert, J. P.; chapter in this book.

[75] Singhal, R. and Avasthi, D.K. Chapter in this book

[76] Pivin,J.C. ; Esnouf, S. ; Singh,F.; Avasthi,D.K.; J. Appl. Phys. 2005, 98, 023908.

[77] Pivin, J.C.; Singh,F.; Angelov,O.; andVincent, L. ; J. Phys. D: Appl. Phys. 2009, 42, 025005.

[78] Reyntjens, S.; and Puers, R. ;, J. Micromech. Microeng. 2001, 11, 287.

[79] Tseng, A.A. ; J. Micromech. Microeng. 2004,14, R15.

[80] Orloff,J. ; Utlaut, M.; and Swanson,L.; *High Resolution Focused Ion Beams* (Kluwer Academic, New York, 2003)

[81] Giannuzzi, L.A.; and Stevie, F.A.; *Introduction to Focused Ion Beams, Instrumentation, Theory, Techniques and Practice* (Springer, New York, 2005)

[82] Kulkarni, V.N. ; chapter in this book

[83] Satyam, P.V. Chapter in this book

[84] Kalkura, S.N. Chapter in this book

[85] Mookherjee, S. chapter in this book

[86] Avasthi,D.K.; and Pivin, J.C.; Current Science 2010, 98,780.

In: Synthesis and Engineering of Nanostructures…   ISBN 978-1-62100-261-1
Editors: Devesh Kumar Avasthi & Jean Claude Pivin   © 2012 Nova Science Publishers, Inc

Chapter 2

NANOFABRICATION BY FOCUSED ION BEAMS

Vishwas N. Kulkarni [1]

Indian Institute of Technology Kanpur
Kanpur-208016, India

ABSTRACT

This Chapter describes the Focused Ion Beam (FIB) technique which has emerged as a promising method for rapid manufacturing of complex 3D micro and nano size structures, nano sensors and actuators and nanosize components for fabrication of prototype Micro and Nano electromechanical systems (MEMS and NEMS). The technique is very powerful in reducing enormously the validation time for testing concepts and new ideas in the field of micro and nano devices. The basic principles of the micro fabrication processes are explained along with a few examples based on the research performed at IIT Kanpur.

1. INTRODUCTION

The scope of conventional techniques for producing micro parts is restricted to 2½ Dimensional features. All these techniques are based on top down approach involving removal of material. To produce truly 3D objects at the micro and nano level, one has to adopt a judicious combination of top down and bottom up approaches based on addition and removal of material in a gradual manner. The Focused Ion Beam (FIB) has provided a very convenient tool for building features in such manner.

In the past two decades the technical advancements in directed energy sources such as lasers, electron accelerators and ion accelerators have made it possible to use these sources in the form of very fine, narrow and intense beams for removing material from a solid surface

---

[1]   (vnk@iitk.ac.n).

with great precision. In addition, energetic focused ions have been very successfully exploited for material addition on the surface. As a result, FIB systems have paved a novel way of manufacturing 3D micro and nano structures of complex geometry rapidly and directly without involving any other processing steps. FIB systems have already become important for the semiconductor industry where they are used for repairing the defects in the masks used for photolithography, doping of elements and for elemental analysis on nano scales. As far as micro/nano scale engineering is concerned numerous applications of FIB are on horizon due to its rapidity, versatility and distinctive nature of the basic fabrication process as compared to the traditional techniques of microfabrication. The micromilling applications of FIB have been reviewed by Reyntjens and Pures [1] and Tesng [2]. The details of FIB instrumentation, theory and modes of the usage are given in the books by Orloff etal [3] and Lucille etal [4]. In this chapter we describe main features of a FIB system, explain the physical principles underlying the machining and deposition mechanisms, illustrate the typical steps involved in the fabrication of a three dimensional structure and present a few examples based on the work carried out at the Indian Institute of Technology Kanpur.

2. FOCUSED ION BEAM SYSTEM

The schematic of a FIB system equipped with electron beam imaging is shown in figure 1 [5] and the photograph of a typical dual beam FIB system with details of the chamber are shown in figure 2 and 3 respectively. The combined ion and electron beam facilitates on-site and in-process inspection by high resolution imaging using the secondary electrons. The system which is built around an ultra high vacuum chamber equipped with Turbo molecular and other ultra high vacuum pumps consists of the following major components:

An ion column (the details of which are shown in figure 4) for milling and deposition,
An electron column for imaging,
Scan generators for ions and electrons,
Secondary electron detectors,
A precision 5-axes goniometer for sample mounting and manipulation,
A gas injection system (GIS) to spray a precursor gas on the sample surface,
CCD Camera
Computer control.

In addition, there are arrangements for beam blanking for milling and/or deposition over a selected pattern, ion current measurement for controlling the milling/deposition process and a load lock for efficient sample interchange. A liquid metal ion source is used to produce ion beams of high brightness of the order mega ampere per square centimeter per steradian. For electron beam, a field emission tungsten source is generally used for achieving high resolution. Both the ion and electron beams can be focused at the same spot on the sample. With the advancements in ion beam optics it has now become possible to obtain ion spot size of less than 5 nm and electron beam spot size of about an nm on the target and such systems are now commercially available.

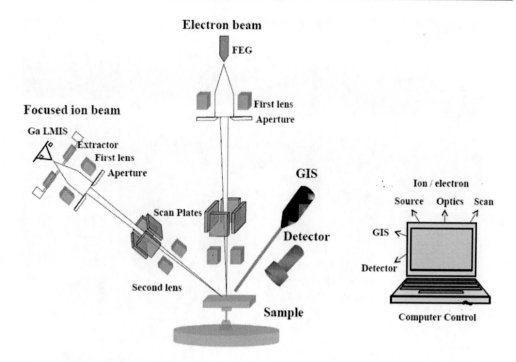

Figure 1. Schematic diagram of dual beam FIB system showing ion and electron columns (from Ref 5, copyright (2010) by Elsevier).

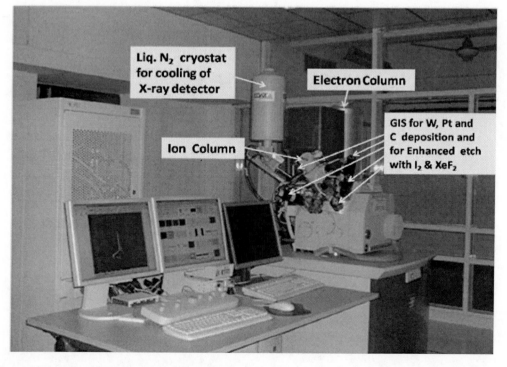

Figure 2. Actual outer details of the FIB system.

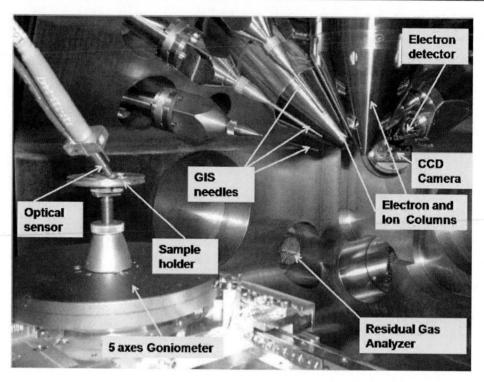

Figure 3. Actual tagged Inner details of the FIB chamber.

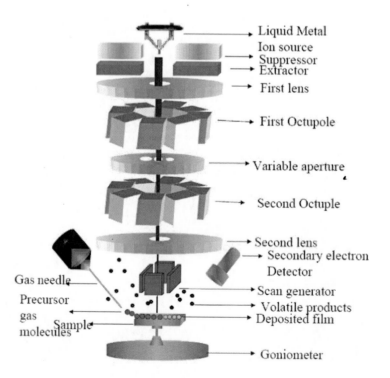

Figure 4. Schematic diagram of the ion column and FIB assisted deposition process.

Ion energies in the range of 1-30 keV are generally used since the performance is optimum for both milling and deposition processes for a wide variety of materials. For micromachining and film deposition purpose, the choice of the ion is governed, in principle, by its i) efficacy of atom removal ii) efficacy of molecular dissociation and iii) its inertness with the substrate. From the basic theory of ion matter interaction it turns out that at these energies the processes of atom removal (sputtering) and molecular dissociation depend primarily on the mass and energy of the incident ion for a given solid. However, since some of the incident ions get embedded in the solid, the solid would get contaminated with these elements and the properties of the machined part will get affected if these atoms react with the host atoms. On this basis, one can infer that ions of noble gases are the most suitable candidates for micromachining purpose. However, appropriate ion sources having high brightness are not yet easily available for noble gases and for other important elements needed for doping etc. Therefore, most of the commercial FIB systems utilize Ga ions for micromachining since the ion source technology for Ga is well developed for producing beams of high brightness. A commercial FIB set up gives ion currents on target that can be varied from 1 pA to 50 nA in steps depending on the spot size. A high current density of a few Amp/cm^2 which corresponds to the ion flux of the order of $10^{10}/\mu m^2$s can be achieved on the target. A commercial system provides possibility for injection of different gases to be sprayed over the sample. The different operations such as sample manipulation, gas choice and flow rate and ion beam current etc. are generally computer controlled. For carving out different patterns or for constructing a three dimensional micro or nano structure by deposition of material, suitable software for beam scanner and beam blanker is used. In the next section we explain the principle of micro fabrication by FIB, on the basis of fundamental ion matter interaction.

3. PRINCIPLES OF FIB MICRO FABRICATION

Micromachining of materials by focused ion beam is based on the different processes which occur when energetic heavy ions hit the surface of a solid sample. The ions loose their energy to the electrons and atoms of the solid resulting in ionization, electron emission, atomic displacements and removal of atoms (sputtering) from the solid, phonon generation, and dissociation of molecules by breaking the chemical bonds. Most of these effects are dominant at energies ranging from a few keV to few hundreds of keV and depend on mass of the incident ion and that of the target atoms. Among these effects, sputtering and dissociation of the molecules form the basis of micromachining and fabrication using FIB. Figure 5 shows a typical trajectory of a 2 keV Ga ion in Si substrate along with the displacements of the Si atoms. The trajectory has been obtained from the Monte Carlo simulation code TRIM [6]. These calculations show that the 2 keV Ga ion traverses a distance of about 4 nm in Si and it removes, on an average, 4 Si atoms from the surface. The implementation of this sputtering effect for achieving material milling is illustrated in figure 6. A focused ion beam is scanned in a programmed manner over the sample, causing material removal from a selected region of desired geometry. A fast material removal rate of the order of a micrometer cube per second can be achieved and complex patterns can be carved within a short interval of time.

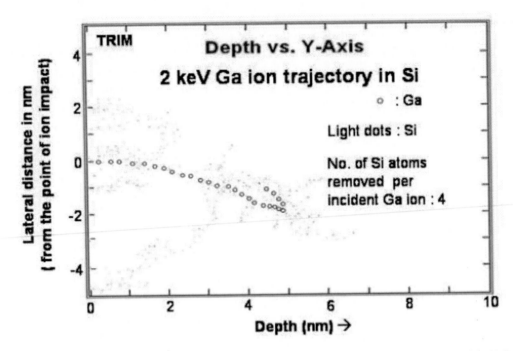

Figure 5. 3 A typical ion trajectories obtained from Monte Carlo Simulation code TRIM. The 2 keV Ga ion comes to rest at a distance of about 4 nm in the Si target. The average sputtering yield (calculated from 1000 ion trajectories) is about 4 Si atoms per Ga ion.

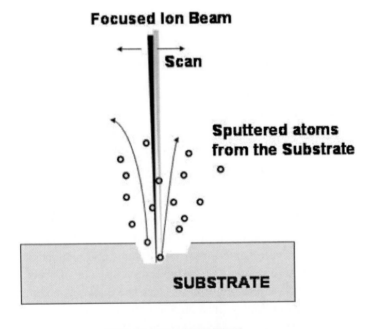

Figure 6. The process of nanoscale milling in FIB. Typical material removal rate is about $1\mu m^3$ per second.

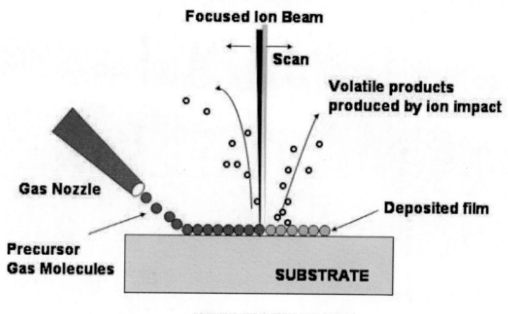

Nanoscale Deposition

Figure 7. The process of localized material deposition by FIB. The precursor gas molecules stick to the sample surface which are dissociated by the energetic Ga ions leaving the nonvolatile component (typically Pt, W , SiO$_2$ etc) of the molecule on the surface where the ion beam hits.

The ion beam current can be tuned such that the material removal is fast enough, the surface finish is good and no debris is produced during milling. In order to enhance the material removal rate of metals and insulators, chemically assisted sputtering is achieved by spraying I$_2$ and XeF$_2$ gases respectively.

On the other hand, complex structures can be built, layer by layer, by spraying appropriate gas on the sample surface and dissociating the gas molecules adhered to the surface by the energetic ions. The volatile components which are mainly hydrocarbons leave the sample, leaving behind the metallic element which is then firmly attached to the surface. This process of localized deposition is illustrated in figure 7. Varieties of precursor gases are used for deposition of thin metallic films or insulators. For example, for Platinum deposition C$_9$H$_{16}$Pt (trimethyl-methycyclopentadienyl-platinum), and for W the organo-metallic gas W(CO)$_6$ are used while for the deposition of an insulating film like SiO$_2$ a mixture of O$_2$ and 1,3,5,7-tetramethylcycloetrasiloxane is used. This process is appropriately called as FIB-Chemical Vapor Deposition (FIB-CVD). In the next section, the steps involved in the construction of a typical 3 D structure which is difficult to make by conventional techniques, is described.

4. FABRICATION STEPS

A schematic illustration of the steps involved in the fabrication of a micro bridge on a substrate is given in figure 8 (a-d).

36   Vishwas N. Kulkarni

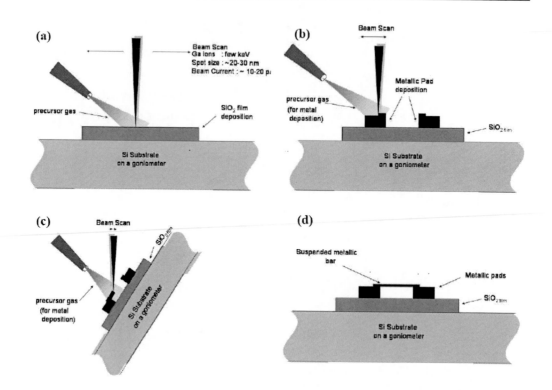

Figure 8. Steps involved in the fabrication of a metallic micro bridge (Pirani Gauge) (a) Deposition of SiO₂ film (b) Deposition of metallic pads (c) Deposition of the bridge portion by tilting the sample (Tilt shown are not actual: only for illustration) (d) Pirani structure of the metallic micro-bridge.

An insulated layer of desired dimension of SiO_2 is first built (Figure 8a) by dissociating the molecules of 1, 3, 5, 7-tetramethylcycloetrasiloxane by the focused Ga ions on the surface. The metallic pads are then constructed on this insulating film by decomposition of a suitable organo-metallic gas (Figure 8b). The micro bridge is then grown by tilting the sample such that the focused ion beam hits the portion of the vertical plane of the metallic pads as shown in figure 8(c). The bridge starts growing in the horizontal direction towards the other metallic pad which eventually leads to the final microbridge structure shown in figure 8(d). There could be alternative ways which would involve deposition of a wall type structure followed by milling of the middle portion of the wall for constructing the same structure. A 3-D branch structure of carbon fabricated using FIB –CVD following the approach mentioned above is seen in figure 2 on the display of the computer monitor. One of the important features of FIB-CVD is its ability of fabricating an overhanging structure. This is illustrated in figure 9 along with a schematic diagram for the fabrication of a nano spring. Although, growth during FIB-CVD process occurs along the direction of the beam, at the edges it occurs a little bit along the lateral direction as well since the over layer of the precursor gas exists at the edges. Thus by shifting the beam slightly (about 20-100 nm) in the lateral direction during each pass, the overhanging structure can be realized as shown schematically in the figure 9. The time needed to fabricate a structure of this kind turns out to be less than an hour. This point is especially stressed since it reduces the time between new ideas and concepts and their validation.

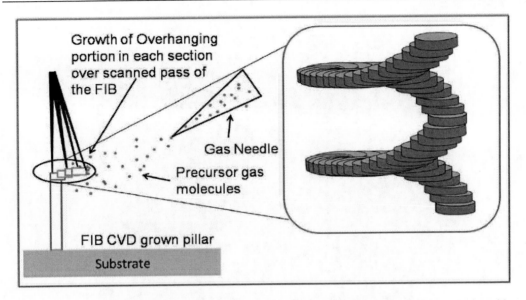

Figure 9. (a) Schematic Principle of Fabrication of step by step overhanging portions by FIB deposition (in-set shows the schematic for making a nano spring).

Reyntjens et al [7] have reported the fabrication of a nano pirani gauge (which is essentially a suspended W bridge with a gap of 400 nm between the substrate and the bridge) on an existing Si CMOS chip and have successfully demonstrated its response for measuring the pressure in the range of 10 mbar to 1 bar. Fabrication of several complex structures and micro components have been reported [1, 2, 4-10] in the literature. A few examples are given in the next section.

5. APPLICATION WITH EXAMPLES

5.1 Nanostructures by FIB Milling

The simplest application of FIB machining is removal of material to make a mesh of patterned blind holes either circular or other shapes. A lattice of holes drilled in Ag film on a quartz substrate is shown in Figure.10. The milled portions are highly smooth, which is one of the advantages of FIB milling. The aspect ratio (diameter/depth) of such holes is normally about 25. Beyond this ratio the holes become tapered at the bottom due to a variety of phenomena taking place viz; redeposition etc. The minimum hole size which has been obtained by the present group is 11 nm. Holes of sizes as small as 5 nm have been reported in the literature [11]. These sub wavelength array of patterned holes on metals are important for photonic and plasmonic applications eg; extra ordinary transmission of light. For the futuristic technology electrical characterization of organic polymers on molecular dimensions is required for which interdigited electrode assemblies with nano meter separation of electrodes are needed. A schematic diagram of such an interdigited electrode assembly and its realization by FIB milling is shown in Figure. 11. The substrate is Si and the electrode material is Al having electrode spacing of 16 nm. The characteristics of the electrodes in air and in the presence of Alq 3 polymer are also shown in the figure 11 [12].

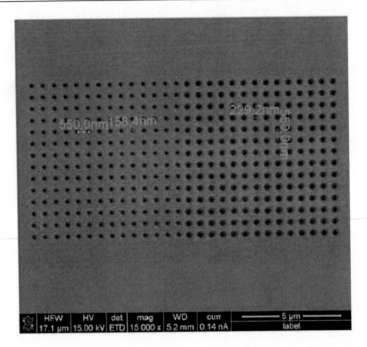

Figure 10. Array of holes of different diameters 158.4 nm and 229.2 nm having periodicity 550nm patterned on 300 nm thick silver film grown on quartz substrate.

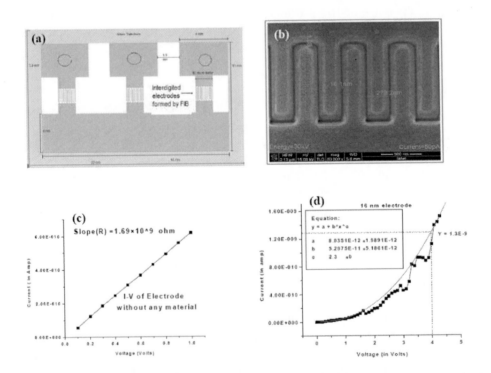

Figure 11. (a) Schematic of basic module to be patterned (b) An inter-digitated nano electrodes having narrow gap of 16 nm (c) I-V characteristics curve for Al nano electrodes having channel separation 16 nm (d) I-V characteristics of Alq3 molecule with Al nano electrodes 16 nm apart [from Ref. 12].

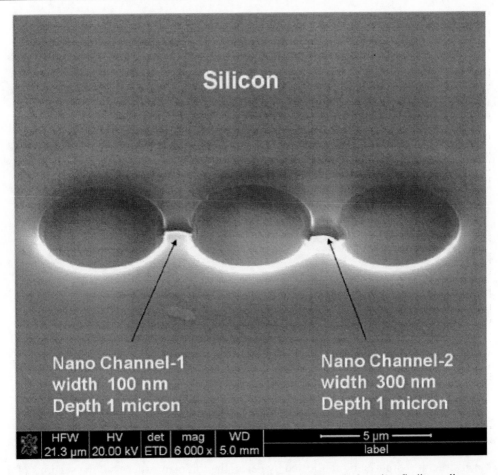

Figure 12. FIB made micron size pits on Si connected by nano channels for microfludic studies.

Another useful structure for micro fluidic and electrophoresis studies at nano dimensions is shown in figure 12. The molecules could be guided through the nano channels under suitably applied potential difference. One of the challenging tasks is to make contacts of such nanostructures with macro domain for measurements. Various strategies of fabrication have to be adopted for this purpose. A simplest procedure is to build the structure around prefabricated electrical contacts having dimensions in the range of 100 -500 micron. Such contacts can be easily made by evaporation of a suitable metallic element through a mask. One of the major problems in FIB milling is the incorporation Ga in the milled portion. Its amount can be as high as few atom percent in the milled portion. Being a metal, incorporated Ga can interfere with the electrical measurements in certain cases. Different methods of removing incorporated Ga atoms have been reported which utilize annealing and radio frequency radiation exposure [13]

5.2 3D nanostructures by FIB CVD deposition

Different types of 3D nano structures fabricated using FIB-CVD are shown in figure 13 (a-d). All these structures are made by molecular cracking of naphthalene gas under Ga FIB.

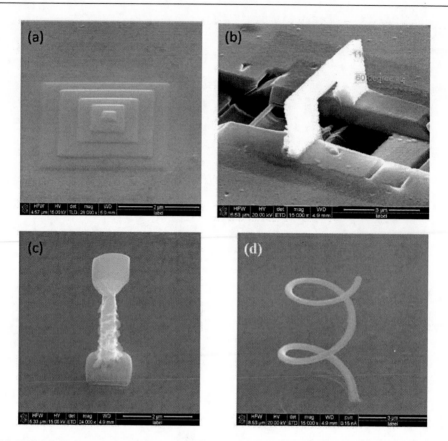

Figure 13. FIB fabricated various overhanging and 3D structures.

Such structures are usually fabricated by generating bit map patterns of the sections of the structures along the beam direction. The patterns are given as input to the ion beam control software which executes the beam scanning in a sequential manner as per the given patterns. The overhanging structures described above can also be generated in this particular way. The minimum feature size of 20 nm or less can be obtained. The structures shown in figure 13 (c and d) could be realized because of a slight overhanging portion which is produced during layer by layer deposition. The fabrication of the nano spring (Figure 13d) was achieved by many consecutive depositions each consisting of a disc of 20 nm in diameter and 20 nm in height by rotating the beam by a few degrees with respect to the previous one as depicted in the schematic diagram of figure 9.

5.3 Morphology and Stoichiometry

The nanostructures of C, Pt W etc fabricated by (FIB-CVD) are not elementally pure. They invariably contain carbon and Ga whose amount can be as high as 40%. In addition, the structures show irregularly grown protrusions or whiskers at the edges of the structure. These effects become more prominent in case of fabrication of nano pillars or cantilevers. The dumbbell structure of figure-13(c) shows such protrusions. A clear illustration is given figure 14(a-c) which shows the protrusions on carbon, Pt and W nano pillars grown by FIB-CVD.

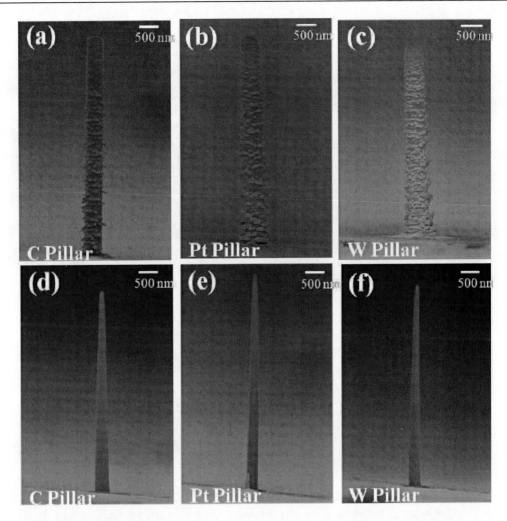

Figure 14. SEM images of as deposited (a) Carbon, (b) Platinum and (c) Tungsten pillars. (d) - (f) shows the smoothened C, Pt and W pillars using ion beam milling, respectively (from Ref. 14, copyright (2009) by Elsevier).

These irregularly grown protrusions limit the design ability and electrical / mechanical properties of the nanostructures. The growth of such protrusions occurs due to the deposition of atoms liberated from the cracking of the precursor gas under secondary ion or electron impact [14]. While the beam parameters can be optimized to reduce the protrusion growth, these can be micro machined by Ga ion milling to make their surface smooth as shown in figure 14 (d-f).

As stated above, most of the Ga FIB-CVD depositions of carbon show presence of Ga. The Pt and W pillars show presence of C as well. The amount of these elements depend on different process parameters such as, ion flux and energy, substrate temperature, precursor gas pressure around the growth region etc. Figure 15 presents EDS (Energy Dispersive Spectroscopy) data of nano pillars of C, W and Pt of similar dimensions grown using different Ga ion flux. The carbon depositions initially show almost equal amount of C and Ga for ion flux upto 3×10^{19} ions-cm^{-2}-sec^{-1}. Above this flux it is dominated by increased Ga incorporation. On the other hand, Pt depositions show quite low Ga and C contamination of less than 10 at% which is uniform over the entire flux range.

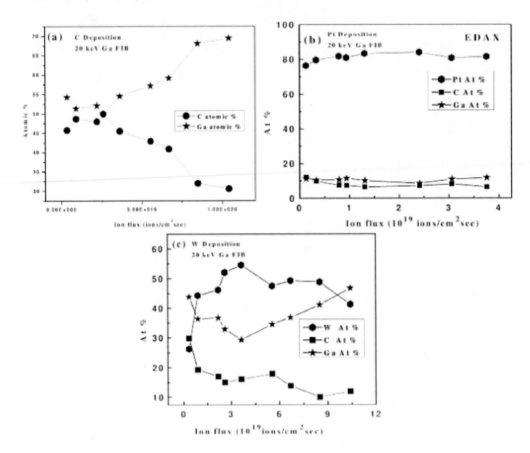

Figure 15. Elemental analysis of (a) Carbon, (b) Platinum and (c) Tungsten pillars grown by 20 keV Ga FIB as a function of ion flux at constant ion fluence 6.6×10^{21} ions-cm^{-2} for C and W and of 2.4×10^{21} ions-cm^{-2} for Pt (from Ref.15, copyright (2008) by Elsevier).

The W depositions show variation in the contents from 30 at. % to about 55 at.%. The C contents in these depositions continuously reduce as a function of flux. On the other hand the amount of Ga initially decrease and then increase as function of fluence. In general, for slower growth rates more energy is deposited per adsorbed molecule which enhances the metallic contents of the film [15]. The problem of contamination of the structures grown by FIB puts limit to its utility in making nano size semiconducting devices, however this problem is of less consequence if the mechanical or some specific photonic aspects are to be exploited for nano device fabrication. In the next section we present a few examples of prototype devices made by FIB.

5.4 Nano Size Sensors

After its development and commercialization in 1990's FIB technology became popular in semiconductor research and processing fields for failure analysis, device modification and repair [1, 4]. In the successive years the capability of localized milling and deposition down to few nanometer scale was utilized in combination with other lithographic machining processes to produce nano-manipulators [16], accelerometers [10] etc. In all these cases, FIB is mostly used as an intermediate or final step to either create nano size spacing at a desired place by ion milling or to make nano size extensions by deposition. Attempts to fabricate complete prototype nano devices such as nano pirani gauge [7], nano thermo probe [17], mass sensors [18] etc. have recently been started. In the following we illustrate fabrication of two types of sensors, one to measure temperature over a micron size space and the other to measure small masses of the order of atto gram which get accumulated on the tip of a nano pillar.

A scheme showing the geometry used for the fabrication of nano / micro thermocouple is illustrated in figure-16. The substrate is a Si wafer having 250 nm SiO_2 film grown by either SiO_2 deposition or grown by wet oxidation of Si. These substrates are then used to for make planar nano thermocouples and micro heaters. The electrodes are first made by deposition of Au through a mask and subsequent milling of the central portion by FIB. Nano thermocouple having junction area 100 nm x 100 nm is then fabricated in the gap region by depositing platinum and tungsten ribbons using FIB-CVD as shown schematically in figure 16. Figure 17(a) shows a nano thermocouple along with a micro heater fabricated in this fashion. The response of this Pt-W nano thermocouple due to the heating of the micro heater under an applied potential difference in the range of 0-180 mV is shown in figure 17(b). The thermocouple shows nearly linear response from 1-4 mV of thermo emf, towards sensing the heat generated in the micro heating wire. The maximum thermo emf of 6 mV generated by the micro heater measured by Pt –W thermocouple suggests a temperature rise of approximately 350 ^{0}C when thermo emf was compared by calibration curve of Pt-W thermocouple [19]. This data show that the planar Pt-W combination grown by FIB-CVD can be implemented for the measurement of temperatures in micro / nano dimensions. Due to the Ga and C contamination of Pt and W, Seebeck coefficient of the Pt-W nano thermocouple fabricated by Focused ion beam would not be same as that for pure Pt-W thermocouple and the actual temperature rise could be slightly different. Appropriate procedures for calibration of such thermocouples are yet to be developed. This nano size thermocouple has been utilized for the measurement of the local temperature rise over a region of few microns square due to ion beam irradiation [17] and it exhibits a fast response. Also, in a recent work [20] it has been shown that such nano thermo probes are capable of sensing the radiation emitted from a heated nano filament. All these reports demonstrate the feasibility of temperature measurement over a micro / nano region during ion beam irradiation or other similar processes where local temperature rise can take place. Arrays of such nano thermocouples can be made to study the temperature gradients over a small region.

One of the most basic structures, which are implemented in many MEMS devices, is a resonator in the form of a cantilever or a pillar. Nano size cantilevers and pillars on a suitable substrate can be easily fabricated by FIB or FEB (Focused Electron Beam) which offer the ability to detect very small motions thereby improving the ability of mass sensing down to atto grams (10^{-18} gm). A scheme of measuring mass accumulation on the tip of a nanopillar is shown in figure-18. The resonant frequency of a uniform pillar is given by

$$f = (\beta^2 d/8\pi L^2) (E/\rho)^{1/2} \qquad\qquad (1)$$

where d is the diameter, L is the length, E is Young's modulus and ρ is the density of the pillar. β is a constant whose value is 1.8751 for the first mode of vibration .

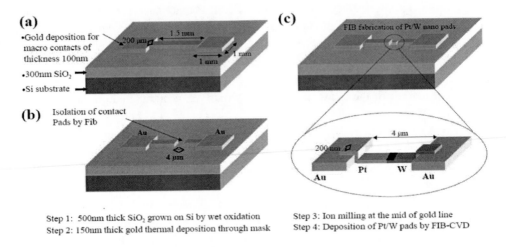

Step 1: 500nm thick SiO₂ grown on Si by wet oxidation   Step 3: Ion milling at the mid of gold line
Step 2: 150nm thick gold thermal deposition through mask   Step 4: Deposition of Pt/W pads by FIB-CVD

Figure 16. (a)-(c) Schematic process of making planar nano / micro Pt-W thermocouple by focused ion beam chemical vapor deposition (FIB CVD) (from Ref 17, copyright (2009) by Elsevier).

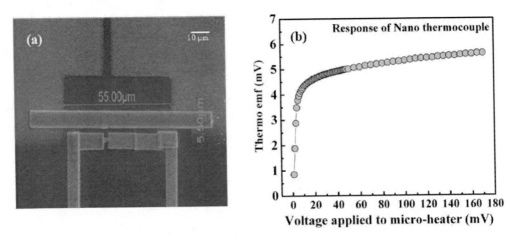

Figure 17. (a) FIB-CVD fabricated planar nano Pt-W thermocouple where nano thermocouple junction is at a distance of 2.5 μm from the tungsten micro heater (b) Thermo emf of the FIB –CVD fabricated Planar Pt-W thermocouple of figure 2 as a function of applied voltage across the micro heater (from Ref 17, copyright (2009) by Elsevier).

When a mass Δm gets accumulated at the tip of the pillar (Figure 18b) the resonance frequency changes and the accumulated mass is related to the change in the resonance frequency by the following relation

$$\Delta m = (k/4\pi^2) \, (1/f_b^2 - 1/f_a^2) \tag{2}$$

where f_a and f_b are resonant frequencies before and after mass accumulation at the tip. k is known as spring constant and is given by

$$k = (3\pi^3 \rho L f^2 d)/\beta^4 \qquad\qquad (3)$$

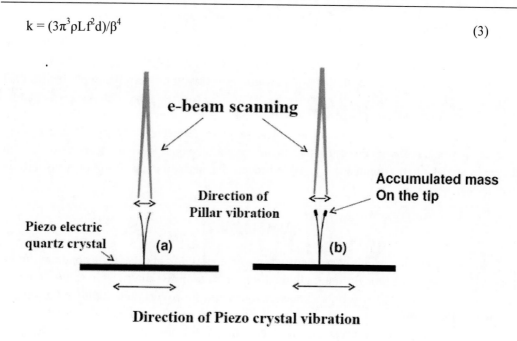

Figure 18. Schematic diagram of the procedure for the measurement of mass accumulation over pillars using SEM (a) pillar in resonance before accumulation of mass (b) after mass accumulation. The resonant frequency for (b) is lower than for (a) .

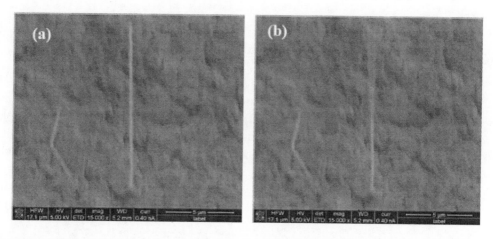

Figure 19. (a) FEB-CVD grown carbon nanopillar, (b) first resonance mode.

Various optical techniques have been developed for the measurement of change in the frequency. For in-situ mass accumulation measurements during SEM scanning, the SEM imaging itself can be used for this purpose. A FEB grown carbon nanopillar in non-resonant and resonant mode is shown in figure 19. The variation in the resonant frequency due to mass accumulation of the pillar surface due to e- beam irradiation is shown figure-20. In this figure, when the entire pillar is exposed to the electron beam, the diameter of the pillar increases thereby increasing the resonant frequency as a function of e-beam irradiation fluence. On the other hand if only the tip of the pillar is exposed the resonant frequency reduces. The resonant frequency for the carbon nano pillar of figure-19 varies between 550 to 600 khz. The typical values for nano pillars lie in the range of few hundred kilohertz to about 2 MHz. These nano pillars exhibit a high Q factor of few thousand enabling high detection sensitivity. A minimum mass accumulation of about 50 atto-grams at the tip of the pillar could be detected [21].

These two simple examples have been presented just to give the reader a glimpse of the prototype fabrication possibilities by FIB. The scope to fabricate a variety of nano sensors with unique features is much wider and there are simultaneous developments which are in progress to make FIB an industrially viable process for mass manufacturing of nano sensors and devices.

SUMMARY

The advancements which have occurred in low energy ion accelerator technology in the past two decades have brought the traditional ion beam tool of a physicist in to the hands of researchers engineers in the form of Focused Ion Beam for a very fine, rapid and advanced manufacturing of micro and nano objects. Complex three dimensional structures can be produced in a very short interval of time facilitating validation of new concepts and ideas quite quickly. One of the emerging possibilities is of fabrication of nanosensors to study the changes occurring in small space of submicron size dimensions. This would facilitate monitoring and control of the processes over a small dimension needed for the futuristic technology.

ACKNOWLEDGMENT

The author would like to thank Prof. G.K. Mehta, for his support in initiating the ion beam program at IIT Kanpur and for many useful discussions and suggestions. Thanks are due to Dr. S. Dhamodaran, Dr. J. Ramkumar, Dr A. Ramkrishna for many useful discussions. The contributions of Sarvesh K. Tripathi, Neeraj Shukla, Tarun Mankad, A. Banerjee, Mihir Sarkar, Abhishek Sing, Nitul Singh Rajput and Sudhanshu Srivastva are gratefully acknowledged.

The financially supported by IIT Kanpur and NSTI, Department of Science and Technology, New Delhi is gratefully acknowledged.

REFERENCES

[1]   Reyntjens,S.; Puers, R. J. *Micromech. Microeng.* 2001, 11, 287.
[2]   Tseng, A.A. J. *Micromech. Microeng.* 2004, 14, R15.
[3]   Orloff, J.; Utlaut, M.; Swanson, L. *High Resolution Focused Ion Beams* (Kluwer Academic, New York, 2003
[4]   Giannuzzi, L.A.; Stevie, F.A. *Introduction to Focused Ion Beams, Instrumentation, Theory, Techniques and Practice* (Springer, New York, 2005)

[5]   Singh, A. K.; Rajput, N. S.; Tripathi, S. K.; Dhamodaran, S.; Kumar, J.; Kulkarni, V.
      N., *Nucl. Instrl and Meth. Phys. Res.* B, accepted, in press
      (doi:10.1016/j.nimb.2010.06.016).

[6]   Ziegler, J.F.; Biersack, J.P.; Littmark, U. *The Stopping and Range of Ions in Solids*
      (Pergamon, New York, 1985). TRIM stands for TRansport of Ion in Mater. The code is
      available at http://www.srim.org.

[7]   Reyntjens, S.; Bruyker, D.D.; Puers, R. *Proceedings of 11 th International conference*
      on Solid-State Sensors and Actuators, Munich Germany, 2001, p. 490.

[8]   Khizroev, S.; Litvinov, D. *Nanotechnology* 2004, 15, R7.

[9]   Adams, D.P.; Vasile, M.J.; Krishnan, A.S.M. *Precision Engg.* 2000, 24, 347.

[10] Daniel, J.H.; Moore, D.F.; Walker, J.F. *Smart Mater. Struct.* 2000, 9, 284.

[11] Lo, C. J.; Aref, T.; Bezryadin, A. *Nanotechnology* 2006, 17, 3264.

[12] Abdin, Z. *Nano Electrode Fabrication Using Focused Ion Beam Suitable For Organic*
      Devices, (M.Tech Thesis, Indian Institute of Technology Kanpur, 2007)
      http://172.28.64.70:8080/jspui/handle/123456789/10361 .

[13] Schilling, A.; Adams, T.; Bowman, R. M.; Gregg, J. M. *Nanotechnology* 2007, 18,
      035301.

[14] Tripathi, S. K.; Kulkarni, V.N. *Nucl. Instrum. Meth. In Phys. Res.* B 2009, 267 1381.

[15] Tripathi, S.K.; Shukla, N.; Kulkarni, V.N. *Nucl. Instrum. Meth. In Phys. Res.*, B 2008,
      266, 1468.

[16] Wang, X.; Vincent, L.; Yu, M.; Huang, Y.; Liu, C. in *"Proceedings of the 2003*
      IEEE/ASME International Conference on Advanced Intelligent Mechatronics", 2003,
      vol 2, 891.

[17] Shukla, N.; Tripathi, S.K. ; Banerjee, A.; Ramana, A.S.V.; Rajput, N.S.; Kulkarni, V.N.
      Appl. Surf. Sci,. 2009, 256, 475.

[18] Banerjee, A.; Mankad, T.; Dhamodaran, S.; Ramkumar, J.; Kulkarni, V.N.
      Nanotechnology 2009, 20, 345501.

[19] Kinzie, P.A. *Thermocouple Temperature Measurement* (Willey Inter Science
      Publication, New York, 1973, chapter 4, p.161.

[20] "Detection and Study of Thermal Radiation Emitted by Focused Ion Beam Fabricated
      Tungsten Nano Filament" presented and submitted at 16th international conference on
      "Surface Modification of Materials by Ion Beams (SMMIB)" held at Odaiba, Tokyo
      (Japan) during 13th-19th of September 2009 to be published in Surface and Coatings
      technology.

[21] Mankand, T. *Exploring vibrational aptitude and atto-gram mass sensing ability of*
      composity nanao-pillars, (M.Tech Thesis, Indian Institute of Technology Kanpur,
      2007).

In: Synthesis and Engineering of Nanostructures…
Editors: Devesh Kumar Avasthi & Jean Claude Pivin

ISBN 978-1-62100-261-1
© 2012 Nova Science Publishers, Inc

Chapter 3

SYNTHESIS OF NANOCOMPOSITE THIN FILMS BY ATOM BEAM CO-SPUTTERING

S. Mohapatra,[1] D. Kabiraj[2] and D. K. Avasthi[2]*

[1]School of Basic and Applied Sciences, Guru Gobind Singh Indraprastha University,
Delhi 110403, India
[2]Inter University Accelerator Centre, Post Box 10502, New Delhi-110067, India

ABSTRACT

Nanocomposite thin films containing Au nanoparticles (NPs) embedded in partially oxidized silicon matrix were synthesized by atom beam co-sputtering technique. The size distribution of Au NPs was tailored by varying the metal fraction in the nanocomposite films. Annealing the co-sputtered films resulted in the formation of Au-Si core-shell nanostructures with tunable surface plasmon resonance. We have also synthesized nanocomposite thin films with Ge NPs embedded in silica and Ni doped ZnO by atom beam co-sputtering. The processes involving the irradiation with energetic sputtered atoms arriving at the substrate are considered in the nucleation and growth of NPs in the co-sputtered films at room temperature. The advantages of atom beam co-sputtering over thermal co-evaporation and ion beam based techniques are also discussed.

1. INTRODUCTION

Nanocomposites are materials consisting of more than one phase in which the dimensions of at least one of the phases is in nanoscale. Nanocomposites are gaining increasing attention due to their combined properties and diversity of applications which can not be achieved with nanostructures of one of the phases alone. Nanocomposites with noble metal nanoparticles (NPs) embedded in a dielectric matrix exhibit unique optical properties due to their strong surface plasmon resonant (SPR) absorption of visible light. The selective photon absorption together with the enhancement in the local electromagnetic field, makes noble metal NPs promising for wide range of applications in optical devices, telecommunications, sub-wavelength lithography, chemical and bio-sensors, and nanoelectronics [1-25]. For these applications, it is important to controllably tailor the SPR wavelength from visible to near-infrared region. The SPR wavelength depends on the size and shape of NPs, inter-particle spacing and the dielectric constant of the embedding matrix [26]. Several methods *viz.,* ion implantation, ion beam mixing, co-evaporation, RF magnetron sputtering, cluster deposition, and sol-gel synthesis have been used to synthesize NPs embedded in dielectric matrices [9-25, 27-29]. In this chapter, we report synthesis of variety of nanocomposite thin films such as: (i) Au NPs embedded in partially oxidized Si and Au-Si core-shell NPs embedded in silica, (ii) Ge NPs embedded in silica and (iii) Ni doped ZnO by a novel process of atom beam co-sputtering. The advantages of atom beam co-sputtering over thermal co-evaporation and ion beam based techniques are discussed.

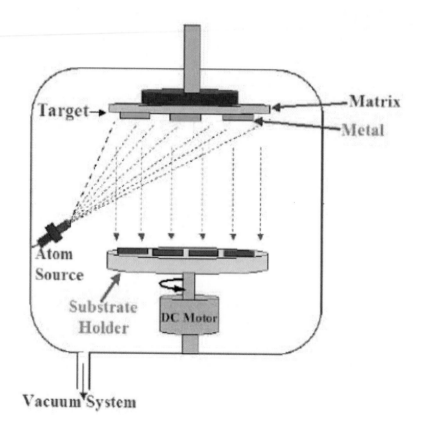

Figure 1. Schematic of diagram of atom beam co-sputtering setup.

2. ATOM BEAM SPUTTERING SET UP FOR SYNTHESIS OF NANOCOMPOSITE THIN FILMS

Nanocomposite thin films containing NPs embedded in partially oxidized Si and silica matrices were synthesized by a unique technique of atom beam co-sputtering [11-25] using the facility at IUAC, New Delhi. The schematic diagram of the set up is shown in figure 1. It consists of a wide beam Ar atom source, a vacuum chamber pumped by a turbomolecular pump, a high voltage feedthrough to supply voltage to the source, a two-inch sputter target holder and a substrate holder. For better film uniformity the substrate holder is rotated during deposition with the help of a DC motor. Metal foils placed on a 3-inch silica or ZnO disc were co-sputtered with neutral Ar atoms of energy 1.5 keV at an incidence angle of 45° and the sputtered films were deposited on silica glass, Si(100) and C coated TEM grids. The metal fraction of the nanocomposite films was varied by controlling the relative area covered by metal foils exposed to Ar atom beam. Some of the samples were annealed in inert (Ar) atmosphere. UV-visible absorption studies in the wavelength range of 300 – 800 nm were carried out on these samples using the dual beam spectrophotometer HITACHI U 3300. FTIR spectra were recorded using a Nexus 670 FTIR spectrometer in the wave number region 400–1500 cm^{-1} with a resolution of 4 cm^{-1}. Raman measurements were carried out at room temperature using the 514.5 nm line of an Ar ion laser as an excitation source. X-ray diffraction measurements were carried out with the Cu K$_\alpha$ line, λ= 0.154 nm in a glancing angle incidence geometry. Transmission electron microscopy (TEM) was used to study the shape, size distribution and crystal structure of NPs in the nanocomposite films, deposited on C coated Cu grids.

3. SYNTHESIS AND CHARACTERIZATION OF PLASMONIC NANOCOMPOSITES

3.1. Gold-Silica Nanocomposites

Figure 2 (a) shows planar TEM image revealing the microstructure of a nanocomposite sample containing 11 % Au. The presence of NPs of spherical shape can be clearly seen. The size distribution of NPs in this sample is shown in figure 2 (b). The average size (diameter) of Au NPs has been found to be $\sim$ 4 $\pm$ 0.8 nm. In figure 2 (c), we show the plan-view TEM micrograph of another nanocomposite film containing 20 % Au. The inter-particle separation of Au NPs in this sample has been found to be much smaller as compared to the sample with 11 % Au. The presence of Au NPs with more irregular shapes can be clearly seen. However, a relatively narrower size distribution of Au NPs with an average size of $\sim$ 5 $\pm$ 0.5 nm has been observed in this sample (figure 2 (d)). The observed overlapping is mainly due to the projections of Au NPs from different depths in the film. In figure 2 (e), we show an HRTEM image of Au NPs in the nanocomposite film. The measured fringe width of 2.29 Å closely matches with the (111) planar spacing of bulk Au. Some of the Au NPs have been found to deviate from spherical shape, which can be seen from the HRTEM image. On the other hand, TEM studies on a sample containing 1.2 % Au couldn't reveal any Au NPs, which indicates that Au in this sample remains in the form of atoms or small clusters, with size below the detection limit of TEM.

The UV-visible absorption spectra of the Nan composite films, deposited on silica glass substrates, are shown in figure 2 (f). All the spectra have been recorded with the bare silica glass substrate in the reference beam. The absence of any SPR peak in the absorption spectra of the sample with the lowest Au content of 1.2 % confirms the absence of Au NPs of appreciable size.

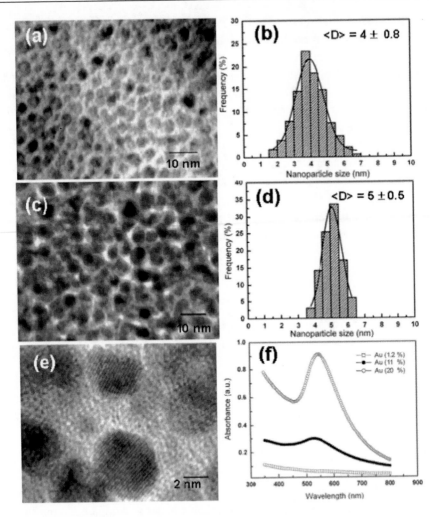

Figure 2. (a) and (c) Plan-view TEM micrographs of nanocomposite samples with 11 % and 20% Au, respectively. The size distributions of Au NPs of the nanocomposite samples with 11 % and 20 % Au are shown in (b) and (d) respectively. (e) High resolution TEM image of Au NPs in the nanocomposite sample with 20 % Au. UV-visible absorption spectra of nanocomposite films deposited on silica glass substrates are shown in (f). (Reprinted with permission from S. Mohapatra, Y.K. Mishra, D.K. Avasthi, D. Kabiraj, J. Ghatak, S. Varma, J. Phys. D: Appl. Phys.2007, 40, 7063. Copyright [2007], IOP Publishing).

Based on this, we expect Au in this sample to be mainly in the form of atoms and small clusters with size below 1 nm. In case of sample with 11 % Au, a broad resonant absorption band at ~ 528 nm has been observed which is due to the SPR of Au NPs present in the co-sputtered film. A significant red shift of ~ 20 nm in the SPR peak position (~ 548 nm) has been observed when the Au content of the film is increased to 20 %. The SPR becomes narrower, indicating an increase of particle size according to theory and more intense with an increase in the metal content of the films. The observed red shift of SPR peak can be ascribed to the increased electromagnetic interaction between the NPs [28-30]. It can be clearly seen from the TEM micrographs (Figure 2) that the inter-particle separation becomes smaller with an increase in Au content of the films. For the nanocomposite sample with 20 % Au, overlapping Au NPs with increased number density have been observed. This is expected to result in an increased electromagnetic interaction among Au NPs resulting in a red shift in the SPR peak. Apart from this, shape anisotropy of Au NPs also contributes to the observed red shift [30]. The observed enhancement in the intensity of SPR peak comes from the increased number density of Au NPs and strong inter-particle interactions among Au NPs of larger size (~ 5nm) [28-30].

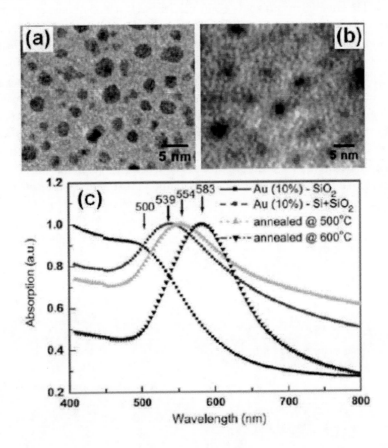

Figure 3. (a) TEM image of Au NPs in as-deposited Au–SiO$_2$ nanocomposite sample. (b) TEM image of Au–Si core-shell NPs in Au–SiO$_x$ nanocomposite sample annealed at 600°C. (c) Optical absorption spectra of as-deposited and annealed Au–SiO$_x$ nanocomposite films deposited on silica glass. (Reprinted with permission from S. Mohapatra, Y.K. Mishra, D.K. Avasthi, D. Kabiraj, J. Ghatak, S. Varma, Appl. Phys. Lett. 2008, 92, 103105. Copyright [2008], American Institute of Physics).

3.2. Au-Si Core-Shell Nps Embedded in Silica

In figure 3 (a) we show bright field TEM image of as-deposited Au-SiO$_2$ nanocomposite film, prepared by atom beam co-sputtering of Au, Si and silica. The presence of spherical Au NPs with average size ~ 3.1 ± 0.5 nm can be clearly seen. The TEM microstructure of Au-SiO$_x$ nanocomposite sample annealed at 600°C is shown in figure 3 (b). Annealing has been found to result in the formation of core-shell particles (average size ~ 4.6 nm) with amorphous Si nanoshells surrounding Au nanocrystals. The average volume fraction of these nanoshells has been found to be ~ 0.39 ± 0.05. EDX studies on these core-shell nanostructures confirmed these nanoshells to be Si rich. UV-visible absorption results revealed the surface plasmonic absorption band around 500 nm of Au NPs which shifted regularly towards red (583 nm) with increase in annealing temperature (Fig 3(c)). The SPR peak at ~ 500 nm in Au-SiO$_2$ nanocomposite confirms the formation of Au NPs. However in case of Si rich Au-SiO$_2$ nanocomposite it occurs at ~ 539 nm, which may be due to increase in refractive index coming from excess Si in the Au-SiO$_2$ nanocomposites. Annealing of Si rich Au-SiO$_2$ nanocomposites up to 600°C results in a large red shift in LSPR peak position from 539 nm to 583 nm [12]. The schematic representation of mechanism of formation of Si nanoshells due to annealing is shown in figure 4. Since annealing temperature is higher than the eutectic temperature of Au-Si system (359°C), formation of molten Au-Si alloy liquid nanodroplets occurs due to large inter-diffusion of Si in Au in Au-SiO$_x$ nanocomposite. During cooling, out-diffusion of silicon leads to the formation of nanoshells surrounds the Au NPs resulting in formation of core-shell nanostructures [12]. The thickness of Si nanoshells increases with increase in annealing temperature which results in larger refractive index and thus enables to tune the LSPR absorption. Our theoretical calculations for surface plasmon peak positions of Au-Si nanostructures under assumption that Au NPs are surrounded by thin Si nanoshells are also in good agreement with experimentally observed LSPR peak positions [12]. Thus, controlled tunability of LSPR peak position of Au NPs can be achieved by appropriate selection of Au and Si fractions in silica and annealing temperature [12].

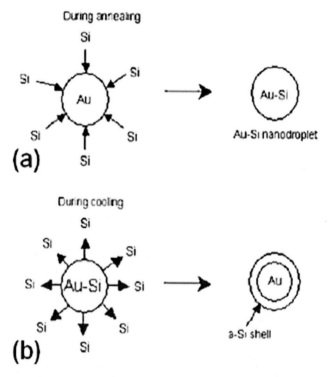

Figure 4. Schematic diagram showing mechanism of Au–Si core-shell formation in annealed Au–SiOx nanocomposite.(Reprinted with permission from S. Mohapatra, Y.K. Mishra, D.K. Avasthi, D. Kabiraj, J. Ghatak, S. Varma, Appl. Phys. Lett. 2008, 92, 103105. Copyright [2008], American Institute of Physics).

4. SYNTHESIS AND CHARACTERIZATION OF GE-SILICA NANOCOMPOSITES

Ge-silica nanocomposites were synthesized by co-sputtering of Ge pieces placed on 3-inch silica disc with 1.5 keV Ar atoms [23]. The Ge concentration in the nanocomposites was controlled by varying the relative area covered by Ge pieces on silica disc. Raman spectroscopy studies revealed the presence of a broad peak with very low intensity at 270 cm^{-1}, which corresponds to amorphous Ge. Annealing at 700°C in reducing atmosphere resulted in the emergence of a sharp symmetric peak at 300 cm^{-1}, indicating the formation of Ge nanocrystals. Thus, Ge-silica nanocomposite thin films are synthesized. Annealing at still higher temperatures resulted in growth of Ge nanocrystals, evidenced by the sharp and intense peak at 300 cm^{-1}, along with the appearance of peaks at 410 cm^{-1} and 480 cm^{-1} indicating the formation of Ge-Si nanocrystals [23], buried in silica matrix.

5. SYNTHESIS ND CHARACTERIZATION OF NI DOPED ZNO

Ni doped ZnO films have been synthesized by co-sputtering of Ni and ZnO with 1.5 keV Ar atoms [24]. XRD studies revealed the polycrystalline nature of ZnO films and the absence of any peaks characteristic of metallic Zn or Ni. X-ray photoelectron spectroscopy studies showed a clear satellite structure at 860 eV in the Ni 2p3/2 peak, which can be ascribed to O(2p)-to-Ni(3d) charge transfer transition or hybridization [31]. The presence of the satellite peak in Ni-doped ZnO films indicates that Ni is present in an oxygen environment in the film. Ni is in solid solution in ZnO crystallites. However, the binding energy position (854 eV) of Ni 2p3/2 is quite close to the one reported for NiO. Therefore, present XPS measurements strongly suggest that in the doped films Ni^{2+} ions partly substitute Zn in the ZnO matrix and rule out the presence of Ni in metallic or +3 states. Resistivity measurements showed a significant decrease (more than two orders) of the resistivity value in ZnO:Ni as compared to undoped ZnO film. The resistivity of the ZnO:Ni film (9×10^{-3} Ωcm) is found to be two orders of magnitude smaller as compared to pure ZnO film (1 Ωcm). Two important mechanisms reported in the literature *viz.* influence of *d–d* transition bands and electron scattering from crystallites/grains are discussed as the possible causes for the increase in conductivity on Ni doping in ZnO [32-33]. The reduction in resistivity in the Ni-doped ZnO film and an average transmission across the visible spectrum of 83% qualify this system to be an important candidate for transparent conducting oxide material

6. MECHANISM OF NUCLEATION AND GROWTH OF NPS IN THE CO-SPUTTERING PROCESS

Thin film deposition by atom beam co-sputtering is a dynamic process in which the sputtered atoms impinge the substrate surface at different positions with different energies. Depending on the atom's energy and the position at which it hits the surface, several phenomena can occur.

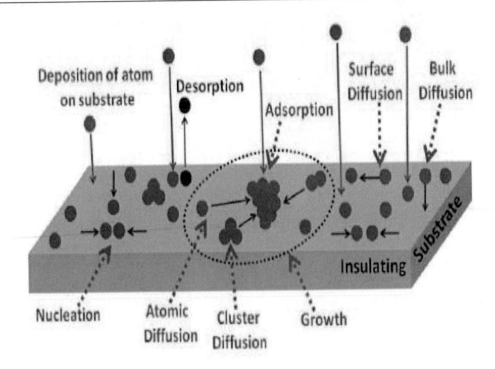

Figure 5. Schematic of basic processes involved in growth of nanoparticles during thin film deposition [from Ref. 34].

The different basic phenomena, which occur when energetic atoms arrive at the surface of insulating substrate, are illustrated in Figure 5. Thus the synthesis of nanocomposite films with energetic atoms arriving at the substrate can be understood in following steps: (i) adsorption and desorption of atoms, (ii) bulk and surface diffusion of atoms, (iii) clustering of atoms leading to nucleation and growth of nanoparticles [34]. Energetic atoms, when arriving at the substrate can get adsorbed or desorbed. Then adsorbed atoms diffuse in surface or bulk with certain diffusion length depending on type of atoms, their energy and also the properties of substrate. The diffusing atoms combine to form dimers, trimers and so on which finally results in formation of stable nuclei when a critical size is reached. If atoms directly arrive on dimer/trimer or on nanoparticle, they are adsorbed to it and directly involved in nucleation and growth.

The formation of nuclei is a competitive process between surface free energy and volume free energy and creation of small particles of solid always leads to an increase free energy. Nuclei of critical size have maximum free energy. The critical nuclei are also effectively in unstable equilibrium with surrounding and hence they further grow by addition of small nuclei and atomic species or dissolve if further atoms are not added. Nucleation and growth depend on (i) liquid phase instability, which again depends on driving force towards equilibrium and (ii) diffusion of atoms into clusters which is larger for higher temperatures. There are two types of nucleation, homogeneous and heterogeneous. In homogeneous nucleation nuclei of pure materials grow at random. However in case of heterogeneous nucleation, some sites such as steps, grain boundaries favor the segregation of the new phase.

In order to understand the processes underlying the formation of NPs in a matrix by co-sputtering process we have considered one of the cases, i.e, Au NPs in silica and carried out

SRIM (Stopping Range of Ions in Matter) simulations [35] for 1.5 keV Ar atoms incident on Si and Au targets at an incidence angle of $45°$. The energy distributions of sputtered Si and Au atoms are shown in figures 6 (a) and (b) respectively. It can be clearly seen that energies of sputtered Si and Au atoms vary from few eV to few hundreds of eV. These energetic sputtered atoms get deposited onto the substrate leading to the formation of ultra-thin films containing Au, Si and O atoms. The relative concentrations of Au, Si and O atoms in the films depend on (i) the coverage of Au foils on Si wafer and (ii) the sputtering yields of Au and Si by 1.5 keV Ar atoms. The sputtering yields for Si and Au have been estimated to be 2.7 and 5.6 atoms per individual Ar atom respectively from SRIM calculations [35]. These sputtered Si and Au atoms with energies varying from few eV to few hundreds of eV continuously irradiate the films, with decreasing fluence, during deposition. Decrease in fluence with increasing energy is due to the energy distribution of the sputtered atoms as shown in figure 6 (a) and (b). The projected ranges of these sputtered atoms are estimated to be in the range of few angstroms to about 2 nm depending on their energy. The estimated projected ranges of Si and Au atoms in the nanocomposite with 11 % Au are shown in figure 6 (c) as a function of their energy. The sputtering yield of Au as a function of the energy of Si and Au atoms irradiating the nanocomposite are shown in figure 6 (d). It can be clearly seen that the majority ($\sim$ 90 %) of sputtered Si and Au atoms having energies lower than 60 eV get deposited into sub-nm thick surface layers without sputtering Au atoms. However, irradiations with Si and Au atoms with still higher energies lead to sputtering of Au atoms from the films. But, the rates of sputtering are rather low, with the maximum rate reaching only 0.06 Au atoms/atom. From this it is clear that sputtering does not play a very significant role in the growth kinetics.

Irradiations with energetic sputtered atoms lead to enhanced diffusivity of Au in the films. This combined with the low solubility of Au in SiO_2 favors clustering and leads to the growth of Au NPs. However, the nucleation and growth of Au NPs critically depends on the average inter-particle separation (r_a) of Au atoms in the film, which is controlled by areal coverage of Au foils on Si target. Using our RBS results, the values of r_a have been estimated to be $\sim$ 1.5, 0.64 and 0.5 nm for nanocomposite films with Au concentrations of 1.2, 11 and 20 % respectively. The nucleation and growth of Au NPs occurs when the inter-particle separation (r_a) is comparable or smaller than the diffusion length (l_d) of Au in SiO_2 matrix and does not occur if r_a is greater than l_d. In the present case, r_a is smaller than l_d for films with Au concentrations of 11 and 20 % which favors the formation of NPs in the co-sputtered films. The present data indicates that the diffusion length of Au atoms in silica is larger than 0.64 nm but smaller than 1.5 nm. The size of NPs formed depends on the Au content of the films and energies of the sputtered atoms irradiating the films during its growth. An increase in the Au content of the films is expected to help in the growth of Au NPs with increased density. However, the observed narrowing of the size distribution with increasing Au content of the films is noteworthy and is an attractive feature of the present technique. This indicates that irradiations with energetic sputtered atoms during deposition play an important role. Stepina et al. [36] have shown that irradiation of Ge NPs with 100-200 eV Ge ions during their growth leads to the formation of an increased density of Ge NPs with a narrower size distribution. In our case, irradiation of film with sputtered Si and Au atoms with energies > 100 eV can lead to desorption of Au atoms from bigger NPs onto the surface, which agglomerate forming smaller NPs. We believe an interplay between the above processes leads to the formation of an increased density of Au NPs with a narrow size distribution.

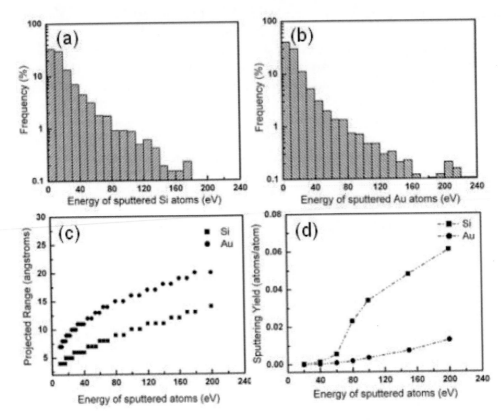

Figure 6. SRIM simulation results showing the energy distributions of (a) Si and (b) Au atoms sputtered by irradiation with 1.5 keV Ar atoms at an incidence angle of 45°. (c) The projected range of sputtered Si and Au atoms in the nanocomposite film (11 % Au) as a function of their energy. The estimated sputtering yields of Au as a function of the energies of sputtered Si and Au atoms, irradiating the nanocomposite with 11 % Au, are shown in (d). (Reprinted with permission from S. Mohapatra, Y.K. Mishra, D.K. Avasthi, D. Kabiraj, J. Ghatak, S. Varma, J. Phys. D: Appl. Phys. 2007, 40, 7063. Copyright [2007], IOP Publishing).

Synthesis of nanoparticles embedded in dielectric matrix (nanocomposite thin film) by atom beam sputtering results in a better size distribution as compared to thermal co-evaporation and ion implantation. Synthesis by ion implantation results in non-uniform depth distribution of NPs. The restricted amount of incorporated metal and depth inhomogeneity of the implanted profile due to range straggling puts severe limitations in the synthesis of NPs of well-defined size and size distribution. In case of synthesis by thermal co-evaporation annealing is required for the formation of NPs since the average energy of evaporated atoms is very low (fraction of eV) which is insufficient for the growth of NPs in the as-deposited films. However, the present technique of atom beam sputtering results in the formation of NPs in the as-deposited films. The most important advantage of this technique is that the thickness of films, with NPs uniformly distributed over it, can be easily increased by increasing the deposition time. This in particular is bit tedious by ion implantation, which has to involve multiple energy implants with varying fluences. Atom beam sputtering is much simpler than ion implantation since by controlling the metal fraction on the target, NPs with uniform size and depth distribution can be easily synthesized. Further, nanoparticles of any material, available in solid form, can be easily synthesized by atom beam sputtering while it is difficult by ion beam techniques.

CONCLUSION

In summary, we have synthesized Au NPs with controlled size by atom beam co-sputtering, a novel approach. Annealing of Si rich Au-SiO$_2$ nanocomposite above eutectic temperature of Au and Si resulted in the formation of Au-Si core-shell nanostructure with tunable surface plasmon resonant absorption. Ge NPs embedded in silica were also synthesized by atom beam co-sputtering followed by annealing. Annealing of Ge-silica nanocomposites at higher temperatures resulted in growth of Ge NPs together with the formation of Ge-Si NPs. We have also synthesized Ni doped ZnO films by atom beam co-sputtering, which showed two orders of magnitude variation in the resistivity as compared to undoped ZnO films. The processes involving the nucleation and growth of metal NPs by atom beam co-sputtering are discussed. The superiority of atom beam sputtering over thermal co-evaporation and ion implantation for the synthesis of NPs in insulating matrix is demonstrated.

REFERENCES

[1]   Ozbay, Ekmel. *Science (2006) 311, 189-193.*

[2]   Yin, Y. ; Alivisatos, A. P. *Nature (2005) 437, 664-670.*

[3]   Alivisatos, A. Paul. *Nature Biotechnology (2003) 22, 47-52.*

[4]   Shenoy, D.; Fu, W.; Li, Jane; Crasto, C.; Jones, G.; Dimarzio, C.; Sridhar, S., and Amiji, M. *Int. J. Nanomedicine (2006) 1, 51-57.*

[5]   Aslan, K.; Lakowicz, J. R.; Geddes, C. D. *Anal. Biochemistry (2004) 330, 145-155.*

[6]   Pitsillides, C. M.; Joe, E. K.; Anderson, R. R.; and Lin, Charles P. *Biophysical Journal (2003) 84, 4023-4032.*

[7]   Sokolov, K.; Follen, M.; Aaroa, J.; Pavlova, I.; Malpica, A.; Lotan, R.; and Kortum, R. R. *Cancer Research (2003) 63, 1999-2004.*

[8]   Huang, X.; Sayed, I. H. El.; Qian, Wei; and Sayed, Mostafa El. *J. Am. Chem. Soc. (2006) 128, 2115-2120.*

[9]   Biswas, A.; Aktas, O. C.; Schurmann, U.; Saeed, U.; Zaporojtchenko, V.; Faupel, F.; and Strunskus, T.; *Appl. Phys. Lett. (2004) 84, 2655-2657.*

[10]   Takele, H.; Greve, H.; Pochstein, C.; Zaporojtchenko, V.; and Faupel, F. *Nanotechnology (2006) 17, 3499-3505.*

[11]   Kabiraj, D.; Abhilash S. R.; Vanmarcke, L.; Cinausero, N.; Pivin, J. C.; and Avasthi, D. K. *Nucl. Instr. and Meth. B (2006) 244, 100-104.*

[12]   Mohapatra, S.; Mishra, Y. K.; Kabiraj, D.; Avasthi, D. K.; Ghatak, J.; and Verma, S. *Appl. Phys. Lett. (2008) 92, 103105.*

[13]   Mishra, Y. K.; Mohapatra, S.; Singhal, Rahul; Avasthi, D. K.; Agarwal, D. C.; and Ogale, S. B. *Appl. Phys. Lett. (2008) 92, 043107.*

[14] Mohapatra, S.; Mishra, Y. K.; Avasthi, D.K.; and Kabiraj, D.; Ghatak, J.; and Verma, S. *J. Phys. D: Appl. Phys. (2007) 40, 7063-7068.*

[15] Mohapatra, S; Mishra, Y.K.; Ghatak, J.; Kabiraj, D.; and Avasthi, D.K. *J. Nanosci. and Nanotech. (2008) 8, 4285-4289.*

[16] Avasthi, D. K.; Mishra, Y. K.; Kabiraj, D.; Lalla, N. P.; and Pivin, J. C. *Nanotechnology (2007) 18, 125604.*

[17] Mishra, Y. K.; Mohapatra, S.; Kabiraj, D.; Mohanta, B.; Lalla, N. P.; Pivin, J. C.; and Avasthi, D. K. *Scripta Mater. (2007) 56, 629-632.*

[18] Mishra, Y. K.; Mohapatra, S.; Avasthi, D. K.; Kabiraj, D.; Lalla, N. P.; Pivin, J. C.; Sharma, H.; Kar, R.; and Singh, Neeta. *Nanotechnology (2007) 18, 345606.*

[19] Agarwal, D.C.; Singh, F.; Kabiraj, D.; Sen, S.; Kulriya, P.K.; Sulania, I.; Nozaki, S; Chauhan, R.S.; and Avasthi, D.K. *J. Phys. D: Appl. Phys. (2008) 41, 045305.*

[20] Agarwal, D.C.; Avasthi, D.K.; Singh, F.; Kabiraj, D.; Kulriya, P.K.; Sulania, I.; Pivin, J.C.; and Chauhan, R.S. *Surf.and Coat. Tech. (2009) 203, 2427.*

[21] Warang, Trupti N.; Kabiraj, D.; Avasthi, D.K.; Jain, K.P.; Joshi, K.U.; Narsale, A.M.; Kothari, D.C. *Surf. and Coatings Tech. (2009) 203, 2506-2509.*

[22] Pandey, B.; Ghosh, S.; Srivastava, P.; Kabiraj, D.; Shripati, T.; Lalla, N.P. *Physica E (2009) 41, 1164-1168.*

[23] Rao, N. Srinivas; Dhamodaran, S.; Pathak, A.P.; Kulriya, P.K.; Mishra. Y.K.; Singh, F.; Kabiraj, D.; Pivin, J.C.; Avasthi, D.K. *Nucl. Instr. Meth. B (2007) 264, 249-253.*

[24] Ghosh, S.; Srivastava, P.; Pandey, B.; Saurav, M.; Bharadwaj, P.; Avasthi, D.K.; Kabiraj, D.; Shivaprasad, S.M. *Appl. Phys. A (2008) 90, 765-569.*

[25] Mishra, Y. K.; Kabiraj, D.; Mohapatra, S.; and Avasthi, D. K.; *Syn. React. Inorganic, Metal-Organic, and Nano-Metal Chemistry (2007) 37, 357-362.*

[26] Kreibig, U.; and Volmer, M. *Optical Properties of Metal Clusters: Springer Series in Materials Science 25*; Springer: Berlin (1995).

[27] Roiz, J.; Oliver, A.; Munoz, E.; Fernandez, L. R.; Hernandez, J. M.; and Cheang, J. C.; and Wong, *J. Appl. Phys. (2004) 95,1783-1791.*

[28] Hanaizumi, O.; Ono, K.; Ogawa, Y.; Matsumoto, T.; Yoda, H.; and Shiraishi, K. *Appl. Phys. Lett. (2004) 84, 3843-3845.*

[29] Daniel, M. Christine; and Astruc, D. *Chem. Rev. (2004) 104, 293-346.*

[30] Maxwell-Garnett, J.C. Philos. *Trans. R. Soc. London (1904) 203, 385-420; (1906) 205, 237-288.*

[31] Kim, K.S.; Davis, R.E. *J. Electron. Spetrosc. Relat. Phenom. (1972/1973) 1, 251.*

[32] Kottman, J. P.; and Martin, O. J. F. *Opt. Lett. (2001) 8, 655-663.*

[33] Lamprecht, B.; Schider, G.; Lechner, R. T.; Ditlbacher, H.; Krenn, J. R.; Leitner, A;.and Aussenegg, F. R. *Phys. Rev. Lett. (2000) 84, 4721-4724.*

[34] Mishra, Y.K.; *Ph.D Thesis;* Jawaharlal Nehru University, New Delhi, (2008).

[35] Ziegler, J.F.; Biersack, J.P.; and Littmark, U. *The Stopping and Range of Ions in Solids*; Pergamon; New York, (1985).

[36] Stepina, N.P.; Dvurechenskii, A.V.; Armbrister, V.A.; Kesler, V.G.; Novikov, P.L.; Gutakovskii, A.K.; Kirienko, V.V.; Smagina, Zh.V.; Groetzschel, R. *Appl. Phys. Lett. (2007) 90, 133120-133122.*

In: Synthesis and Engineering of Nanostructures...
Editors: Devesh Kumar Avasthi & Jean Claude Pivin

ISBN 978-1-62100-261-1
© 2012 Nova Science Publishers, Inc

Chapter 4

LOW ENERGY ION BEAM ASSISTED DEPOSITION OF TiN-Ni NANOCOMPOSITE COATINGS

J. P. Rivière [a], A.Akbari [a,b], M.F Beaufort [a] and C. Templier [a]

[a]Laboratoire de Physique des Matériaux UMR CNRS 6630 - Université de Poitiers Bd M. et P Curie SP2MI, BP 30179, 86962 Chasseneuil Futuroscope, France
[b]Department of Materials Engineering, Sahand University of Technology, PO Box 51335-1996, Tabriz, Iran

ABSTRACT

Using ion beam assisted methods, we have designed and produced novel hard and tough nanocomposite coatings consisting of hard TiN nanograins, embedded in a soft metallic intergranular phase of Ni. The microstructural properties: phases, grain size, and texture of the coatings, have been investigated by X-Ray Diffraction and High Resolution Transmission Electron Microscopy. In the composition range 0-22,5 at% Ni, δ-TiN is the only crystalline phase and Ni appears as an X Ray amorphous phase. The hardness increases up to a maximum of 41 GPa at ~7 at.% Ni, which corresponds to a TiN crystallite size of ~ 8 nm and a Ni intergranular phase thickness of roughly 1 monolayer. It is shown that the hardness enhancement in TiN-Ni nanocomposite coatings is not correlated with residual stresses, instead with the intrinsic properties of the nanostructure. An important improvement in wear resistance is obtained for the coatings, exhibiting the highest toughness and not the highest hardness. These results show that ion assisted processing is an effective tool for producing dense TiN-Ni nanocomposite coatings and tailoring their structure and mechanical properties.

1. INTRODUCTION

Decreasing the grain size of a crystalline material to the nanometer range, leads to considerable changes in plastic deformation mechanisms, which are controlled by new grain boundary mediated processes, responsible of the decrease of hardness known as "inverse Hall-Petch" effect [1,2]. One solution for preventing this softening effect has led to the concepts of superhard nanocomposite coatings, composed of hard nanocrystalline grains, covered by an amorphous phase of only one or two monolayers [3-5]. This new category of coatings has recently attracted increasing research interest, due to the possibility of synthesizing materials, with new physical and mechanical properties [6-8]. The extremely high hardness values obtained with such coatings are the consequences of the combination of grain refinement, hardening and blocking of grain boundary sliding by formation of a strong interface between both phases [5-8]. Most of PVD methods [9-11], used to deposit nanocomposite coatings are based on reactive magnetron sputtering, however ion beam assisted deposition technique could be very useful for controlling independently, the atomic vapour and reactive assistance with nitrogen ions [12,13]. It is also well known that the bombardment of a growing film with more or less energetic ions or the energetic condensation of atoms are very successful techniques to produce much denser films and at lower temperatures than by conventional deposition methods. Nanocomposite nc-TiN/a-Si$_3$N$_4$ coatings have been the deeply studied during the last ten years [3,6,7,14] and hardness values up to 50 GPa have been measured. However, hardness is not a functional property and for wear resistant applications, nanocomposite coatings must exhibit a high resistance to brittle fracture, which implies that a high toughness is also necessary, in addition to a high hardness [15-17]. It appears that nanocomposites coatings made of a hard nanocrystalline phase and a soft one such as TiN-Ni, could be of particular interest for tribological applications [13,18]; however none of the previous works, using either cathodic arc or reactive magnetron sputtering [19,20], has resulted in this system in the formation of a nanocomposite structure because of an inefficient phase segregation during deposition.

In this work, we will use the specific advantages of ion beam assisted deposition for producing and tailoring the structure and properties of TiN-Ni nanocomposite coatings.

2. DEPOSITION AND CHARACTERIZATION OF HARD COATINGS (TIN-NI NANOCOMPOSITES)

2.1. Deposition

TiN-Ni films (~0.5 μm thick) containing from 0 up to 21,5 at.% Ni were deposited at different temperatures RT, 200°C, 300°C, 400°C using an ultrahigh vacuum NORDIKO-3000 ion beam sputtering system, equipped with two RF plasma sources and two cryogenic pumps (base pressure $\leq 1.33 \times 10^{-6}$ Pa). The target was a 15 cm water-cooled 99.99% pure Ti circular plate, covered with two 99.99% pure Ni plates. The Ni surface proportion under beam was adjusted to obtain the desired Ni composition. Sputtering was carried out with a primary Ar ion beam with an acceleration voltage of 1200 V and an incident angle of 45°. Prior to deposition, the composite target was sputter cleaned for 10 min, with the primary Ar ion beam. A secondary ion source feeded with a mixture of Ar and N$_2$ gases was used for reactive assistance during the deposition. In order to obtain high deposition rate, to stay close to the stoichiometry of the TiN phase and to limit the re-sputtering effects during growth, the voltage and current of the assistance ion gun were chosen at 50 V and 40mA, respectively [21]. The angle between the secondary beam and the substrate was 45°. The N$_2$ and Ar flows of the assisted beam were held constant and both equal to 2 sccm for the whole set of samples. During deposition, the total pressure in the chamber was 3.33×10^{-2} Pa and the target-to-substrate distance was 30 cm. Different types of substrates were used: Si(100) wafers covered with native oxide (approx. 2 nm thick), for chemical and structural analysis and for tribological tests and hardness measurements mirror polished ($R_a \sim 0.01$-$0.014 \mu m$), M2HSS steel disks and TA6V alloy discs either untreated (hardness ~3 GPa) or plasma nitrided 12 hours at 600°C (hardness ~9 GPa). All substrates were successively cleaned for 15 min in two ultrasonic baths, containing acetone and ethyl alcohol respectively. Coating thickness was determined measuring a step height using a surface profilometer Dektak II system.

2.2. Chemical Composition and Phase Characterization

The film composition was obtained from Rutherford backscattering spectroscopy (RBS) using 3.2 MeV He^{+2} ion beam at the ARAMIS facility, Orsay France. The analysis of the RBS spectra was carried out using the SIMNRA software [22], in order to obtain elemental composition. The results are in good agreement with those from energy dispersive spectroscopy (EDS) analysis. The existing phases and crystallographic structure of the deposited films were examined using a Siemens (D5005) diffractometer operating at 40 kV and 30 mA, equipped with a secondary monochromator selecting the Cu K_α radiation. XRD scans were recorded, either in the conventional θ–2θ or in the Grazing Incidence X-ray Diffraction (GIXRD) configurations. The average grain size was deduced from the Scherrer's equation applied to the (200) GIXRD peaks, whose width was corrected from the instrumental broadening. Transmission electron microscopy (TEM) observations were performed using Jeol 200 CX microscope and a JEOL 2200FS. The latter was used to obtain high-resolution image and elemental maps of Ti and Ni, operated at 200 kV, with point resolution of 2.3 Å and energy resolution of 1eV. Samples for cross sectional observations were prepared, using tripod polishing followed by ion beam thinning.

2.3. Residual Stress Measurement

Stress analysis was performed using the crystallite group method (CGM), based on $Sin^2 \Psi$ method, developed to stress evaluation, in textured materials and coatings [23]; all crystallites with the same orientation are treated as being one crystal. After determining the strains for TiN (200) and TiN (111) oriented grain groups, the stress state evaluated using elastic data of single crystalline TiN presented by Zhang et al [24] and respected formula developed for given lattice and crystallographic planes. Measurements were performed on a four-circle SIEFERT diffractometer, using a Cu X-ray source with a 1×1 mm^2 point focus equipped with a Ni filter in the direct beam path to absorb the Cu K_β radiation. The incident beam was collimated using a 1 mm-diam fibre optics and focused on the sample mounted on an Eulerian cradle, for ψ tilting, where ψ is the angle between the specimen surface and the scattering plane.

2.4. Hardness and Tribology

Hardness tests were performed, using a nanohardness tester (CSEM Instruments), equipped with a Berkovich diamond pyramid. The tests were performed at RT, in the force-control mode of the machine. A three steps loading, holding and unloading cycle was used, every step lasting 30 sec. The calibration procedure suggested by Oliver and Pharr [25], was used to correct for the load-frame compliance of the apparatus and the imperfect shape of the indenter tip. The maximum load was varied between 0.2 mN and 300 mN, and it appeared that 1.5 mN, was the optimum load according to the 10% penetration depth rule [26]. The given results are the average of 15 measurements, with standard deviation used as error bars. Tribological tests were carried out using a ball on disc tribometer, at room temperature with humidity of about 50-55%, under normal loads of 2 and 4 N during 1500 and 5000 loading cycles. Test samples were 32 mm diameter discs and 8 mm height sliding against 5 mm diameter sapphire balls. The wear life was obtained from abrupt changes in the friction coefficient curves; more quantitative informations on the net removed volume of material (difference between the volume of the track below the initial surface and the pile-up volume each side of the track) were obtained from 3D analysis of wear tracks, coupled with SEM analysis for wear mechanisms.

3. ANALYSIS OF CHARACTERIZATION OF TIN-NI NANOCOMPOSITE THIN FILM

3.1. Chemical Composition and Microstructural Analysis

RBS analyses were performed using a 2 and 3.2 MeV He^{+2} ion beam. High energy of 3.2 MeV was selected for better peak separation. Standard Au, Pt, Al, Si samples were used in each series of samples for energy calibration. All coatings contain ~2 at.% of argon, which comes from the sputtering beam and is trapped during coating growth, and ~0.8 at.% of molybdenum, which comes from the accelerating grid of the ion source. Oxygen was always found to be lower than the detection limit of RBS; indicating that it is present at very low level; due to the high vacuum of $3 \ 10^{-6}$ Pa in the chamber prior deposition. For all deposition temperatures, the N/Ti ratio in TiN films is around 0,85, however the formation of stoichiometric TiN crystallites was identified from the analysis of the N-K-NEXAFS spectra [27]. Therefore, it can be stated that since the [N]/[Ti] concentration ratio is below 1 in all studied samples, the excess of the Ti atoms are located in the intergranular phase, forming intermetallic Ti-Ni bonds.

The XRD measurements in θ-2θ and grazing incidence configurations for films deposited at the different temperatures, indicate the presence of TiN peaks and no reflections from neither Ni nor Ni containing compounds indicating that Ni appears as an amorphous phase, even up to 22.5 at.% Ni. Figure 1 shows typical θ-2θ XRD patterns of TiN and TiN-Ni nanocomposite coatings deposited at T_s=300°C, on single crystalline Si; XRD patterns, obtained from the coatings, deposited on metallic substrates are very similar. However, the existence of a peak from the substrate close to the (200) TiN peak, makes more difficult calculations on that peak.

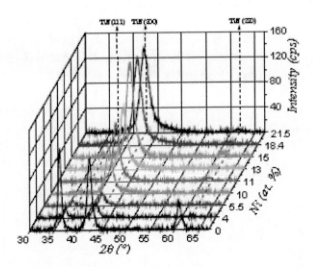

Figure 1. XRD patterns in θ-2θ configuration of ~0.5 μm thickTiN-Ni coatings deposited at 573 K.

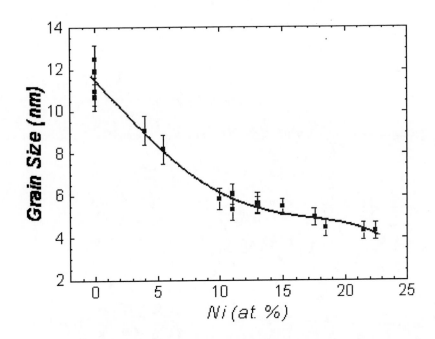

Figure 2. Variation of the grain size deduced from (200) peak as a function of the Ni content in TiN-Ni nanocomposite coatings deposited at 573 K.

The only observed crystalline phase is the NaCl type crystalline TiN structure (JCPDS 38-1420). It is noticed that a texture evolution takes place from TiN (111) to TiN (200) with Ni content and beyond 10 at.% Ni a pure (200) texture develops. Addition of Ni causes also a (200) peak broadening, which is the signature of a grain size decrease. This later on was estimated using the integral breadth method with peak integral breadth corrected for instrumental peak broadening using the Cauchy-Gauss method, applied to the (200) reflection. A monotonous decrease in grain size from about 12 nm for single phase polycrystalline TiN to about 4.5 nm for a TiN-22.5 at.% Ni nanocomposite coating is determined (Figure 2). The estimation of the average thickness of the Ni amorphous layer around the TiN crystallites was done, using simple geometrical considerations. The calculated values have been normalized by dividing the data by the first neighbour distance, in crystalline nickel (0.249 nm) and are expressed in terms of monolayer of nickel (ML). Figure 3 shows the variation of the Ni amorphous layer thickness (Ni coverage) as a function of the Ni content, which increases up to about 2 monolayer at 22.5 at.% Ni.

The schematic representation of the coating structure is given in Figure 4.

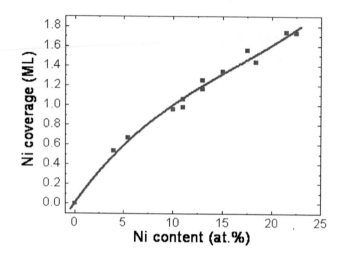

Figure 3. Calculated Ni coverage(number of monolayers) around TiN grains as a function of the Ni content.

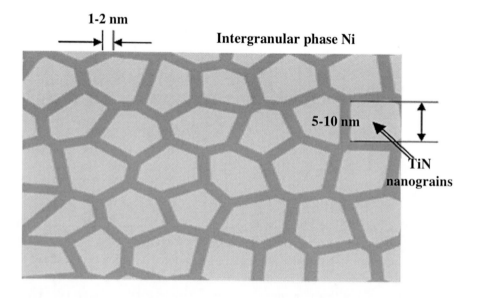

Figure 4. Schematic representation of a TiN-Ni nanocomposite film.

3.2. Internal Stresses

The ion beam assisted deposition technique used for the synthesis of TiN-Ni nanocomposite coatings results in a high level of biaxial compressive stresses in the films and an important question to address is whether hardness increase is mainly due to the nanostructure or the compressive stress in the coatings [28]. They have been determined using XRD analysis and crystallite group method (CGM) that is adapted to textured coatings and films. The true strain for a given {hkl} reflection in φ and ψ directions, is defined as:

$$\varepsilon_{\psi,\varphi}^{hkl} = \ln \frac{a_{\psi,\varphi}^{hkl}}{a_0} \tag{1}$$

where $a_{\psi,\varphi}$ and a_0 are the lattice parameters deduced from $d_{\psi,\varphi}(a_{\varphi\phi}^{hkl} = d_{hkl}\sqrt{(h^2 + k^2 + l^2)})$ corresponding to the lattice plane spacing of the {hkl} planes in a given direction and unstrained lattice parameter respectively. Linear elasticity leads to the relation between strain and stress, $\varepsilon_{ij} = s_{ij}\sigma_{ij}$, where s_{ij} are the material elastic compliances.. In the case of thin films the stress field can be modeled to be biaxial leading for (111) and (200) textures of fcc crystal the following equations:

$$Lna_{\psi,\varphi} = \left(2S_{12} + \frac{2}{3}J + \frac{S_{44}}{2}\sin^2\psi\right)\sigma + Lna_0 \text{ (111) fiber texture} \tag{2}$$

$$Lna_{\psi,\varphi} = \left[2S_{12} + (S_{11} - S_{12})\sin^2\psi\right]\sigma + Lna_0 \text{ (200) fiber texture} \tag{3}$$

where $(J = S_{111} - S_{12} - S_{44}/2)$ is the anisotropy factor of the material plotting of $Lna_{\psi,\phi}$ against $Sin^2\psi$ yields a straight line whose slope is proportional to the residual stress amplitude and the intercept corresponds to the stress free lattice parameter a_0 using single crystal TiN elastic constants obtained from ref. [23]. We have represented on Figure 5 the variation of the intrinsic stresses, calculated after removing the thermal stress contribution, as a function of Ni concentration at substrate temperature of 573 K. A monotonous stress decrease is observed from 6.6 GPa for TiN to 3.8 GPa for TiN-22.5 at.% Ni coatings.

3.3. Hardness and Thermal Stability

The variations of the nanocomposite coatings hardness as a function of the Ni content for coatings synthesized at 300°C are presented in Figure 6. One can notice that the hardness increases with Ni content, with a maximum hardness of 41 GPa reaching at about 6-7 at. % Ni, corresponding to a hardness enhancement of about 30%, with respect to the single phase TiN deposited under the same conditions. Beyond 10 at.% Ni the hardness decreases slowly and at 22.5 at.% Ni the hardness value is till about 23 GPa. When comparing the hardness variations with the intrinsic stresses variations in Figure 5, we can see, there is no correlation between hardness enhancement and residual stresses indicating that the hardness enhancement is an intrinsic effect, due to the nanocomposite structure. An important characteristic of hard ceramic-ceramic nanocomposite is their thermal stability up to high temperatures; in the case of metal-ceramic nanocomposite, the problem of their thermal stability is an open question. We have compared the hardness variation of TiN-Ni nanocomposite coatings before and after annealing under vacuum (~10^{-4} Pa), for 1 hour at 700°C; the results are presented in Figure 7. There is no evolution of the hardness after annealing even though a ~1-2GPa increase is observed depending on Ni content, with respect to the as deposited coatings. However the values are in the uncertainty intervals of measurements and this increase cannot be taken into account, but this clearly indicates a thermal stability of the coatings hardness up to 700°C.

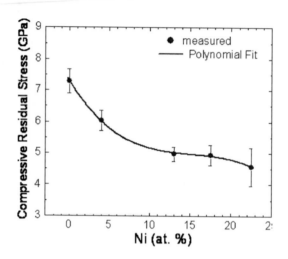

Figure 5. Variation of residual stresses as a function of the Ni content in nanocomposite TiN-Ni coatings deposited at Ts=573K.

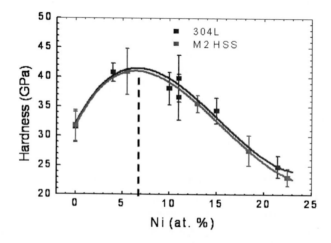

Figure 6. Hardness variation of nanocomposite TiN-Ni coatings deposited on two different steel substrates (AISI 304L and M2 HSS) as a function of the Ni content for coatings synthesized at 573K.

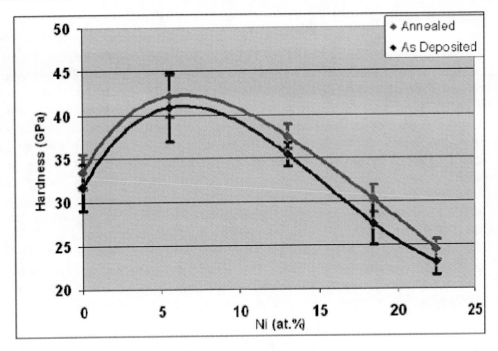

Figure 7. Comparison of hardness variation of nanocomposite TiN-Ni coatings deposited on M2 HSS for coatings synthesized at 573K (as deposited) and after annealing of 1 hour ay 973 K.

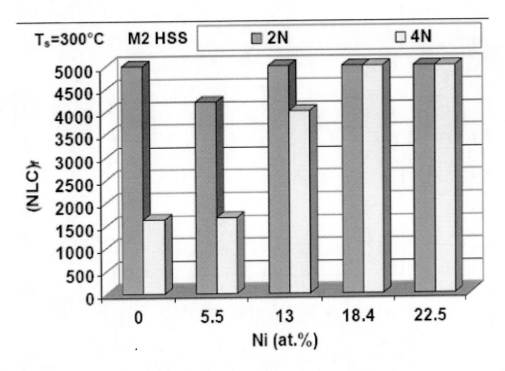

Figure 8. Wear life (NLC)f of TiN-Ni coatings deposited at Ts=573 K on M2 HSS for applied loads of 2N and 4N.

3.4. Wear Resistance

The wear resistance of series of TiN and TiN-Ni coatings (composition range 0-22.5 at.%
Ni), deposited at 300°C, on hardened M2 HSS were studied. The wear life of these coatings
for 2N and 4N normal loads is presented in Figure 8. The coatings supported the 5000 loading
cycles under 2N, without any failure at the exception of the coating with 5,5 at% Ni that
failed at 4000 cycles. For the wear tests under 4N load, an important wear life improvement is
noticed above 10 at% Ni. We have calculated the wear rate of the coating from the 3D
profilometry analysis of the wear tracks in the whole Ni composition range. Figure 9
represents the evolutions of the net removed material volume (NRV), during ball on disc wear
tests after 5000 revolutions for a 2N load. The net removed material volume increases as a
function of the Ni content up to 5.5 at.% Ni coating. This coating has a lower wear resistance
than the TiN coating, whereas its hardness is higher. The minimum material removal was
obtained for TiN-18.4 at.% Ni coatings, after 5000 revolutions. For this coating, an
enhancement in wear resistance of 20 times, is obtained with respect to the TiN coating, and
of 140 times with respect to uncoated M2 HSS. These results show that wear resistance of the
TiN-Ni nanocomposite coatings is not correlated with their hardness enhancement.

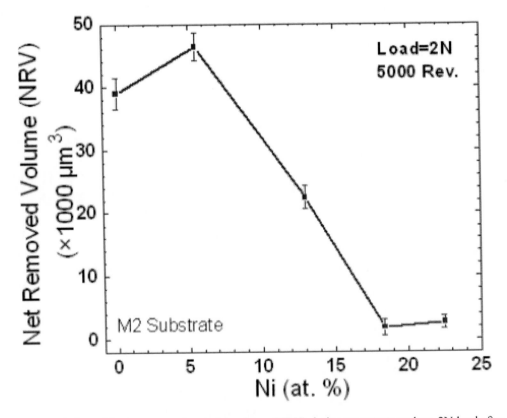

Figure 9. Variation of the net removed material volume (NRV) during wear tests under a 2N load after
5000 revolutions for TiN-Ni nanocomposite coatings deposited on M2 HSS.

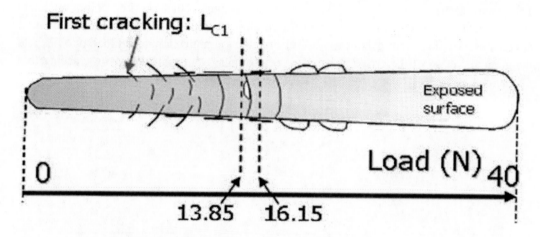

Figure 10. Schematic representation of scratch tests experiments.

Table I. Critical load for first cracking L_{C1} as a function of the Ni content in TiN-Ni nanocomposite films deposited at 300°C on M2HSS steel substrate

Ni at%	L_{C1} (N)
0	8.3
5,5	12.8
11	20
18.4	26
22.5	32

3.5. Qualitative Coating Toughness Evaluation

The failure mechanisms of high strength coatings are controlled by brittle failure and toughness is a key mechanical property, for designing wear resistant material, instead of strength or hardness alone. Most of the methods adapted to assessment of thin film toughness or fracture toughness, give mainly a qualitative evaluation [29,30]. The toughness of TiN-Ni nanocomposite coatings was evaluated, using scratch tests at increasing load and the results were compared qualitatively with those for the TiN coatings. Different failure modes can occur in a scratch test at increasing load but a few of them depend on adhesion and most of the other failure modes, which depend on plastic deformation and fracture within the coating are useful in the assessment of coating mechanical properties, for tribological applications [31,32]. The critical loads related to the longitudinal, angular, transverse semicircular cracks and coating chippings are the criteria for comparison of the intrinsic coating brittleness and the lower critical load L_{C1} can be used for comparing qualitatively the coating toughness as it is schematically shown in Figure 10 and the measured values are given in Table I. The single phase TiN coating starts to crack under the load L_{c1} = 8.3 N, but for the TiN-Ni nanocomposite coatings, the cracking threshold increases as a function of the Ni content. Schematic representation of scratch tests experiments at increasing load is shown in figure 10.

The comparison of scratch tracks in Figure 11 suggests that an important toughness enhancement is observed for TiN-Ni nanocomposites coatings. Other important effects of Ni are the absence of spallation and exposed substrate up to the maximum test load of 40 N, and the gradual change of the cracking behavior of coatings, from a brittle tensile cracking to a ductile one.

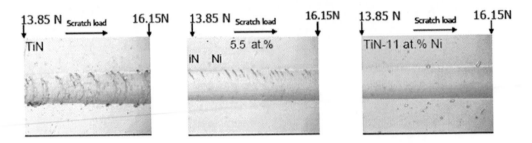

Figure 11. Scratch tracks in the load range 13,85-16,15 N for TiN-Ni nanocomposite coatings compared with TiN.

DISCUSSION- CONCLUSION

Under the present ion beam assisted deposition conditions, the growing film is continuously hit by energetic particles, which greatly affect the resulting microstructure as compared to that predicted from classical structure zone model diagrams, established for thermal evaporation or magnetron sputtering, for which the average incident particle energies are ~0.1 and ~2–5 eV, respectively. According to the SRIM computer code, ion beam sputtering of Ti and Ni targets by 1.2 keV Ar^+ ions gives sputtered Ti and Ni atoms with an average energy of 38 eV and 25 eV, respectively and reflected Ar (about 10% of the incident beam) with an average energy of 33 eV. All these particles have energy tail contributions extending up to 100–300 eV. At the working pressure, the mean free path is about 0.5 m, higher than the target to substrate distance. Therefore, these energetic particles are not thermalized before arriving the growing film and they contribute to the incident energetic flux, in addition to energetic ionic species (Ar^+, N^{2+}, and N^+), arriving from the assistance beam, with energy of 50 eV. Using the deposition rate, the Ar and N_2 flow rates, the ionization yield of the assistance gun, the current of the assistance beam and assuming that ionized species are Ar^+, N_2^+ and N^+, a rough estimate of the ion-to-atom flux ratio gives J_i /$J_{Ti} \cong 5.4$ for I_a=40 mA. Thus, ion irradiation effects are prevailing factors in the present deposition conditions. This continuous bombardment produces shallow collision cascades at the film surface and the transfer of additional energy to depositing atoms, increases the surface mobility, resulting in a dense microstructure and the enhancement of the phase segregation and the nucleation of TiN nanograins as well as the formation of the percolation network of the intergranular phase.

The growth mode of nanocomposite coatings can be explained by fundamental structure-forming phenomena of polycrystalline films [33,34]. The formation of the film structure starts with nucleation of TiN grains (major phase), with concurrent segregation of Ni atoms, as the size of nuclei increases. This leads to the formation of a tissue of Ni around TiN grains, limiting their growth and coalescence as well. In fact, the size of the TiN crystals at which their surface coverage will be complete, depends on the Ni concentration in the condensing vapour beam. A complete coverage blocks effectively, the grain growth and their coarsening during coalescence. At this stage, the condensation proceeds by repeated nucleation of the TiN phase on the formerly surfaces of TiN crystallites covered by the tissue of Ni, and the whole process repeats itself. At higher Ni concentration, as more Ni atoms segregate on the growing TiN crystallites, the process of repeated nucleation takes place rapidly, leading to effective grain refinement. While at low Ni concentrations partial coverage may occur, increasing the Ni deposition rate leads to a complete coverage with Ni of one or several monolayers (not clear). It is evident that for such a thin thickness, Ni will appear as an amorphous phase.

The enhanced ductility is the result of the ability of plastic deformation in the Ni phase boundary. The enhanced toughness is caused both by the three dimensionally modulated structure and the geometrical toughening mechanisms. Crack deflection, crack splitting and crack tip blunting, are possible operating mechanisms. The presence of "soft" metallic amorphous phase, instead of the hard ceramic phase reduces the possibility of brittle fracture, when cracks are deflected. Nanocomposite coatings offer high wear resistance, in terms of coating wear life and removed material volume. Finally, this review shows that toughness is an important property to take into account for designing wear resistant coatings.

REFERENCES

[1]   Chokshi A.H., Rosen A., Karch J. and Gleiter H., *Scripta Metallurgica* 1989, *23*, 1679-1684.

[2]   Valiev R. Z., Chmelik F., Bordeaux F., Kapelski G., and Baudelet B., *Scripta Metallurgica et Materialia* 1992, *27*, 855-860.

[3]   Vepřek S., Reiprich S., *Thin Solid Films* 1995, *268*, 64-71.

[4]   Vepřek S., *J. Vac. Sci. Technol. A* 1999, *17(5)*, 2401-4220.

[5]   Karvankova P., Vepřek-Heijman M.G.J., Azinovic Vepřek D., S., *Surface and Coatings Technology* 2006, *200*, 2978-2989.

[6]   Procházka J., Karvánková P., Vepřek-Heijman M.G.J. and Veprek S., *Materials Science and Engineering A* 2004, *384*, 102-116.

[7]   Vaz F., Rebouta L., Goudeau P., Pacaud J., Garem H., Rivière J.P., Cavaleiro A., Alves E., *Surface and Coatings Technology* 2000, *133-134*, 307-313.

[8]   Patscheider J., Zehnder T. and Diserens M., *Surface and Coatings Technology* 2001, *146-147*, 201-208.

[9]   Musil J. and Vlček J., *Surface and Coatings Technology* 2001, *142-144*, 557-566.

[10] Martin P.J and Bendavid A., *Surface and Coatings Technology* 2003, *163-164*, 245-250.

[11] Carvalho S., Rebouta L., Ribeiro E., Vaz F., Denannot M. F., Pacaud J., Rivière J.P., Paumier F., Gaboriaud R.J. and Alves E., *Surface and Coatings Technology* 2004, *177-178*, 369-375.

[12] Colligon J.S., Vishnyakov V., Valizadeh R., Donnelly S. E. and Kumashiro S., *Thin Solid Films* 2005, *485*, 148.

[13] Akbari A., Riviere J.P., Templier C., LeBourhis E., *Surface and Coatings Technology*. 2006, *200*, 6298.

[14] Diserens M. and Patscheider J., F. Lévy, *Surface and Coatings Technology* 1999, *120-121*, 158-165.

[15] Holmberg K., Ronkainen H., Matthews A., *Tribology of thin coatings*, Ceramics *International* 2000, *26*, 787-795.

[16] Sundgren J.E and Hentzell H.G., *J. Vac. Sci. Technol. A* 1986, *4(5)*, 2259-2279.

[17] Zhang S., Sun D., Fu Y. and Du H., *Surface and Coatings Technology* 2003, *167*, 113-119.

[18] Akbari A., Riviere J.P. and Templier C., *International Journal of Moder Physics B*, 2008, *122, Nos18-19*, 2979-2988.

[19] Nakayama A., Yoshioka T. and Nomura T., *Fundamental studies on Ni-TiN nano-composite films synthesized by vacuum arc deposition method*, in: *T.S. Sudarshan, K. Ishizaki, M. Takata, K. Kamata (Eds.), Surface Modification Technologies VII, by The Institute of Materials, London*, 1994, 315-325.

[20] M. Irie, H. Ohara, A. Nakayama, N. Kitagawa, T. Nomura, *Nucl. Instr. Meth. Phys. Res. B* 1997, *121 (1)*, 133-136.

[21] Abadias G. and Tse Y.Y., *Surf. Coat. Technol.* 2004, *180-181*, 33-40.

[22] Mayer M., SIMNRA, a Simulation Program *for the Analysis of NRA, RBS and ERDA*, Proceedings of the 15th International Conference on the Application of Accelerators in Research and Industry, J. L. Duggan and I.L. Morgan (eds.), American Institute of Physics Conference Proceedings 1999, *475*, 541.

[23] Hauk V., *Elsevier, New York*, 1997.

[24] Zhang M. and He J., *Surface and Coatings Technology* 2001, *142-144*, 125-131.

[25] Oliver W.C., Pharr, G.M. *J. Mater. Res.* 1992, *7*, 1564-1593.

[26] Pharr G.M. and Oliver W.C., *MRS Bulletin* 1992, *17(7)*, 28-33.

[27] Pinakidou F., Katsikini M., Paloura E.C., Akbari A., Riviere J.P., *IC4N Conference Halkidiki Grèce, June 16-18 2008 Materials Science and Engineering B (to appear in 2010)*

[28] Akbari A., Riviere Templier J.P. C., Bourhis E. Le, Abadias G., *Rev.Adv.Mater.Sci.* 2007, *14*, 14-34.

[29] Zhang S., Sun D., Fu Y., Du H., *Surface and Coatings Technology* 2005, *198*, 74-84.

[30] Bull S.J., Berasetegui E.G., *Tribology International* 2006, *39*, 99-114.

[31] Darbeïda A., Von Stebut J., *Actes des Journées d'études, Ecole des mines, Nancy, France* 1995.

[32] Bull S.J., *Tribology International* 1997, *30*, 491-498.

[33] Barna P.B. and Adamik M., *Thin Solid Films*, 1998, *317(1-2)*, 27-33.

[34] Barna P.B., Adamik M., Lábár J., Kövér L., Tóth J., Dévényi A. and Manaila R., *Surface and Coatings Technology* 2000, *125(1-3)*, 147-150.

In: Synthesis and Engineering of Nanostructures…   ISBN 978-1-62100-261-1
Editors: Devesh Kumar Avasthi & Jean Claude Pivin   © 2012 Nova Science Publishers, Inc

Chapter 5

NANOSTRUCTURED SOFT MAGNETIC FILMS: ELABORATION, PERFORMANCES AND APPLICATIONS FOR TRILAYERED SENSORS BASED ON MAGNETO-IMPEDANCE EFFECT

F. Alves[1], L. AbiRached[1], Y. Le Bihan[1], J. Moulin[2], E. Dufour-Gergam[2], C. Schwebel[2] , A. Gupta[3] and V. Raghavendra Reddy[3]

1 LGEP, CNRS UMR 8507, Univ. Paris Sud , UPMC Univ. Paris 6 ; Supelec, plateau du Moulon, 11 rue Joliot-Curie, 91192 Gif sur Yvette, France
2.IEF, CNRS UMR8622, Univ Paris Sud, 91405 Orsay, France
3. UGC-DAE Consortium for Scientific Research, University Campus, Khanda Road, 452017 Indore, India

ABSTRACT

This chapter deals with elaboration and characterization of soft magnetic FeSiBCuNb thin films, patterned for magnetic sensors based on the magneto-impedance (MI) effect. Simulation tools based on finite elements method are also presented for the design optimization of these MI sensors.

1. INTRODUCTION

The sensors, we developed are based on the magneto-impedance (MI) effect, has attracted great interest, since it was discovered in Co-based wires by K. Mohri [1]. This effect has a classical electromagnetic origin (skin effect) and it consists on the change of impedance of the sensor with an applied external magnetic field. The variation can be of 1000% with sensitivities up to 400%/Oe, much higher than in the case of the giant magneto-resistance (GMR) effect (15%) [2]. This later was discovered in 1988 in Fe/Cr/Fe trilayers and Fe/Cr multilayers. They consist in anti-parallel ferromagnetic layers separated by a very thin (few nm) non ferromagnetic layer. Under external field, the magnetization of the anti-parallel layer turns along the external magnetic field direction. The electrical resistance of the device (high in the anti-parallel configuration) decreases with the field magnitude. 1D, 2D and 3D MI sensors produced by Aichi Micro Intelligent Corporation [3] are promising competitors in the magnetic sensors world market which expand 883 million US$ in 2002 (81% for Hall effect, 17% for anisotropic magneto-resistance (AMR) and GMR, 2% other technologies) [4] with 10% annual growth rate. The main user is the automotive market (70% of sales), 20% for process control applications. Medical devices, a growing market [5], are expected to reach 2-20 billion US$ in 2010. Requirements are smaller, faster, cheaper, more reliable sensors.

2. WHY A MI SENSOR? WHY TRILAYERED STRUCTURE? WHY INDUSTRY WANTS TO REDUCE SENSOR SIZE?

Among small sized and cheaper sensors, magneto-impedance effect offers a good compromise between transfer curve, sensitivity and resolution (see table 1). Magnetic macro-sensors (*i.e.* millimeter width), using annealed FeSiBCuNb (Finemet[TM]) ribbons have been already tested [6-7], the advantage of multilayer form (ferromagnetic alloy/ conductor/ ferromagnetic alloy) lies in the increase of MI ratio and the decrease of frequency of driven alternating current, compared to wire shaped structures, simply due to the skin effect δ figure

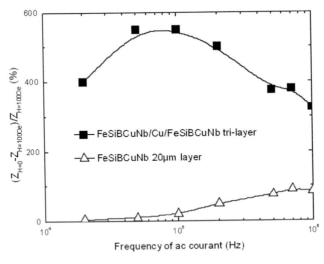

Figure1. Comparison of MI effect between one and tri-layer structures elaborated with ribbons 20μm thick (taken from ref [6], copyright (2008) by Elsevier).

In such kind of structure, impedance expression Z depends on geometrical, electrical and magnetic parameters namely length (l), width of the sensor(b), conductor thickness ($2d_1$), conductor conductivity (σ_1), ferromagnetic layer thickness (d_2), ferromagnetic layer conductivity (σ_2) and μ_t the transversal effective permeability obtained through Landau-Lifshitz-Gilbert (LLG) equations.

$$Z = R_{dc}\left(\frac{coth(x_1)coth(x_2)+\xi}{coth(x_1)+\xi coth(x_2)}\right)(\xi x_1 + x_2) \quad (1)$$

With $R_{dc}=\dfrac{\ell}{2b(\sigma_1 d_1+\sigma_2 d_2)}$, $x_1 = (1+j)\dfrac{d_1}{\delta_1}$, $x_2 = (1+j)\dfrac{d_2}{\delta_2}$, $\xi = \dfrac{\sigma_1 \delta_1}{\sigma_2 \delta_2} = \sqrt{\dfrac{\sigma_1 \mu_t}{\sigma_2}}$ (2)

Commercial magneto-impedance sensor has been tested in position feedback control on conveyor with superconducting magnetic levitation [8], in non destructive testing (NDT) application [9]. For high sensitive sensors, the main parameter is the intrinsic magnetic noise level, which should be as small as possible; one solution proposed by L.G.C. Melo *et al.* is the use of dc current biasing technique [10], reducing the white noise level down to $fT/\sqrt{Hz}$.

Table 1. Comparison of characteristics of some sensor technologies

Technology	Transfer curve	Size (length)	Sensitivity (pT/Hz$^{1/2}$)@10Hz	Resolution (Oe)
Anisotropic MR	0.4 (%/Oe)	1-100μm	10000	0.1
Giant MR	0.8 (%/Oe)	1-100μm	700	0.01
MI in FeCoNi wires	400 (%/Oe)	1-2 mm	300	10^{-6}
Hall with magnetic concentrators	0.2 (Ω/Oe)	μm	77000	
Search coil			4	10^{-8}
Fluxgate	0.003 (V/Oe)	1-100mm	5	10^{-6}
Squid		1μm-100mm	0.6	10^{-9}

Nowadays, the huge advantage of designing micro-sensors using clean-room facilities, is the implementation of large amount of sensors on small area. As an example, we elaborate multi-element sensors, based on MI effect (Figure2) for eddy-current non destructive testing (EC NDT) applications, in order to detect embedded defects, which requires high sensitivity to field at low frequency.

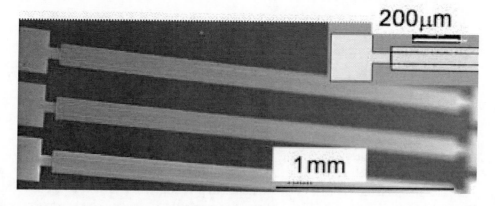

Figure 2. Photograph of multi-element trilayer structures.

Other application lies to dc-ac space magnetometers by introducing a "dc sensor" as MR, MI or Hall in the air gap, located between the magnetic concentrators of two search coils, to enhance the bandwidth of the space magnetometers [11].

Third application developed within an UniverSud Paris Consortium, between LGEP, IEF and PPSM laboratories, is the magnetic detection of assembly of FeNi@SiO_2 or Co@SiO_2 nano-particles, which includes synthesis of insulated (with silica) ferromagnetic nano-particles and realization of high sensitive MI sensor arrays compared to classical GMR sensor arrays, already developed by many academic or industrial research groups. These nano-particles are widespreadly used in biochemical laboratories for bio-separation. As an example, scientists at the Naval Research Laboratory (NRL) in Washington, D.C., have developed a DNA detector that relies on magnetic fields, rather than optics and fluorescence. The NRL's device, called BARC (Bead ARray Counter), comprises an array of magnetic field micro-sensors able to detect single micro-beads, and so in principle it could detect a single DNA molecule. To date, the BARC system has only been tested with samples of at least a few thousand bio-agent molecules [12].

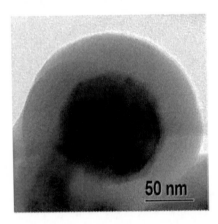

Figure 3. MET picture of Co@SiO2. Courtesy of M. Ammar, IEF, France.

3. ELABORATION ROUTE AND CHARACTERIZATIONS

The need for thin films deposition covers a wide range of industrial domains: optics (antireflection coatings), metallurgy (surface passivation or hardening) and of course microelectronics and Micro-Electro-Mechanical-systems (MEMS) fabrication. Among available deposition techniques, one can distinguish reactive techniques, that involve a chemical reaction, generally used for oxides layers deposition (CVD), non-reactive techniques for metal or metallic alloys deposition (evaporation, electrodeposition) and sputtering that is applicable for both types of materials.

Mass production requires equipments, with low cost, poor maintenance, large deposition zone and continuous functioning. Sputtering techniques are good candidates, for this. In addition, they are versatile enough to allow depositing conductive and non conductive thin films of complex alloys (Finemet^{TM} for instance) or materials containing refractory elements. Each element can be deposited separately, from pure targets (co-sputtering) or together from a target, containing the alloy. In the latter case, a shift in the composition can be observed, due to the different yield factor of each element. Nevertheless, the shift is constant and can be balanced by a judicious target. Finally, thick materials (several microns) can be deposited. For these reasons, ion beam and plasma sputtering have become the most current deposition techniques in industry. The former has the advantage to allow controlling separately the ions energy and flux through the measurement of the current (i.e. film thickness). The latter does not need expensive maintenance of the ion source.

Magnetic sensors had to fit numerous industrial requirements; high sensitivity, high spatial resolution in some applications, high thermal stability, low magnetostriction coefficient, linearity, low hysteresis...

FeSiBCuNb alloys after ad-hoc thermal annealing exhibit all these features as comparison to amorphous or crystalline systems. The layers are deposited on a silica/silicon substrate by RF (*13.56 MHz*) sputtering in Ar plasma at residual pressure 10^{-7} mbar and working pressure $3 \ 10^{-2}$ torr. The copper layer is obtained by 50 W dc sputtering. The thickness of the layers varies from 45 to 970 nm. The sensors are patterned using a lift-off technique of a 3 µm layer of AZ5214 photo-resist and are constituted of strips 50-500 µm wide and 0.25-5 mm long.

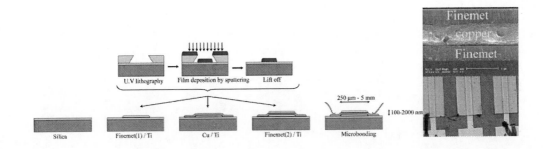

Figure 4. process steps of elaboration of tri-layer structures (taken from ref [13]).

Our first thin layers obtained in 2006, revealed magnetic hardness, coercive field around 15Oe. To understand this result, composition of the films has been checked using XPS and EDS experiments. The XPS analysis coupled with 1 keV Ar+ ion beam etching (Figure 5), shows unfortunately, despite its convenience, the sputtering technique leads to oxygen contamination in thin films, as deposition is most of the time realized in medium quality vacuum. O/Fe ratio is in the range of 75 % at the surface of the film. Oxygen contamination decreases from surface to core. Oxygen contamination depends on process parameters. To check the composition through the depth, EDS measurements were computed, using Noran commercial software and were related to Monte Carlo simulations, allowing an estimation of the e-beam penetration depth in the material, from 70 to 650 nm for 2 to 20 keV respectively (Figure7). Figure 8 shows that the film composition changes from surface to volume and reaches target nominal values at a depth of 160 nm. From Figure 6 and table 2, the Cu content is high (5%), compared to 1% of the target, which implies higher nucleation rate for FeSi nano-crystallites, as expected. Furthermore, low silicon content does not allow the magnetostriction volumetric averaging of the two phases ($\lambda_s^{FeSi} < 0$ and $\lambda_s^{amorphous \ phase} > 0$) and then films exhibit positive magnetostriction and are stress dependent.

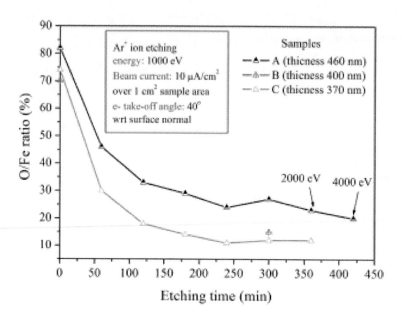

Figure5. X-Ray Photoelectron spectroscopy of FeSiBCuNb RF sputtered films.

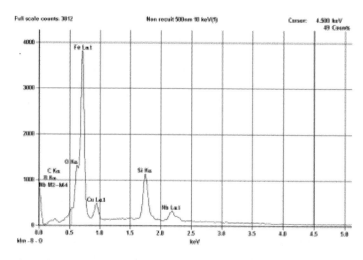

Figure 6: Energy Dispersive X-Ray spectroscopy.

Table 2. Quantitative Results of Atom % for as- deposited 500nm film

Element Line	5 keV	10 keV	15 keV
B K	8.06	7.95	7.78
Si K	7.03	11.57	14.73
Fe L	77.95	70.44	69.46
Cu L	5.32	7.59	4.95
Nb L	1.64	2.45	2.55

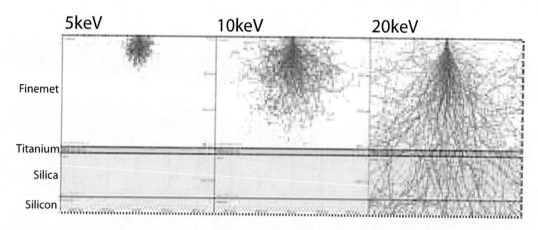

Figure 7. Monte Carlo simulations, allowing an estimation of the e-beam penetration depth in the material.

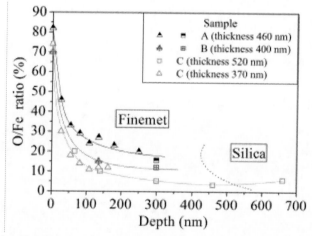

Figure 8. Depth related O/Fe atomic ratio for different samples using EDS (square) and XPS (triangle) (taken from ref [14]).

4. BENEFITS OF ANNEALINGS

As-deposited FeSiBCuNb films had to be annealed in order to relax stresses, induced during deposition process and to nanocrystallize the structure (Figure 9). As we observed on the hysteresis loops of samples 500 nm (ferromagnetic layer) thick annealed one hour in the chamber (residual pressure : $3 \ 10^{-7}$ mbar, heating rate 10°C min^{-1}) at different annealing temperatures, coercivity decreases up to 250°C (stress relaxation) and then increases (crystallization). Increasing the thickness of ferromagnetic layer also implies a lowering of coercivity. For enhanced magneto-impedance effect, magnetic anisotropy perpendicular to measuring field is required, which is easily obtained with a field annealing after deposition.

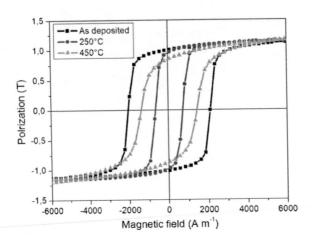

Figure 9. Effect of annealing on hysteresis loops of RF sputtered FinemetTM films (500nm).

Random Anisotropy Model (RAM) [15] in nano-crystalline alloys can be invoked to understand the thickness-coercivity relationship. In this model (Figure 10), the local magneto-crystalline anisotropy of the ferromagnetic FeSi grains is averaged in an exchange volume:

$K_{eff} = \dfrac{xK_1}{\sqrt{N}}$, where K_{eff} and K_1 are the effective and the intrinsic magneto-crystalline energy

respectively. In addition, the exchange length depends on material properties: $l_{ex} = \sqrt{\dfrac{A}{K_{eff}}}$.

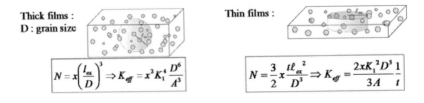

Figure 10. Random anisotropy model in thick or thin films.

$\lambda_{ex} \sim$ 1-2 μm in FeSiBCuNb systems, consequently in a film thinner than 1 μm, the RAM explain that $H_c \, \alpha \dfrac{1}{t}$.

Theoretically, we calculated for coercivity $H_c = p_c \dfrac{K_{eff}}{\mu_0 M_s} (0 \leq p_c \leq 1)$; $H_c(Oe) = \dfrac{65}{t(nm)}$ taking x = 80 %, K_1 = 10 kJm^{-3}, A = 10^{-11} J.m^2 and D = 10 nm). But experimentally, we obtain: $H_c(Oe) = \dfrac{5000}{t(nm)}$. This difference is due to the fact that we have to take into account both magneto-crystalline energy and stress due to thermal expansion effect in the contribution to local anisotropy energy [16]:

$$K_1 = K_{crist} + \lambda_f \sigma_{dilat} = K_{crist} + \lambda_f \left(\mu_w - \mu_f\right)\frac{E_f}{1-\upsilon_f}\,\Delta T$$

10 kJ m^{-3} 70-100 kJ m^{-3}

The thermal dependence of coercivity is mostly influenced by internal stress, that decreases at low temperature (below glassy transition) and increases with the crystallisation, because of thermal expansion effect. In conclusion, both stress and oxidation are responsible in the high coercivity, observed in the former thin films, which are partially removed in 2007, by using a liquid nitrogen trap, as shown by mass spectrometer investigation presented below. In 2009, by using this Nitrogen trap, combined with increased deposition rate, we succeeded (Figure 11) in obtaining ultra-soft magnetic films (coercivity less than 0.1Oe) with ad-hoc magnetic anisotropy orientation (see in Figure 12 the domain patterns observed by magneto-optical Kerr effect imaging). We observe on as-deposited samples well defined domain configurations with stripe domains at the edges of the sample delimited by dash lines. The sample 162, annealed under dc magnetic field of 45 kA/m magnitude, exhibits transversal anisotropy, as also confirmed by AGFM hysteresis measurements.

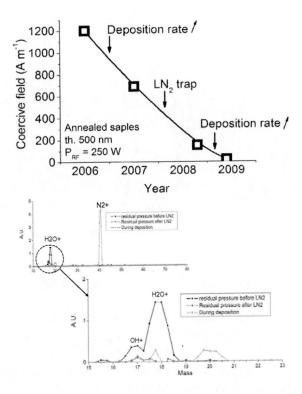

Figure 11. Analysis by mass spectrometer of the vacuum inside the chamber before/after using Liquid Nitrogen trap.

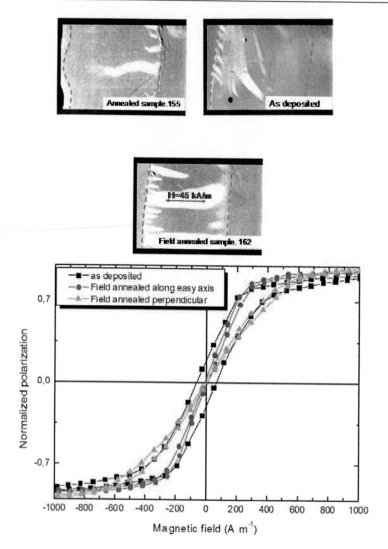

Figure 12. MOKE images and AGFM hysteresis loops of structured film deposition using shadow masking on 2*2mm² squared samples obtained in 2009 (taken from ref [17]).

5. SENSOR: FIRST MAGNETO-IMPEDANCE RESULTS

MI sensors have been tested under two-axis field H_{dc}, generated by the set of four Helmholtz coils. By means of the lock-in amplifier, we measure both real and imaginary parts of MI voltage. Results, presented here are relative to the TP configuration, namely, anisotropy field H_k perpendicular to the sample axis and H_{dc} parallel to I_{ac}. The impedance is function of frequency f, current amplitude I_{ac} and external field H_{dc} due to skin effect. MI ratio is defined as the relative variation of impedance between two magnetic states (demagnetized and saturated). Figure 13 shows that performances in term of sensitivity to field are mainly determined by shape factors (length/width, thickness ratio or width ratio between ferromagnetic and conductive layers).

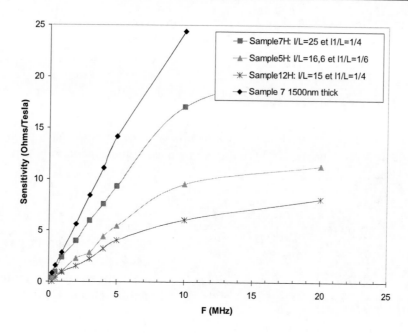

Figure 13. Frequency dependence of field-sensitivity (in ohms/Tesla) of MI sensors with different shape ratios. l, L, l1 represent the length of the sensor, the ferromagnetic layer and copper widths respectively. Cu/ferromagnetic thickness ratio is 1.5:1. Thickness of ferromagnetic layer of samples 5H, 7H, 12H is 500 nm.

The modeling of MI sensors allows us the evaluation and the improvement of their performances without the need to multiply the realization of costly prototypes. A fine modelling of MI sensors requires the use of numerical modelling methods. Among them, the finite element method (FEM) is particularly adapted, since it allows considering structures of arbitrary geometry and taking into account of anisotropic or nonlinear behavioral laws [18-19]. The FEM is based on a weak variation formulation of the problem. The solution of this formulation is done on a discretized space, obtained by meshing the study domain with elements. The fields to be calculated are obtained by a linear combination of simple functions (shape functions), deduced from the size and shape of the elements. These functions are generally defined at the nodes of the elements and are expressed as a linear combination of polynomial functions. The FEM leads to a matrix system which is generally symmetric and sparse. The solving of the algebric system provides an approximate solution of the problem. For the modeling of the MI sensor a magneto-dynamic formulation was used, taking into account the eddy currents and neglecting the displacement currents. It is based on the calculation of the magnetic vector potential and of the electric scalar potential at the nodes of the meshing with an applied current as source. Taking into account the high length of a MI sensor, compared to its depth and width, a bi-dimensional representation of it was adopted. A cross-section of the sensor is then considered and meshed with 2D elements (triangular in our case since it allows meshing of arbitrary shaped areas, (Figure 14). After solving the system, the electric and magnetic fields are deduced from the potentials. These fields allow computing of the power losses and the magnetic energy, which provide the sensor impedance real and imaginary parts, respectively (Figure 15). The simulations presented in figs 16-18 show how MI effect changes with shape ratios. The MI ratio is defined as follows:

$$MI(\%) = \frac{Z(H=0) - Z(H=Hsat)}{Z(H=Hsat)} \qquad (3)$$

The state, corresponding to H=0, is to consider in computations a relative permeability μ_r of ferromagnetic layer equal to 4000 (confirmed by measurements) and to take $\mu_r = 100$ for the state H=Hsat.

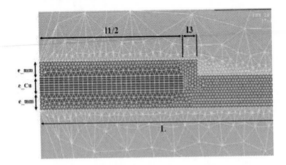

l1 : copper width
l3 : lateral ferromagnetic layer
e_Cu :Copper thickness
e_mm :ferromagnetic layer thickness
L :ferromagnetic layer width

Figure 14. Half meshed cross-section of the MI sensor. Red, purple and blue areas are related to copper, ferromagnetic layers and air, respectively.

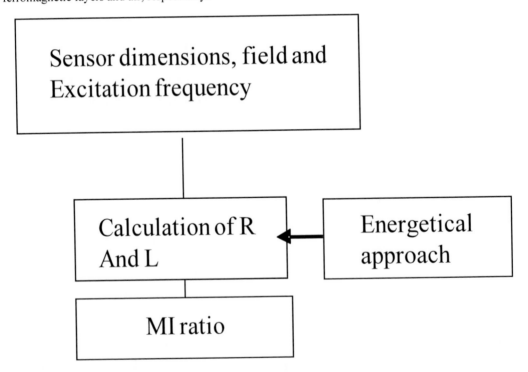

Figure 15: Flow chart of the design procedure.

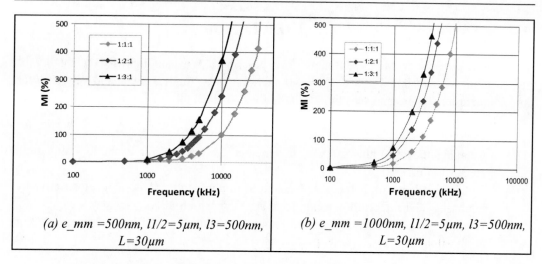

Figure 16. Thickness-frequency dependence of MI effect in trilayered ferromagnetic/conductor/ferromagnetic structure.

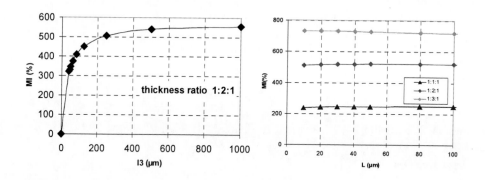

Figure 17. Effect of lateral ferromagnetic layer (l3) and ferromagnetic layer width (L) on MI effect.

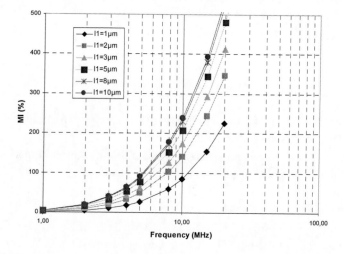

Figure 18. Incidence of copper layer width on MI effect.

CONCLUSION

Various aspects of MI based sensor are described. We can improve the quality of FeSiBCuNb nanocrystalline films for GMI sensors: MI ratio expected and required for application around 100% and sensitivity of 80%/Oe. To reach this goal, investigations have to be done in:

- Relaxing the remaining stresses in Finemet^{TM} films by, for example, using high energy ion irradiation,
- Obtaining films with homogeneous composition in depth and no-magnetostrictive by exploring others deposition techniques: laser deposition, IBS…
- Finding other ultra-soft magnetic films exhibiting significant MI effect for applications.

ACKNOWLEDGMNTS

This work was supported by the French ANR, through the IMAGINE project #05-NANO-067-01.

REFERENCES

[1]　Panina, L.V.; Mohri, K.; Bushida, K.; Noda, M. *J. Appl. Phys.* 1994, *vol 76,* 6198–6203.

[2]　www.nve.com.

[3]　www.aichi-mi.com.

[4]　www.frost.com.

[5]　www.intechnoconsulting.com

[6]　Alves,F.; Moutoussamy, J.; Coillot,C.;Abi Rached,L.;Kaviraj,B. *Sensors and Actuators A* 2008, *vol. 145-146,* 241-244.

[7]　Alves,F.; Bensalah,A-D. *Journal of Materials Processing Technology* 2007, *vol.181,*194–198.

[8]　Lizuka, T.; Sakai, N.; Fujita,H. *Sensors and Actuators* 2009, *vol. 150,*110-115.

[9]　Vacher, F.; Alves, F.; Gilles-Pascaud,C. *NDTandE International* 2007, *vol. 40,* 439–442.

[10]　Melo, L.G.C.; Ménard, D.; Yelon, A.; Ding, L.; Saez, S.; Dolabdjian,C. *J. Appl. Phys.* 2008, *vol.103, n°3,*33903-33906.

[11]　P. Leroy, "Mesures des champs magnétiques alternatifs et continus dans les plasmas naturels : développement d'un magnétomètre search–coil à bande étendue", *Thesis* 2007, UVSQ, France

[12]　www.spectrum.ieee.org/print/1534

[13]　Pascaud-Gilles, C.; Jaffres, H.; Nguyen van Dau, F. ; Alves, F. ; Moulin, J. ; Dominguez, D. ; Ruaud, C., *Contrôles-essais-mesures, March 2009, Sogi communication editions*

[14] Moulin, J. ; Kaviraj, B. ; Oubensaïd, E.H.; Alves, F.; Deshpande, U.P.; Gupta, A.; Dufour-Gergam, E. *Solid State Phenomena* 2009, *vol. 152-153,* 3-6.

[15] G. Herzer, *IEEE Trans. Magn.* 1990, vol. *26,* 1397-1402.

[16] J. Moulin *et al,* "Magnetic properties of stressed amorphous and nanocrystalline FeCuNbSiB thin films", communication JEMS'08 conference, September 2008, Dublin, Ireland.

[17] Moulin, J. ; Ammar, M.; Shah-Hosseini, I.; Alves, F. ; Mazaleyrat, F., *Journal of Physics, conference series 200/2010/082020*

[18] Ida, N.; Bastos, J.P.A. In *Electromagnetics and calculation of fields.* Ed. Springer, 1997.

[19] Sadiku, M.N.O. In *Numerical Techniques in Electromagnetics.* Ed.;CRC Press, 1992.

In: Synthesis and Engineering of Nanostructures…
Editors: Devesh Kumar Avasthi & Jean Claude Pivin

ISBN 978-1-62100-261-1
© 2012 Nova Science Publishers, Inc

Chapter 6

FORMATION AND INTERROGATION OF METAL AND SEMICONDUCTOR NANOSTRUCTURES BY keV ION BEAMS

Prasanta Karmakar[1]

Variable Energy Cyclotron Centre, 1/AF, Bidhannagar,
Kolkata 700 064, India

ABSTRACT

Nanostructure materials have opened the possibilities of new technology and basic science research from micro electronics to catalysis. Therefore, there is a formidable effort to develop experimental techniques, which are able to provide controlled nanostructures as well as their characterization. The low energy ion beam is a promising candidate for fabrication and characterization of nanostructures. The formation of ripples, dots, and kinetic roughening in a number of thin metal films, e.g. Au, Pt, Ag, Cu and Co and semiconductors such as Si(100) and TiO_2(110) under keV energy ion bombardment is discussed. The influence of initial surface roughness (perturbation) on the development of ion induced Si surface morphology is studied and the beginning of nanostructure formation by ion bombardment is explored. Low energy ion beams are also used to characterize the ion beam synthesized nanostructures. Neutralization of scattered Na^+ and K^+ ions is used to probe the electronic states of the sputter-induced Au nanoclusters. In contrast to the well known kinetically induced ion beam sputtering process, multi-charged Ar ion beam induced potential sputtering of the oxidized part of Si nano ripples is also illustrated.

---

[1] E-mail: prasantak@gmail.com.

1. INTRODUCTION

The study of interaction of ion beams with solids has both scientific and technological importance and there is a growing use of ion beams in the modification and analysis of solid materials. During keV energy ion solid interactions, the ions lose their energy by elastic and inelastic collision processes (Figure 1-1). The elastic collision results in sputtering, surface diffusion, implantation, recoil implantation, atomic mixing and backscattering of incident ions, while the inelastic part of the interaction may lead to emission of secondary electrons, secondary excited and ionized particles, optical photons and x rays [1,2]. Multiply charged ion solid interaction leads to some additional phenomena such as hollow atom formation, potential sputtering, radiation from projectile etc. due to the substantial potential energy stored in the projectile.

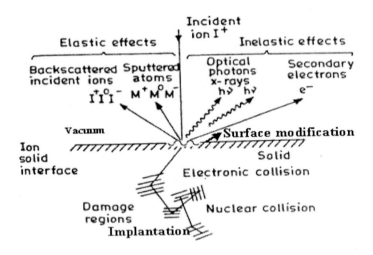

Figure 1.1. Schematic diagram of ion-solid interaction.

Here, I concentrate the discussion on single and multiple charge ion induced surface modification in nano scale. The energetic ion beam sputters as well as tends to mobilize the surface atoms. Due to the combined effect of sputtering and diffusion, the initial surface topography is modified and characteristic structures like cone, sphere, ripple, nano-dot or nano-hole are found to develop on the surface [3,4]. In contrast to the well- known kinetically induced ion beam sputtering process, a new phenomena called potential sputtering, i.e. the erosion of surfaces, exploiting the potential energy of the projectile, has also been illustrated.

The fabrication of nano scale structures has attracted considerable attention due to its applications in various optical, electronic and magnetic devices. Different techniques have been proposed for realization, but only a few can be operated on extended areas and have process parameters which can be easily controlled. Low energy ion sputtering belongs exactly to such type of technique for producing nano scale structure. When a collision cascade intersects the surface and sufficient energy is transferred to the surface atoms, exceeding the surface binding energy, the target atoms are ejected from the solid (Figure 1-2). This phenomena is called sputtering. The sputtering yield is defined as the number of emitted target atoms per incident ion $Y = J_{sp}/J_i$, where J_i and J_{sp} denote the flux of incident ions and sputtered atoms, respectively. A detailed understanding of sputtering requires target surface and bulk properties, projectile kinetic and potential energy, incidence angle, atomic masses and atomic numbers of collision partners and perhaps most importantly, an appropriate model of ion-atom and atom-atom interaction potential. However, during ion bombardment, an equally important phenomenon is ion induced surface diffusion [2].

The interplay between ion erosion and diffusion leads to a modified surface topography [3]. In 1956, Navez et al. [4] observed for the first time wave like structures by bombarding a glass surface by air ion beam. Later, a large variety of characteristic surface structures, ranging from stochastic rough surface to the formation of well-defined conical protrusions [5] are reported. Different scaling theories for the evolution of the surface roughness have been proposed [6], in order to understand the underlying physical processes involved and eventually determining a way of optimizing control of the process.

The review is organized as follows: section 2 deals with the theoretical approach developed to describe the morphology of ion sputtered surface. Section 3 contains a brief overview of the experimental results on surface morphology developed under ion sputtering. In section 4 our experimental results of surface roughening, dot and ripple formation on various polycrystalline thin films are described and compared with the existing theory. The detection of quantum confined states in sputtered induced Au nano clusters by neutralization of alkali ion during scattering is also illustrated in the same section. Finally, formation mechanism and dynamics of ion induced ripple structures of Si are presented in section 5 where multi charged ion induced Coulomb explosion sputtering of the selectively oxidized Si ripple is also discussed.

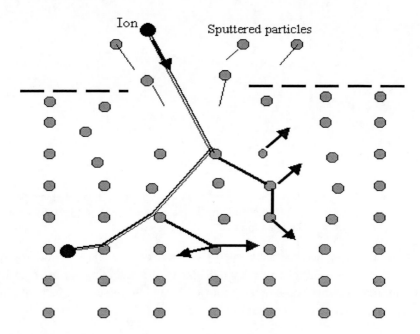

Figure 1.2. Scematic diagram of the sputtering process.

2. Theory of Ion Induced Surface Morphology

Based on Sigmund's [7] theory of sputtering, Bradley and Harper (B-H) [8] made a successful description of the morphological evolution of sputtered surfaces. Ion sputtering is determined by atomic processes, taking place within a finite penetration depth inside the bombarded material. The ions penetrate the surface and transfer their kinetic energy to the atoms of the substrate by inducing cascades of collisions among the substrate atoms, or through other processes, such as electronic excitations [2]. Fig 2.1 shows the ion bombardment process. An ion releasing its energy at point P at a distance 'a' in the solid contributes energy to the surface point O, that may induce the atoms in O to break their bonds and the dislodged atoms either leave the surface or diffuse along it. The average energy deposited at point O due to the ion arriving at P follows the Gaussian distribution

$$E(r^{'}) = \frac{\varepsilon}{(2\pi)^{3/2} \sigma\mu^2} \exp\left[-\frac{z^{'2}}{2\sigma^2} - \frac{x^{'2} + y^{'2}}{2\mu^2} \right]$$

(2.1)

$z^{'}$ is the distance measured along the ion trajectory, $x^{'}$ and $y^{'}$ are measured in the plane

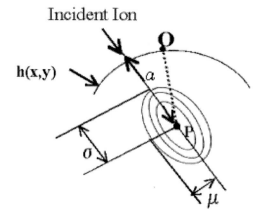

Figure 2.1. Schematic illustration of the energy distribution by an incident ion. The ion penetrates the solid and is stopped at point P. 'a' is the penetration depth. The kinetic energy of the ion is released and spreads around P following a Gaussian form.

perpendicular to it; ε denotes the kinetic energy of the ion and σ and μ are the widths of the distribution in directions parallel and perpendicular to the incoming beam respectively. A quantity of central importance is the range of the ion beam into the target i.e. the mean energy deposition depth a, which depends on incident ion energy as-

$$a(\varepsilon^{'}) = \frac{1-m}{2m} \gamma^{m-1} \frac{\varepsilon^{2m}}{NC_m},$$

(2.2)

where N is the target atom density, γ is a constant of the order of unity, C_m is a constant dependent on the parameters of the interatomic potential and the exponent $m = m(\varepsilon)$,

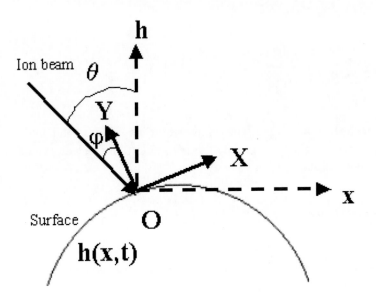

Figure 2.2. The reference coordinate system used for a two-dimensional model.

where m is a number between 0 and 1. $m = 1$ for Rutherford scattering, $m = 1/2$ for keV energy range and medium-mass ions and atoms and $m = 1/3$ for lower keV energies [7].

A large number of ions penetrate the solid at different points and the velocity of erosion at O depends on total the energy contributed by all the ions deposited within the range 'a', of the distribution (Figure 2.1), such that

$$v = p \int_a \phi(r) E(r) dr, \tag{2.3}$$

where $\phi(r)$ is a local correction of the uniform flux J due to variation of the local slopes, p is the proportionality constant between power deposition and erosion rate [7] and is given by

$$p = \frac{3}{4\pi^2} \frac{1}{nU_0 C_0}, \tag{2.4}$$

where n is the target atomic density, U_0 is the surface binding energy and C_0 is a constant dependent on radius of the interaction potential.

For simplicity the model is reduced to (1+1) dimension [3], as shown in Figure 2.2. The incoming beam direction forms an angle φ with the direction normal of the local surface. φ changes point to point along the surface. The radius of curvature at O is R_x (positive when surface is concave and negative when the surface is convex). The sputtering yield Y (φ) is related to the velocity of erosion v(φ,Rx) by the following expression:

$$Y(\varphi) = \frac{n v(\varphi, R_x)}{J \cos \varphi} \tag{2.5}$$

$$v(\varphi, R_x) = \frac{J \cos \varphi}{n} Y(\varphi) \tag{2.6}$$

where n is the number of atoms per unit volume in the amorphous solid and J the flux of the incoming ions. Since a $\ll$ R_x, taking only the first order terms of a/R_x, equation (2.6) gives the following expression for erosion velocity

$$v(\varphi, R_x) = \frac{J}{n} Y_0(\varphi)[\cos(\varphi) - \Gamma_x(\varphi)a / R_x], \tag{2.7}$$

where $Y_0(\varphi)$ is the sputtering yield for a flat surface ($R_x = \infty$) at an incident angle φ.

For a $= \sigma = \mu$, i.e for a spherical distribution

$$\Gamma_x = \sin^2(\varphi)\sin^2(\varphi/2) - \cos^2(\varphi/2) \tag{2.8}$$

The term $\Gamma_x(\varphi)$a/R_x corresponds to the curvature dependence of erosion velocity. At normal incidence, the term $\Gamma_x(\varphi)$a/R_x is negative for trough and positive for crest. This means when ion beam is incident on a periodic disturbance, the troughs are eroded faster than the crest Figure 2.3. Thus sputtering increases the amplitudes of the perturbation and so leads to an instability.

Eq. (2.7) can be transformed to the laboratory frame (x, h). h(x) describes the surface where h is the normal to the initial flat surface. Ion beam forms angle θ with h. The ion trajectory forms a plane with h and x. The time evolution of the surface is described by the height function h(x, t), measured from the initial flat configuration. θ is fixed angle where φ changes from point to point, along the surface as $\varphi = \theta + \partial h/\partial x$. If it is assumed that the surface height varies slowly with time, the equation of motion obtained by taking the normal component of the velocity of erosion (Eq. 2.7):

$$\frac{\partial h}{\partial t} = -\frac{J}{n}Y_0(\theta)\cos\theta + \frac{J}{n}\frac{\partial}{\partial \theta}[Y_0(\theta)\cos\theta]\frac{\partial h}{\partial x} + \frac{J}{n}Y_0(\theta)\left[\Gamma_x(\theta)\frac{\partial^2 h}{\partial x^2}\right] \tag{2.9}$$

Here $v_0 = \dfrac{j}{n} Y_0(\theta) \cos \theta$ is the rate of erosion of the unperturbed flat surface and

$\gamma = \dfrac{J}{n} \dfrac{\partial}{\partial \theta} [Y_0(\theta) \cos \theta]$. Now it is easy to generalize the above equation to an arbitrary surface: $h(x, y, t)$ [10]

$$\frac{\partial h}{\partial t} = -v_0(\theta) + \gamma \frac{\partial h}{\partial x} + \frac{Ja}{n} Y_0(\theta) \left\{ \left[\Gamma_x(\theta) \frac{\partial^2 h}{\partial x^2} \right] + \left[\Gamma_y(\theta) \frac{\partial^2 h}{\partial y^2} \right] \right\} \qquad (2.10)$$

or

$$\frac{\partial h}{\partial t} = -v_0(\theta) + \gamma(\theta) \frac{\partial h}{\partial x} + v_x(\theta) \frac{\partial^2 h}{\partial x^2} + v_y(\theta) \frac{\partial^2 h}{\partial y^2} \qquad (2.11)$$

where $v_x = \dfrac{Ja}{n} Y_0(\theta) \Gamma_x(\theta)$ and $v_y = \dfrac{Ja}{n} Y_0(\theta) \Gamma_y(\theta)$

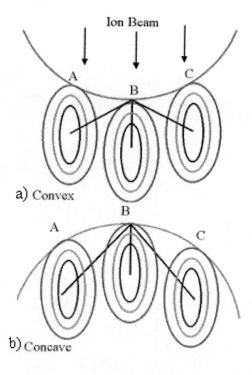

Figure 2.3. Schematic illustration of physical origin of the instability, during ion erosion of non-planar surfaces. A surface element with convex geometry (a) is eroded faster than that with a concave geometry (b), due to the smaller distances the energy has to travel from the impact point to the surface.

SURFACE DIFFUSION

The complete description of the surface topography evolution incorporates the surface diffusion which generates a surface current density j(x, t), tangent to the surface. Since the total number of particles remains unchanged due to diffusion, the current must obey the equation of continuity –

$$\frac{\partial h}{\partial x} = -\nabla . j(x,t).$$
(2.12)

Since the surface current is driven by the difference in the local chemical potential μ(x, t)

$$j(x,t) \propto -\nabla \mu(x,t).$$
(2.13)

The simplest assumption is that chemical potential μ(x, t) is proportional to the $-1/R_x$, which in turn proportional to $\Box^2 h(x, t)$. Thus we obtain the equation, describing relaxation by diffusion [6] as

$$\frac{\partial h}{\partial x} = -K\nabla^4 h(x,t).$$
(2.14)

where K is a coefficient depends on the surface self diffusivity D, the free energy per unit area z and the number of atoms per unit area moving across the surface ρ as

$$K = \frac{2DF\rho}{n^2 k_b T}$$
(2.15)

2.1. Linear B-H Equation

The sputter erosion causes roughening of surface whereas the diffusion leads to smoothening the surface. The competition between these two processes forms a final surface morphology. Now combining Eq. (2.11) and Eq. (2.14) we obtain:

$$\frac{\partial h}{\partial t} = -v_0(\theta) + \gamma(\theta)\frac{\partial h}{\partial x} + v_x(\theta)\frac{\partial^2 h}{\partial x^2} + v_y(\theta)\frac{\partial^2 h}{\partial y^2} - K\nabla^4 h(x,t)$$
(2.16)

This is the linear B-H equation for sputtering induced surface growth [8]. During bombardment, there is an inherent randomness, coming from the fluctuations in the intensity of the incoming ion beams. At large length scale, the beam is homogeneous with an average intensity but there is a local random fluctuation η(x, y, t) with zero mean uncorrelated in space and time. If noise term is included, the more complete form of the Eq. 2.16 is

$$\frac{\partial h}{\partial t} = -v_0(\theta) + \gamma(\theta)\frac{\partial h}{\partial x} + v_x(\theta)\frac{\partial^2 h}{\partial x^2} + v_y(\theta)\frac{\partial^2 h}{\partial y^2} - K\nabla^4 h(x,t) + \eta(x,y,t) \quad (2.17)$$

Here, v_0 describes the erosion velocity of a flat surface. This term doesn't affect the ripple characteristics and can be eliminated from the surface evolution equation by coordinate transform $\overline{h} = h + v_0 t$. The coefficient γ contributes only to the velocity of ripples along the x direction for oblique ion incidence ($\theta \neq 0$). Similar to the v_0 term, γ does not affect the ripple characteristics and can be eliminated using the transformation $\overline{h} = h(x - \gamma t, t)$. The coefficients v_x and v_y are the origin of the instability, responsible for ripple formation. Consequently, they play important roles in determining the final surface morphology. At $\theta \neq 0$, the v_x and v_y are not equal. v_y is always negative while v_x can change sign as ion beam parameters are varied. The sign and magnitude of the coefficients v_x and v_y determine the wavelength and orientation of the ripples. For $v_x < v_y < 0$, the ripple structure is oriented along the x direction with ripple

$$\Lambda_x = 2\pi\sqrt{\frac{2K}{|v_x|}} \tag{2.18}$$

whereas for $v_x > v_y$, the ripple structure is oriented in the y direction, with ripple wavelength,

$$\Lambda_y = 2\pi\sqrt{\frac{2K}{|v_y|}} \tag{2.19}$$

LIMITATIONS OF THE LINEAR B-H EQUATION

1) Linear B-H theory successfully predicts the ripple formation and its orientation but it can not account for surface roughening or other types of periodic structure formation due to ion bombardment.
2) B-H theory predicts an ultimate exponential increase of the ripple amplitude in contrast to the observed saturation of the ripple amplitude.
3) According to B-H theory, the ripple wavelength should increase with temperature, whereas a number of experiments show that the ripple wavelength is independent of the substrate temperature, and finally-
4) The ripple wavelength is found to increase linearly with incident ion energy, in contrast to the BH prediction, where there is a decrease with the increasing ion energy.

2.2. The Continuum Equation of Makeev, Cuerno and Barabasi (MCB) for Ion Bombarded Surface

The observed linear B-H theory could not explain all the experimental results of ion bombarded surfaces. To overcome the demerits of B-H theory and limitations of continuum theories, Makeev et al. [9], starting from Eq. (2.3) derived a continuum equation, where higher order and non linear terms with a random Gaussian white noise, are added to the linear B-H equation. This presents a general equation of surface growth during ion bombardment of solid surfaces. The main steps they followed are –

(i) The normal component of the erosion velocity v at the point O (Figure 2.1) is calculated. The calculation is done in a local frame of reference (Figure 2.4).
(ii) The quantities measured in local frame have been related to the laboratory frame.
(iii) Finally, to obtain the equation of motion for the surface profile h(x, y, t), normal component of the erosion velocity is projected on to the global h axis (Figure 2-4). The time derivative of h(x, y, t) at any point O on the surface is proportional to the surface erosion velocity v at at that point.

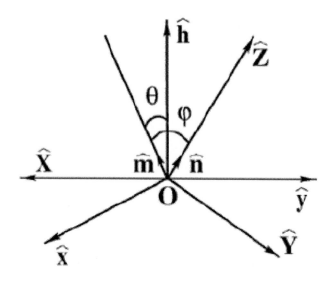

Figure 2.4. Illustration of the local reference frame ($\hat{X}$; $\hat{Y}$; $\hat{Z}$).

The $\hat{Z}$ axis is parallel to the local normal to the surface $\hat{n}$. The ions arrive to the surface along $-\hat{m}$. The $\hat{X}$ axis is in the plane defined by $\hat{Z}$ and $\hat{m}$, while the $\hat{Y}$ axis is perpendicular to this plane. The laboratory coordinate frame ($\hat{x}$; $\hat{y}$; $\hat{z}$) has its $\hat{h}$ axis perpendicular to the flat substrate, $\hat{h}$ and $\hat{m}$ define the ($\hat{x} - \hat{h}$) plane and $\hat{y}$ is perpendicular to it. The incidence angle measured in the local reference frame is φ, and θ in the laboratory frame. Furthermore, taking into account the surface diffusion effect, and the noise term the surface evolution equation is-

$$\frac{\partial h}{\partial t} = -v_0 + \gamma \frac{\partial h}{\partial x} + \xi_x \left(\frac{\partial h}{\partial x}\right)\left(\frac{\partial^2 h}{\partial x^2}\right) + \xi_y \left(\frac{\partial h}{\partial x}\right)\left(\frac{\partial^2 h}{\partial y^2}\right) + v_x \frac{\partial^2 h}{\partial x^2} + v_y \frac{\partial^2 h}{\partial y^2} + \Omega_1 \frac{\partial^3 h}{\partial x^3} + \Omega_2 \frac{\partial^3 h}{\partial x \partial x^2}$$

$$-D_{xy} \frac{\partial^4 h}{\partial x^2 \partial y^2} - D_{xx} \frac{\partial^4 h}{\partial x^4} - D_{yy} \frac{\partial^4 h}{\partial y^4} - K\nabla^4 h(x,t) + \frac{\lambda_x}{2}\left(\frac{\partial h}{\partial x}\right)^2 + \frac{\lambda_y}{2}\left(\frac{\partial h}{\partial y}\right)^2 + \eta(x,y,t)$$

(2.20)

The explicit expression for the coefficients and the special cases are described in the Ref [9].

3. A BRIEF REVIEW OF ION INDUCED SURFACE MORPHOLOGY

Energetic ion bombarded surface morphology has fascinated the experimental community. Navaz et al. [4] in 1956, for the first time observed a nanometer sized wavelike structure (ripple) by bombarding a glass surface with an ion beam of air at oblique angle. The author did not provide an accurate explanation at that time, but simply tried to find analogies with macroscopic phenomena, such as ripple structures formed by wind over a sand bed. Recently, with the development of high resolution observation techniques, such as atomic force microscopy, scanning tunneling microscopy and transmission electron microscopy, this field received a new life. Investigations on ion bombarded surfaces showed the formation of cone, pit, dot and ripple structures with dimensions ranging from micrometer to a few nanometer [5,9]. However, a number of experiments reported no well defined patterns but only the development of apparently random and rough surfaces. Some representative works on ion induced surface morphology are briefly reviewed, below-

3.1. Ion Induced Kinetic Roughening

It is observed that under certain experimental conditions the ion bombarded surface does not form any regular structure rather undergoes a random roughening. The properties of such rough surface can be described by the kinetic roughening theory. Eklund et al. [10] bombarded a pyrolytic graphite by 5 keV Ar^+ at 45^0. Examined by STM, it was observed that the eroded surface becomes rough with the roughness exponent $\alpha = 0.2 - 0.4$ and dynamic exponent $z = 1.6 - 1.8$. These values are consistent with the theoretical prediction based upon KPZ equation [11]. It was pointed out, however, that the scaling exponents strongly depend on the ion bombardment condition, such as energy, flux, fluence, angle of incidence and target temperature. Koponen et al. [12] performed simulation for 5 keV Ar^+ ions on amorphous carbon surface for wide range of primary ion incidence angles from 0^0 to 60^0. The roughness exponent was observed to decrease with increasing angle of incidence. They found that the roughness exponent $\alpha = 0.37 - 0.45$ for normal incidence while $\alpha = 0.25$ for the angle of incidence closer to 60^0. The growth exponent $\beta = 0.8$ was observed to be nearly independent on angle of incidence.

3.2. Formation of Regular Structures by Ion Bombardment

By changing only the angle of ion incidence, different surface morphology can be developed. The well defined periodic structures appear only for a limited range of ion incidence angle, which depends on the material and ion involved. Stevie et al [13] observed the ripple formation on Si and GaAs by O_2^+ ion sputtering at incidence angles between 39^0 and 52^0. Similarly ripple formation on Si [14] and on GaAs [15] were observed at angles 30^0 to 60^0 for oxygen ion bombardment. Erlebacher et al. [16] monitored Ar^+ ion induced periodic ripple formation on Si (100) by in situ light scattering spectroscopy. Analysis indicates that under high ion flux the concentration of mobile species on the surface is temperature and flux independent, the measured migration energy of Si surface being 1.2 ± 0.1 eV. They also observed that for sufficiently long time bombardment, the ripple amplitude does not continue to grow exponentially, as predicted by B-H model. This observation suggests the development of non linear effect due to long time ion sputtering. The topography of (001) graphite (HOPG) surfaces eroded by a 5 keV Xe^+ ion beam, has been investigated by Hebenicht et al. [17]. For oblique angle ion incidence, quasi periodic ripple topography has been formed. They estimated a critical angle between 60^0 and 70^0, below which the ripples are formed perpendicular to the ion beam, while for angle above the critical angle, the ripple orientation is parallel to the ion beam projection. Kahng et al. [18] theoretically predicted the quantum dot and hole formation in ion beam sputtering. They demonstrated that sputtering under normal incidence leads to the formation of spatially ordered uniform nano-scale island or holes. Facsko et al., [19] while investigating low energy normal incidence Ar^+ ion sputtering of GaAs (100) surface, observed that nano-scale islands are remarkably well ordered and have uniform size distribution. On the other hand, experiments of Ar^+ ion sputtering of Cu (110), and Ne^+ sputtering of Ag (001) under normal incidence showed relatively uniform depression or holes [20].

4. ION INDUCED NANOSTRUCTURES ON METAL THIN FILMS

Nanostructured materials have opened possibilities for new technology and basic science research in areas ranging from microelectronics to catalysis. Polycrystalline metal thin films have wide industrial applications in electronic, magnetic, and optical devices. It will, therefore, be interesting to explore the possibility of formation of correlated surface features, such as random rough surface [21], wavelength selected ripple structures [22], or dot like structure at nanometer length scales, in these systems. Changes in electronic structure that scale with the cluster dimensions, i.e., quantum size effects, can strongly contribute to the chemical, electrical and optical properties of the materials [23,24]. Here, the development of rough surface, dot like structure at near normal and ripple topography at grazing ion beam sputtering on a number of thin metallic films at ambient temperature are reported and the results are discussed.

4.1. Kinetic Roughening of Thin Pt Films on Si Substrate

We have investigated the development of morphologies in thin Pt films evaporated onto Si substrates. Morphological data were quantitatively analyzed within the frame work of dynamic scaling theory, described in ref. [25] and the results are discussed with appropriate physical mechanisms, responsible for the growth of the structures [21].

Thin Pt films (~ 30 nm) were deposited by d. c. magnetron sputtering onto commercially available polished Si (100) wafers, previously degreased and cleaned. The Pt/Si samples were then sputtered with 9.7 keV Ar^+ ions at different fluences, in a low energy ion beam set-up. The angle of ion incidence with respect to the surface normal was 45^0. The average current density was 10 $\mu A/cm^2$. The samples were exposed to total ion fluences between 1×10^{15} and 2×10^{18} ions/cm^2. The base pressure in the target chamber was less than 5×10^{-8} mbar. The surface morphology of the ion-irradiated samples was examined by a Park Scientific AFM (Auto Probe CP).

Figure 4.1 shows the AFM images from the sample surfaces sputtered at successive increasing ion fluences φ (different bombarding times t). Immediately after the start of the bombardment, mound-like or globular structures begin to appear.

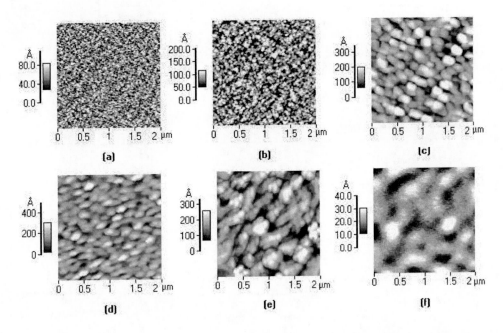

Figure 4.1. Some selected AFM images of Ar^+ sputtered Pt/Si surfaces, showing a sequence of the evolution of the surface topography with increasing ion fluences: (a) 2×10^{15} ions/cm^2; (b) 7×10^{15} ions/cm^2; (c) 2×10^{16} ions/cm^2; (d) 5×10^{16} ions/cm^2; (e) 7×10^{16} ions/cm^2 and (f) 2×10^{17} ions/cm^2. (Ref. [21] copyright (2004) by Elsevier).

The bombardment also produces voids or vacant regions in between the mounds. Both the lateral size and the height of the mounds become larger with increasing ion fluence upto < 10^{17} ions/cm^2; thereafter the heights tend to decrease rapidly as the sputtering further continues. In the fluence region 10^{16} ions/cm^2, the mounds are quite sharp and well developed. However, at fluences $\geq 2 \times 10^{16}$ ions/cm^2, the mounds tend to form clusters and become blurred.

In order to quantitatively characterize the observed morphology, we have studied the scaling properties of the interface. A standard method for investigating surface morphology is to study the height height correlation function G(r,t), which is the mean square of height difference between two surface positions separated by a lateral distance r:

$$G(r) = \left\langle [h(r_1) - h(r_2)]^2 \right\rangle \qquad (4.1)$$

If the surface is scale invariant and isotopic, then G(r,t) has the following propertie:

$$G(r) \sim \begin{cases} r^{2\alpha}, r << \xi(t) \\ 2w^2(t), r >> \xi(t) \end{cases} \qquad (4.2)$$

where $\xi(t)$ is the lateral correlation length which scales $t^{1/z}$. $w(t)$ is given by

$$w(t) = \sqrt{\left\langle [h(r,t) - \langle h \rangle]^2 \right\rangle} \propto t^{\beta} \qquad (4.3)$$

The correlation function was evaluated directly from the AFM micrographs by taking every possible pair of positions, calculating the square of the height difference and averaging for equal distances.

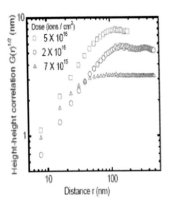
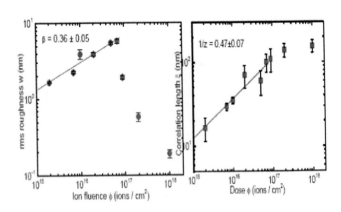

Figure 4. 3. (a) log-log plots of the height-height correlation functions G(r,t), as a function of the lateral distance r for different bombarding fluences φ (b) rms surface roughness w vs the bombarding ion fluence φ. The solid line of the growth part represents the fit according to the power scaling relation w ~ φ$^\beta$. (c) The plot of the correlation length ξ versus ion fluence φ; the fitting line indicates the slope yielding the value of z. (Ref. [21] copyright (2004) by Elsevier).

Shown in Figure 4-3 (a), are the typical log-log plots of G(r, t) vs lateral distance r at three different bombarding ion fluences, φ. From the figure, it is seen that G(r, t) increases with a simple power law at small r following a plateau at large r, consistent with the asymptotic behavior predicted in Eq. (4.2). The lateral position corresponding to the plateau point is equal to ξ, which is a representative measure of the average dimension of the mound. The roughness exponent α was determined by least-squares fitting to the linear slope of G(r, t) at small r. In the fluence range investigated here, we observed α in the range $0.65 - 0.87$. The weighted average of these α's gives a value of 0.77 ± 0.04.

The rms roughness or the interface width w, at each time (or fluence) was obtained from the in-built software of the AFM instrument, and it was found that they all agree to those calculated from the asymptotic value of G(r, t) for $r \gg \xi(t)$ as stated in Eq. 4.2. These data of w versus ion fluence in a log-log plot are shown in Figure 4.3 (b). It is interesting to note that after a certain bombarding fluence when the film material is eroded enough away, the rms surface roughness values show a sharp fall. The exponent β was determined from the linear fit of the ascending part of the roughness curve and is found to be 0.36 ± 0.05. The lateral correlation length ξ can be determined from the auto-correlation function $C(r) = < h(r)h(0) >$, in which ξ is defined as the value of r at which $C(\xi) = C(0)/e$, where e is the base of the natural logarithm [26]. Figure 4.3 (c) shows a power law increment of the correlation length ξ with increasing ion fluence φ, as expected, with the dynamic exponent $1/z = 0.47 \pm 0.07$, which is quite close to that obtained from the scaling relation $z = \alpha/\beta$.

For thin films, one should consider a further effect of ion beam responsible for the decay of kinetic roughening at the later stages of bombardment (cf., Figure 4.3(b)), namely, the excessive loss of material due to sputter erosion from the sample. After prolonged bombardment, when the film is thin enough, the dynamic balance between the erosion and growth tends to break down. This seems to occur above the bombarding fluence $\phi = 7 \times 10^{16}$ ions/cm^2, where the linear fit to the w vs. φ curve (Figure 4.3(b)) yields quite a high value of $\beta \ (\approx -1)$. The negative sign of the exponent indicates the decay of the structures. Furthermore, inspection of Figure 4.3(c) reveals a slower increment of the correlation length ξ above $\phi \approx 7 \times 10^{16}$ ions/cm^2 suggesting the scaling relation $z = \alpha/\beta$ not operative after this fluence.

4.2. ION BEAM SPUTTERING INDUCED DOT AND RIPPLE FORMATION IN THIN METAL FILMS

Thin films of Au, Pt, Ag, Cu and Co were deposited by d. c. magnetron sputtering onto commercially available polished Si(100) wafers, as described earlier. The film thicknesses were in the range of 30 to 200 nm. These samples were then sputtered with mass analyzed $5 - 27$ keV Ar$^+$ ions in a low energy ion beam (LEIB) system. The angle of ion incidence with respect to the surface normal was varied from 10^0 up to 85^0. The beam current through a 4 mm diameter aperture was in the range of $2 - 3$ μA. The samples were exposed to ion fluences in the range $5 \times 10^{15} - 5 \times 10^{17}$ ions/cm^2. The surface morphology of the ion-irradiated samples was examined by AFM in the contact mode. All the measurements were carried out in air at room temperature.

Variation of Surface Morphology with Ion Incidence Angle

Earlier, I have discussed kinetic roughening of Pt thin films by Ar^+ ion bombardment at 45^0, with respect to the surface normal. Here, we have studied the evolution of surface morphology on a Pt thin film as a function of ion incidence angle θ, for a given ion fluence and energy. It has been found (Fig 4.4) that at near normal Ar^+ incidence, dot like structures are developed while at larger angles of incidence (20^0-60^0), checkerboard and mound structures are developed. At 70^0 a remarkable transition of the topography occurs, showing the development of arrays of tiny cones, inclined along the ion beam direction. Further increase of the incidence angle shows the beginning of distinct changes of the surface morphology which ultimately ends up with regular ripple structures at grazing ion incidence (80^0-85^0). The present results are not only typical to Pt films but also valid for other metallic films, namely, Co, Cu, Ag and Au.

Metal Dot Formation

Kahng et. al. [18] predicted by numerical simulation that sputtering under normal incidence leads to the formation of specially ordered uniform nano-scale islands or holes. Under normal ion incidence, the coefficients of Eq. 2.20 are isotropic and are given by

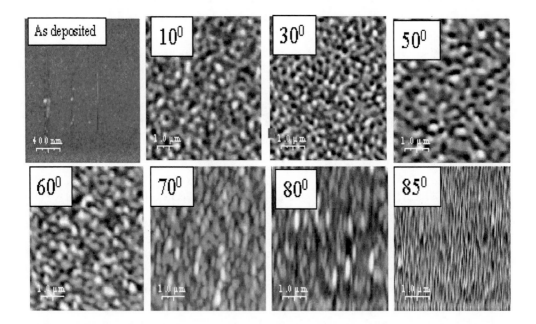

Figure 4.4. AFM images showing a sequence of the evolution of the surface topography of the Pt film with increasing bombarding angle. The projectile is 16.5 keV Ar^+ with a fluence of 5×10^{16} ions/cm^2. The ion beam direction is from the bottom to the top.

$$v \equiv v_x = v_y = -\frac{faa_\sigma^2}{2a_\mu^2},$$

$$D \equiv D_x = D_y = \frac{D_{xy}}{2} = \frac{fa^3 a_\sigma^2}{8a_\mu^4},$$

$$\lambda \equiv \lambda_x = \lambda_y = (f/2a_\mu^2)(a_\mu^2 - a_\sigma^4 - a_\mu^2)$$

For $\lambda > 0$, in the early stages of sputtering process, the surface is dominated by small, wavy perturbations, generated by the interplay between the ion- induced instability and surface relaxation. However, since the system is isotropic in the (x, y) plane, these ripple precursors are oriented randomly, generating short wormlike morphologies on the surface. After some characteristic time τ, these structures turn into isolated but closely packed island [18]. A similar scenario was observed for $\lambda < 0$ [18], only the difference being that the islands are replaced by holes. The results also indicate that the quantum dots and holes are inherently nonlinear objects and therefore the formation of such morphological structures depends on the nonlinear term (Eq.2.20) of the continuum equation.

We experimentally found similar dot like structures of different polycrystalline metal thin films under normal or near normal Ar^+ ion bombardment at room temperature. These structures are found to be stable for long time at room temperature. A thin film of Co deposited on Si (100) was bombarded with 16.5 keV Ar^+ ion at an angle of 10^0. As shown in Fig. 4.5, dot-like structures are formed at an ion dose 5×10^{16} ions/cm². Similar structures are also observed for 16.5 keV Ar^+ ion bombarded Ag thin film at an angle 10^0 and for Pt thin film at 0^0 ion incidence.

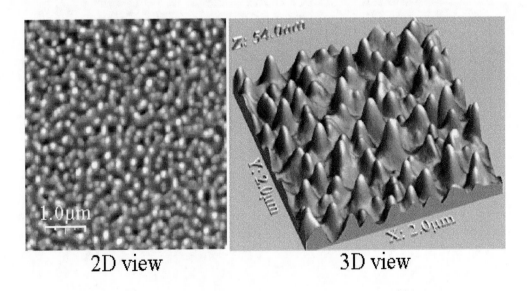

2D view   3D view

Figure 4.5. Surface morphology showing dot-like structures after 16.5 keV Ar^+ ion bombardment at an incident angle of 10^0 on Co thin film. The ion fluence is 5×10^{16} ions/cm².

Metal Ripple Formation

Figs. 4.6(a) - (t) show some selected AFM images of the sputtered Co, Cu, Ag, Pt and Au films, respectively, at the angles of 60^0, 70^0, and 80^0, because at these angles the gradual morphological transitions are clearly visible and this is a general feature for all the metallic films, studied in the present sputtering conditions. At 60^0 weakly pronounced ripples with wave vector parallel to the ion beam direction, especially in Co and Cu films, appear, at projection of the ion beam direction. Finally, at 80^0 regular ripple-like surface instability, with the wave vector perpendicular to the ion beam direction is developed. In passing we mention that the AFM images of the ripples, including that of the other morphological structures are found to be quite reproducible even after several weeks of bombardment.

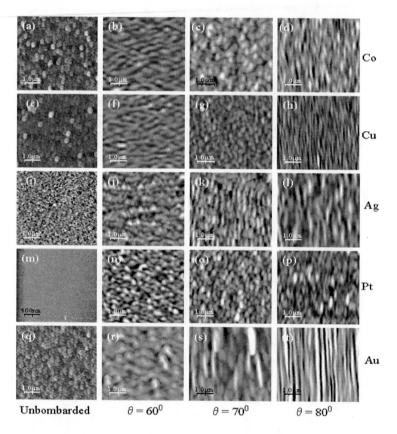

Unbombarded $\theta = 60^0$ $\theta = 70^0$ $\theta = 80^0$

Figure 4.6. AFM images of the unbombarded and 16.7 keV Ar^+ sputtered Co, Cu, Ag, Pt and Au surfaces at different angles of incidence θ as indicated. The bombarding fluence φ for Co, Cu, Ag, and Au is 1×10^{17} ions/cm^2, while that for Pt is 5×10^{16} ions/cm^2. The ion beam direction is from the bottom to the top. (Ref. [22] copyright (2004) by Elsevier).

Valbusa et al. [3,27], showed that sputtering of metal surfaces involves two types of surface instabilities depending on the angle of ion incidence, θ: the first one arising from erosion process and the other deriving from anisotropic surface diffusion. The erosion-induced surface instability dominating at grazing incidence $\theta > \theta c$ ($\theta c \approx 50^0 - 70^0$) [28] leads to ripple structures aligned parallel to the ion beam projection, independent on the surface crystallinity or orientation. The erosive regime is supposed to govern by the Bradley and Harper (BH) theory [8]. Eq. (2.17) can further be extended to crystalline materials by including the effects of anisotropic diffusion in different crystallographic directions as well as the existence of the ES barrier, at the step edges [29]. One of the consequences of the presence of the ES barrier is that the ripple structure in metal surfaces could be formed even at normal ion beam incidence ($\theta \approx 0^0$), by tuning the surface temperature [29]. However, for polycrystalline thin films, the grains are mainly randomly oriented and the grain sizes are usually much smaller compared to the film thickness [30,31].

For the quantitative analysis of the ripple morphology, we have calculated numerically the height-height auto-correlation function $C(r) = \langle [h(r)h(0)] \rangle$, where h(r) is the relative surface height at the position r and $\langle \ \rangle$ denotes an average over all positions and directions. As an illustration, Figure 4.7 shows a typical AFM image of the rippled structure on a Au film together with the corresponding two-dimensional auto-correlation function. The ripple wavelength Λ is defined as the separation between the central peak and the first correlation maximum while taking linear scans of Figure 4.7(c). Figure 4.8 shows a typical set of data for the ripple wavelength Λ, as a function of the substrate material when sputtered with the same ion fluence and energy.

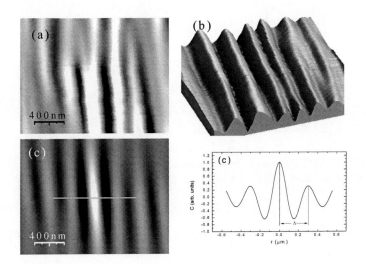

Figure 4.7. AFM image of the rippled surface on Au film after 16.7 keV Ar^+ ion sputtering at $\theta = 80^0$ and $\varphi = 1 \times 10^{17}$ ions/cm^2; the ion beam direction is from the bottom to the top. (a) 2D view; (b) 3D view; (c) 2D-autocorrelation function and (d) 1D-autocorrelation function along the marked line. (Ref. [22] copyright (2004) by Elsevier).

For such a system, the existence of ES barrier is improbable because of the lack of well-defined atomic steps at the surface [30]. Therefore, the approximation of isotropic diffusivity as in amorphous materials seems to be well held in polycrystalline metallic films. The stability of the ripple structure at room temperature indicates that the thermally activated diffusion energy barriers in thin polycrystalline films are comparatively higher than that in monocrystalline metal surfaces.

Rossnagel and Robinson [32] measured the activation energy for adatom surface diffusion on various polycrystalline materials from the Arrhenius plot of the sputter cone spacings for several temperatures. The barrier heights lie typically in the range of 0.3 −1 eV. Similar plots for ripple wavelengths on Ag single crystals yield activation energy around 0.15 eV [3]. At room temperature the surface diffusion is driven by the collisional effects rather than pure thermal effect [33]. The mobility of adatoms is believed to originate from the overlapping collision cascades, due to multiple ion impact [34]. Carter and Vishnyakov [35] proposed to add a ballistic smoothening term of the form | A(E, θ) | □²h in Eq. (2.17), in order to account the effect of recoiling-adatom diffusion, induced by ion irradiation at a given energy E. Makeev et al. [9] showed that fourth-order derivatives of the surface height function h(x, y), may also cause the smoothing effect which does not involve real mass transport.

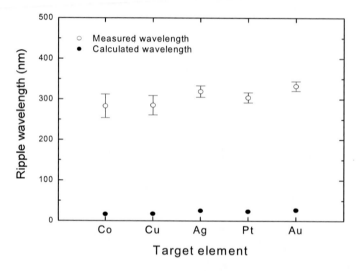

Figure 4.8. The ripple wavelength Λ versus the substrate element after 16.7 keV Ar+ ion sputtering at θ = 80° and φ = 1 × 10^{17} ions/cm². (Ref. [22] copyright (2004) by Elsevier).

For such a case the wavelength of the ripples, in the present experimental conditions, can be derived as $\Lambda = \sqrt{\dfrac{2D_{yy}}{|v_y|}}$, where D_{yy} is the ion induced smoothing coefficient in the y direction. The ratio D_{yy}/v_y can be estimated from the values of the ion penetration depth a and the longitudinal and lateral straggling widths σ and μ , respectively, using the computer code SRIM [36]. Although the experimental data at fixed bombarding ion energy and dose follow the same trend as the theoretically calculated Λ in different target elements, the theory underestimates substantially the experimental wavelength values (cf., Figure 4.8). One of the reasons for this discrepancy is that the ripple wavelength Λ coarsens with the ion dose φ as a power law Λ ~ φ^n with the exponent n = 0.28, e.g. measured for Pt films, whereas the BH theory predicts a fixed ripple wavelength. Nevertheless, such a large discrepancy simply indicates the failure of the model, which is based on curvature-dependent sputtering for the calculation of Λ. Recently, several authors [37-39] have reported that the characteristic wavelengths of the generated sputtered patterns on various semiconductor targets are a factor of 4 to 10 higher than the theoretical expected value.

4.3. FORMATION AND INTERROGATION OF AU NANO CLUSTER BY ION BEAMS

Low energy ion bombardment of a Au thin film by 0.5 keV Ar^+ forms self-organized nanoclusters that display quantum size effects. The reduction of Au coverage with sputtering time is quantified with XPS, and a decrease of both the rms roughness and correlation length is measured by STM. Neutralization of scattered 3 keV Na^+ and K^+ ions is used to probe the electronic states of the sputter-induced nanoclusters [40].

The experiments were performed in an ultra-high vacuum chamber with a base pressure of 1×10^{-10} Torr. The $TiO_2(110)$ single crystal surface was cleaned by cycles of ion bombardment and annealing until a sharp (1×1) low-energy electron diffraction pattern was obtained. A thin Au film (~60 ML) was deposited on $TiO_2(110)$ from an evaporator. The Au film was sputtered by normally incident 0.5 keV Ar^+ (current density = 1 $\mu A/cm^2$), at various ion fluences. Images of the Au clusters after each deposition and sputtering cycle were collected with an *in situ* scanning tunneling microscope. The surface roughness and correlation length, which are related to the vertical and lateral dimensions of the nanostructures, respectively, were quantitatively determined from the STM images. The purity and Au coverage were measured with x-ray photoelectron spectroscopy (XPS), immediately after cleaning and again following each deposition and sputtering cycle.

Time-of-flight was used to measure the charge state-resolved kinetic energy distribution of scattered Na^+ and K^+ ions, as described elsewhere [46]. A thermionic emitter ion gun generated 3 keV alkali ion beams, which were deflected across a 1.0 mm^2 aperture to produce pulses (~10 ns) at a rate of 80 kHz. The beams were incident normally to the surface, and the ions and neutrals scattered at 150° were detected by a microchannelplate (MCP) array after traveling through a 0.55 m long flight tube, containing a pair of deflection plates. "Total Yield" spectra were collected with the deflection plates held at ground, while "Neutrals Only" spectra were collected by placing 300 V between the plates to remove the scattered ions.

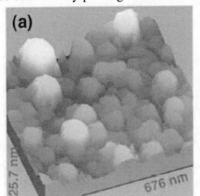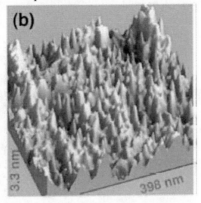

Figure 4.9. 3D STM topographies of (a) a ~60 ML Au thin film deposited on TiO_2, and (b) after 0.5 keV Ar^+ ion sputtering at a fluence of 5×10^{16} ions/ cm^2. (Ref. [40] copyright (2007) by The American Physical Society).

STM topography of the thin Au film is presented in Figure 4.9 (a). The morphology of the thick film is rough and contains large-scale features. Figure 4.9(b) shows a typical STM image collected after Ar$^+$ sputtering at a fluence of 5×10^{16} ions/cm^2. Both rms roughness and correlation length of the features decrease with ion fluence, as shown in Figure 4.10(a). Figure 4.10(b) presents the XPS intensity of the Au 4f and Ti 2p core levels as a function of ion fluence. It shows a decrease of the Au and an increase of the Ti signal with Ar$^+$ sputtering, which indicates that Au is removed, thus revealing the TiO$_2$ substrate. From the STM and XPS measurements, it can be concluded that both the lateral and vertical dimensions of the structures decrease, as the Au is sputtered, leading to the formation of nanoscale clusters.

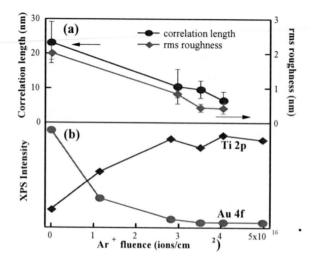

Figure 4.10. (a) The correlation length and rms roughness and (b) the ratio of the Au and Ti XPS signals shown as a function of Ar+ ion fluence. (Ref. [40] copyright (2007) by The American Physical Society).

The morphology and time evolution of ion sputtered surfaces have been described by a continuum equation [8] based on Sigmund's sputtering theory [7] (section 2). The formation of dot-like structures by 0.5 keV Ar$^+$ sputtering on Au/TiO$_2$ is consistent with the existing theory, but the theory cannot explain the decrease of the rms roughness and correlation length with ion fluence (Figure 4-10(a)). Chen, et al. [41] bombarded Ge on Si with 300 eV Ar$^+$ and Krishna, et al. [42] bombarded zinc oxide films on Si(100) with 15 keV Ar$^+$, and both observed that the rms roughness and the diameter of the clusters decrease with ion fluence, similar to the results reported here. Interestingly, nanodots of Si on Si [43] and Pt nanostructures on Si [21] produced by ion sputtering also decrease their dimensions with further sputtering. The existing theory predicts that the rms roughness would initially increase and saturate after a certain time t_x, called the crossover time. This theory fits some experimental observations well, such as when the surfaces of bulk materials or very thick films are sputtered, but it cannot explain a decrease of rms roughness during thin film or nanostructure sputtering. A possible explanation may be that the dynamic balance between growth and erosion is not the same, when ions bombard a nanostructure or very thin film as described in sec.4.1.

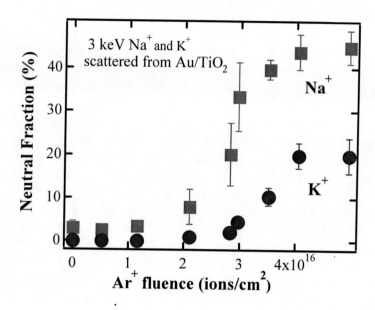

Figure 4.11. Neutral fractions of 3 keV Na+ and K+ ions singly scattered from a sputtered Au film shown as a function of the Ar+ ion fluence. (Ref. [40] copyright (2007) by The American Physical Society).

The electronic properties of the Au nanoclusters produced by ion sputtering are probed by the neutralization of Na^+ and K^+ ions during scattering. When an alkali is in the vicinity of a surface, its ionization level shifts up due to the image charge interaction, while it also broadens due to interaction of the ion and surface wave functions [44]. The measured neutral fraction (NF) is then determined by a non-adiabatic resonant charge transfer process along the outgoing trajectory, typically within about 5 a.u. of the surface. The NF depends on the ionization potential, the degree that the level shifts near the surface, and the local electrostatic potential at the point where the charge state distribution is frozen in.

Figure 4.11 shows the neutral fractions of scattered Na^+ and K^+ ions as a function of Ar^+ ion fluence. The NF for Na^+ scattered from the thick Au film is ~3%, which is the expected value for scattering from bulk Au [44]. As the Ar^+ bombardment produces nanoclusters and reduces their dimensions, the NF increases and eventually reaches a value of ~48%. Similarly large values of the NF for scattered Na^+ were obtained previously from the smallest Au clusters, formed by vapor deposition onto $TiO_2(110)$ [44]. Figure 4.11 also shows the same measurement with K^+ ions, where in this case the NF for the Au film is zero, and gradually increases to 20% with Ar^+ sputtering.

It should be pointed out that changes in the roughness of the Au film with sputtering could possibly contribute to the alkali ion scattering NF changes. To study the effects of roughness, a clean polycrystalline Au foil was sputtered with Ar^+ under the same experimental conditions, used for sputtering the Au film on TiO_2, but no concurrent changes in the scattered alkali ion neutralization were observed. It was also previously observed that Ar^+ sputtering of a Au foil [45] and Au(111) [46] does not change the surface work function or increase the neutralization during alkali ion scattering. Therefore, the increase of NF with sputtering of Au clusters on TiO_2 cannot be explained simply by a change of surface roughness.

In addition, it is possible that the projected band gap and surface states that exist in noble metal (111) surfaces, could influence the measured neutral fractions [47]. The production of Au (111) facets by vapor deposition at room temperature is not impossible, but they would be deformed in the early stages of ion bombardment, before the nanoclusters are produced. Since changes of the NF during the early stages of ion bombardment were never seen, it can be concluded that any contribution of (111) surface states to the NF can be neglected.

The increase of the NF with sputtering for both Na and K, can be explained by the size-dependent electronic structure of the nanoparticles. As the Au film is sputtered, the morphology of the surface is strongly modified and isolated Au clusters are produced. Ion sputtering decreases both the lateral and vertical dimensions of the Au clusters (see Figure 4.10), so that quantum confinement is possible in either direction. In the case of sputtering, 2D confinement is more probable as the cluster's vertical dimension is smaller than the lateral dimension, as observed from STM (Figure 4-10). Hövel and Brake[47] presented size dependent dI/dV curves of STS measurements of small Au clusters on graphite, and found that the peak position changes with cluster height. STS spectra of Ag clusters on alumina showed discrete electronic states along the vertical direction [44]. Accordingly, occupied or partially occupied confined states may appear and shift towards vacuum level with lowering of the cluster dimensions with Ar^+ sputtering. These states can contribute directly to the neutralization of the scattered alkali, as described previously [48].

An additional contribution to the size-dependent neutralization may be the dependence of the magnitude of the image charge potential on the cluster size. It can be shown from classical electrodynamics [19] that the image charge potential is reduced when the clusters become smaller, leading to less of an upward shift of the ionization level. At typical distances of 5 a.u. from the image plane of a flat metal surface, where charge exchange between the projectile and the substrate typically occurs, the image charge potential shift is 1.7 eV, whereas the shift induced by clusters with diameters of 20 a.u is only 0.7 eV.

Thus, a combination of the appearance and upward shift of confined states of Au nanoclusters with a reduction of the image charge potential leads to an increase in the overlap of the alkali ionization levels with the occupied cluster states, which raises the NF as the cluster dimensions decrease with sputtering time. The higher NF observed for Na than for K is understandable because the K ionization level is always positioned above the ionization level of Na.

5. ION INDUCED NANOSTRUCTURES ON SEMICONDUCTORS

Ion sputtering under oblique angles is known to produce self-organized nano-scale ripples on the surfaces of various materials [9]. At low energy sputtering of Si, the ripples are readily obtained with O_2^+ ion, in comparison to Ar^+ ion under the same experimental conditions [49]. However, the development of Si topography due to O_2^+ ion bombardment had not been observed in any systematic way. Most of the works were related to secondary ion mass spectrometry (SIMS), where the main interest was to study the variations in the secondary ion yield and the erosion rate during depth profiling with a report on topography, as an adjunct to the main work. In the present section, ripple formation on Si under O_2^+ ion bombardment as a function of ion fluence and energy is presented in detail [50]. The results are discussed within the framework of Bradley-Harper theory [8] and its nonlinear extension, developed for amorphous materials and semiconductors amorphized by ion bombardment.

5.1. Formation of Ripples and Faceted Structures on Oxygen Bombarded Si Surface

Degreased and cleaned Si(100) wafers were sputtered with mass analyzed oxygen ions (both molecular and atomic) in the energy range $5 - 35$ keV in the low energy ion beam (LEIB). The angle of ion incidence θ with respect to the surface normal was varied from 10^0 up to 80^0. The beam current through a 4 mm circular aperture was in the range of $2 - 5$ μA depending on the ion extraction voltage. The samples were exposed with fluences from 2×10^{17} up to 1.1×10^{19} atoms cm^{-2}. It is assumed that an O_2^+ molecular ion sputters the surface as two O^+ ions of half the incident energy of the molecule. The base pressure in the target chamber was less than 5×10^{-8} mbar. The surface morphology of the sputtered samples was examined by AFM in the contact mode, using a Nanoscope IV from Digital Instruments.

The results show that bombardment-induced topography develops when the angle of ion incidence θ is between 50^0 and 60^0. Figure 5.1 shows the evolution of the topography after 16.7 keV O_2^+ ion bombardment at 60^0, as a function of the ion fluence.

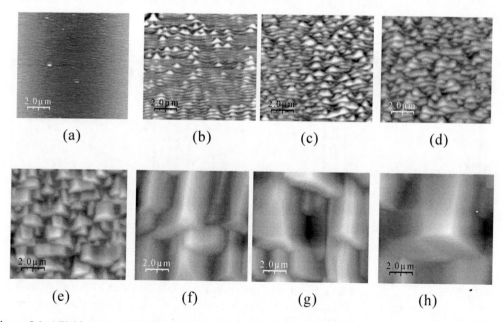

Figure 5.1. AFM images of Si showing the evolution of the surface topography with increasing fluence for 16.7 keV O_2^+ bombardment at $\theta = 60^0$; (a) 2×10^{17} atoms/cm^2, (b) 3×10^{17} atoms/cm^2, (c) 5×10^{17} atoms/cm^2, (d) 8.8×10^{17} atoms/cm^2, (e) 1.4×10^{18} atoms/cm^2, (f) 4×10^{18} atoms/cm^2, (g) 7.5×10^{18} atoms/cm^2 and (h) 1.1×10^{19} atoms/cm^2; the ion beam direction is from the bottom to the top. (Ref. [50] copyright (2005) by Elsevier).

The ripple topography appears at lower fluences ($\leq 8 \times 10^{17}$ atoms cm^{-2}), which is periodic in the direction parallel to the ion beam. At larger fluences, the ripples disintegrate and isolated faceted structures develop. The size of the facets increases with increasing ion fluence. The mechanism of ripple formation is usually discussed within the linear stability framework of Bradley and Harper (BH) [8], as described by Eq. 2.17. The projection of the ion beam on the surface is considered to be in the x direction.

The parameters v_x and v_y can be estimated using the prescriptions as stated in Ref. [8]. For 16.7 keV O_2^+ on Si and a flux of 1×10^{14} atoms cm^{-2} s-1, $v_x = -0.424$ nm^2 s^{-1} and $v_y = -0.154$ nm^2 s^{-1}, where the sputtering yield and the range parameters were calculated using the SRIM program [36]. Since $|v_x| > |v_y|$, the ripples will form with their wave vector parallel to the ion beam direction, which is really observed in the experiment. Eq. 2.17 also predicts that the ripple amplitude should grow exponentially with sputter time t (proportional to ion fluence φ), at constant wavelength as exp(Rt), where $R = |v|^2/4K$ is called the growth rate. The linear model applicable for small slope approximation is further extended by Cuerno and Barabási [51], by including higher order and non linear terms of the derivative of the height function and also taking into consideration the randomness of the erosion, resulting from the stochastic nature of ion arrival. The time evolution of the surface topography h(x, y, t), in this case, is described in section 2 (Eq. 2.17).

In the early stage of sputtering, when the ripple structure begins to develop, the nonlinear term, i.e. $(\lambda/2)(\nabla h)^2$ in Eq. 2.20, is not operative and the ripple characteristics can well be described by the linear BH theory (Eq.2.16). Once the ripples are formed, there exists slope asymmetry that activates the non-linear effect at the late stage of sputtering, thereby changing the law of growth of ripples: from an exponential growth at low fluences to a power law evolution at high fluences [51,52].

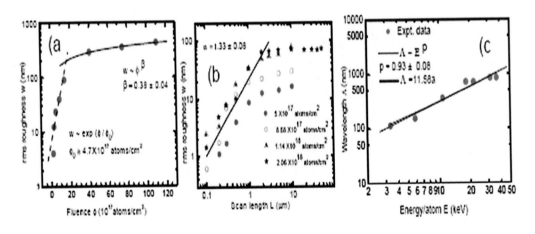

Figure 5.2. (a) rms roughness w as a function of ion fluence φ for 16.7 keV O_2^+ bombardment at θ = 60°. The dashed line represents the fitting by an exponential function w ~ exp(φ/φ0) and the solid line by a power law   w ~ φ$^\beta$. (b) Showing the rms roughness w versus scan length L at different bombarding fluences. The solid line represents the best power law fit w ~ L$^\alpha$ with α = 1.33 ± 0.08. (c) Ripple wavelength versus energy per oxygen atom at a fixed luence 5×10^{17}atoms/cm^2. The solid line represents the power law fit: $\Lambda \sim E^p$ and the dashed line represents the best linear fit using the range values: $\Lambda = 11.58a$. (Ref. [50] copyright (2005) by Elsevier).

Figure 5.2 (a) shows the experimental results of the fluence dependence of the surface roughness. The ripple amplitude (□ w) grows fast exponentially in the early stages, followed by a slower rate of growth consistent with power-law at larger fluences. Similar behavior was observed earlier on Ar^+ bombarded Si(001) and graphite (HOPG) surfaces [53,54]. The dashed line represents the least square fit to the data in the linear regime by an exponential function w ~ exp (ϕ/ϕ_0) with $\phi_0 = 4.7 \times 10^{17}$ atoms cm^{-2}. Dividing the ion flux by ϕ_0, the growth rate of the ripples under the present experimental conditions is found to be about 2.3 $\times$ $10^{-4}s^{-1}$. The solid line represents a power law fitting to the data in the non-linear regime: w ~ ϕ^β, where $\beta = 0.38 \pm 0.04$, is called the growth exponent. We have also measured the roughness exponent α by plotting w of the sputtered surface as a function of the scan length L for different bombarding fluences ϕ (Figure 5.2(b)). The result shows that the local width increases as w~ L^α before it saturates. α is found to be fluence invariant with an average value of 1.33 $\pm$ 0.08. If one considers the corrections for finite tip-size effect [55,56], the true α value will be somewhat less and close to unity. In the limit of long time and length scales, Eq. 2.20 is equivalent to the Kardar-Parisi-Zhang (KPZ) equation [11]. The exponents α and β for the KPZ-type scaling are 0.38 are 0.25, respectively, which are much lower than that of the present work. The near-unity roughness exponent implies that the surface morphology, in this case, is not self-affine.

Figure 5.3(c) shows the measured ripple wavelength as a function of the bombarding energy per oxygen atom for a fixed fluence of 5 $\times$ 10^{17} atoms/cm^2. Λ follows a power law dependence: $\Lambda \sim E^p$ with p = 0.93 $\pm$ 08. At room temperature where ion induced smoothening is thought to be main relaxation mechanism, the dependence of Λ on the ion energy E, is shown to be [2]: $\Lambda \sim a \sim E^{2m}$, where a is the ion range and m is the exponent of the power law interaction potential. Comparing with our experimental results, we find that m $\approx$ ½, which is quite a reasonable value in the energy range investigated. The ripple wavelength is found to scale with ion range as 11.6 A, in contrast to 40 A, as measured by Vajo et al. [39].

Instead of dot or ripple structures, nano scale hole structures are introduced on an atomically clean TiO_2(110) surface in a controllable manner via bombardment with 0.5 keV Ar^+ ions, and the resultant material is probed with scanning tunneling microscopy and x-ray photoelectron spectroscopy. It is shown that ion bombardment leads to a change of stoichiometry and the formation of vacancy clusters, while annealing after prolonged bombardment forms regular rectangular cavities with single atomic layer steps [57].

5.2. Coulomb Explosion Sputtering of Oxidized Nano Structure

In recent years, the interactions of multi-charged ions with solid surfaces have been the subject of active research, both for fundamental interest to understand various emission processes as well as future technological applications. In contrast to the well- known kinetically induced ion beam sputtering process, the erosion of surfaces exploiting the potential energy of the projectile is called Coulomb explosion or potential sputtering. As per the Coulomb explosion model, the potential sputtering depends on the surface conductivity of the target. Here, we have developed different conductive zone in nanometer range on Si(100), by oblique angle oxygen ion bombardment and showed the enhanced sputtering of oxidized zone due to multi charged argon ion impact [58].

The samples were first irradiated with 16 keV O_2^+ ion beam at 60^0 angle, with respect to the surface normal at fluence 2 $\times 10^{18}$ atoms/cm^2. The topography and surface conductivity measurements were carried out in air by Scanning Probe Microscopy (SPM), both in contact

Atomic Force Microscopy (AFM) and conducting Atomic Force Microscopy (C-AFM) modes. The samples were again inserted into the irradiation chamber and bombarded with Ar^{q+} (q = 2, 8) at normal ion incidence. The kinetic energy of the Ar^{q+} was same (32 keV) for all the cases. For MCI irradiation, normal incidence is chosen for isotropic radiation of oxidized and less oxidized part of the ripple structures. All the ions were generated and extracted from a 6.4 GHz Electron Cyclotron Resonance (ECR) ion source of the Radioactive Ion Beam Facility at Variable Energy Cyclotron Centre Kolkata. After Ar^{q+} bombardment the nano structures are again imaged by the Atomic Force Microscope (AFM) in air.

The ripple formation and selective oxidation is evident from Figure 5.3. Once the ripple structures are formed, local ion impact angle on the beam facing surface of the ripple is reduced, resulting in an increase of implanted oxygen concentration and thus SiO_2 forms. This compositional change causes further reduction of sputtering yield from the front side, and thereby the surface of each ripple is decomposed into two phases, the ion beam facing side which is more oxidized and the other side which is comparatively less oxidized. Figure 5.3 (a) presents the topographic AFM image whereas Figure 5.3(b) shows the C-AFM current image of the same area, which measures the leakage current through the sample, for a fixed bias voltage between tip and sample.

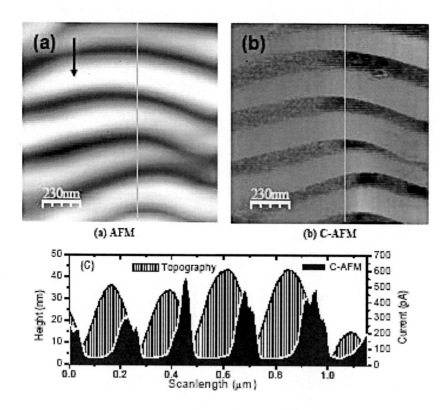

Figure 5.3. Same area (a) AFM and (b) C-AFM images of Si ripple structures produced by 16 keV O_2^+ bombardment at 60^0. (c) Superposition of one dimensional topographic and current profiles corresponding to the marked lines. The arrow indicates the O_2^+ beam direction.

For better comparison, the line profiles of topographic and current images are superimposed in Fig 5.3 (c). It illustrates clearly that only the back side of the ripple shows leakage current which confirms the coexistence of insulating and semiconducting sectors of the nano ripples. Homma et al. reported the similar structure for 2-10 keV O_2^+ bombardment at 45^0 [59]. Auger mapping also showed the asymmetric distribution of implanted oxygen. C-AFM measurement at the bottom of SIMS crater formed by 8 keV O_2^+ ion revealed the same fact [60]. Such ripples having both semiconducting and insulating zones have been chosen to study the MCI induced potential sputtering.

Fig 5.4 (a1) presents the ripple structures formed by 16 keV O_2^+ ion bombardment at 2×10^{18} atoms/cm^2 whereas Figure 5.4 (a2) illustrates the topography after subsequent irradiation by Ar^{8+}. The line profiles of two similar ripple structures before and after HCI irradiation are shown in Figure 5.4 (a3). It is observed that the ripple is eroded asymmetrically, the front (beam facing side during oblique angle oxygen bombardment) surface is eroded more than the other side though the MCI incidence was symmetric (along the sample surface normal). It can be estimated from Figure 5.4 (a3) that the normal sputter loss of the front side is ~ 80 nm, while the one on back side is only ~ 31 nm. Figure 5-4(b2) shows the effect of Ar^{2+} ion bombardment on the similar ripple structures at same fluence and kinetic energy as before. It is observed from the Figure 5-4(b3) that the ripple is eroded almost symmetrically.

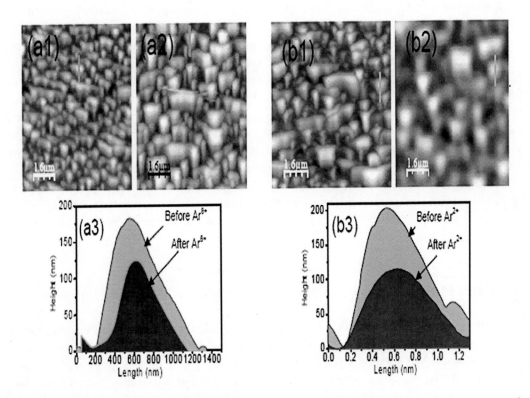

Figure 5.4. (a1) and (b1) AFM topography of Si ripple produced by 16 keV O_2^+ bombardment at 60^0 (a2) AFM topography of (a1) after Ar^{8+} bombardment, (a3) superposition of surface profiles corresponding to (a1) and (a2). (b2) AFM topography of (b1) after Ar^{2+} bombardment, (b3) Superposition of surface profiles corresponding to (b1) and (b2).

In the present experiment, the MCI ions carry both kinetic and potential energy as they are not decelerated. Therefore, sputtering yield due to impact of MCI consists of two components, one due to potential sputtering and the other due to kinetic sputtering. To investigate the effect of potential energy, the same kinetic energy (V × q) of the Ar $^{q+}$ (q = 2, 8) ions were maintained, where V is the extraction voltage and q is the charge state of the ions. Equal erosion from both sides of the ripple by kinetic sputtering during the ion impact at normal to the sample surface is predictable. In case of Ar^{2+}, the stored potential energy is negligible compared to the kinetic energy; therefore, the observed symmetric erosion of the ripple [Fig 5.4 (b3)] is quite likely. The asymmetry in ripple [Figure 5.4(a3)] after Ar^{8+} bombardment reveals that the insulating part of the ripple is preferentially sputtered due to considerable potential energy stored in the incident ions.

The potential energy is the unique parameter of MCI, which plays the main role for the additional sputtering of the insulating part of the ripple by Ar^{8+}, compared to the Ar^{2+}. The well-known kinetic energy deposition forms a collision cascade, and if collision cascade reaches the surface, the target atoms, having energy larger than the surface binding energy are ejected as kinetic sputtered materials, whereas potential sputtering supposed to be for the potential energy stored in the projectile. When the MCI comes close to the target surface, the electrons from the surface fill the high-lying Rydberg states of the projectile. The emission of electrons from the surface forms charge depletion at the impact point. If the surface is good conductor, the conduction electrons quickly diminishes the charged up domain prior to the explosion, but for poor conductor this charge imbalance will probably of sufficient duration, because of the diffusion length of the electron. The electrostatic repulsion between nearby positively charged surface atoms is thought to generate a coulomb explosion or even shock wave [61], which ablates target materials. The erosion of more material from the oxidized, i. e., insulating side of the ripples is qualitatively in agreement with the above model of potential sputtering. Tona et al.[62] studied the secondary ion emission during the impact of I^{q+} on a native SiO$_2$ thin film on a Si(111) as an insulator surface and a clean well defined hydrogen terminated Si(111) as semiconductor material. The direct comparison of sputtering yield of coexisted insulating and semiconducting regions of the nano ripples reduces the difficulties of maintaining the same experimental conditions, which is required for performing the same experiment with separate samples of different conductivity. Although an additional sputtering of insulating sector of the ripple is observed for Ar^{8+} ion bombardment compared to the Ar^{2+}, the evidence may be stronger, if projectile with higher potential and lower kinetic energy is exercised.

5.3. Role of Initial Surface Roughness on Ion Induced Surface Morphology

In the previous sections a number of experimental and theoretical studies on ion induced nano-structure formation are described. Theoretical understanding of ion induced structure formation was given by Bradley and Harper [BH] [8], based on the Sigmund sputtering theory [7]. However, most of the theoretical and experimental studies of nanostructure formation are restricted to the regions of stable ripples, dots and holes formation or to the long time bombardment effects, the beginning stage of such regular structure formation has not been discussed.

Ion-induced surface morphology depends upon the growth or decay of the perturbations, present at the very initial stage of bombardment. The possible origins of perturbations are: (i) stochastic nature and in-homogeneity of the incident ion beam; (ii) preferential sputtering [19,57]; (iii) presence of impurities on the surface [63]; and (iv) initial surface roughness. Single ion impact on clean single crystal surface showed [3], that at the point of impact both vacancies and ad-atoms are created. Because of stochastic nature of incident ion beam, these defects are expected to be randomly distributed on the surface resulting in a rough surface at the early stage of ion bombardment or prior to the regular structure formation. In the case of preferential sputtering and presence of impurities, different elements are sputtered at different rate, which assist the initial roughening process. Thus, rough surface, which is supposed to be the origin of initial perturbations, is necessary for ion induced curvature dependent structure formation. Therefore, if the initial roughness is incorporated by any simple way, the ion induced structure formation is expected to be influenced.

In this section we have studied the effect of initial roughness on well known and well studied ripple formation on Si (100) surfaces [64]. We have incorporated random roughness on Si (100) by simple chemical process and studied the 16.7 keV, molecular oxygen ion beam induced ripple pattern on various initially rough surfaces and compared the results with initial flat surface. We observe that the ripple structures are formed at relatively lower ion fluence, in presence of initial roughness on the surface. For higher values of initial roughness, additionally, we observe the process of kinetic roughening and rotation of surface pattern at moderate ion fluence which are only observed at very high fluence in the case of an initial flat surface.

Si (100) samples were cleaned with trichloroethelene, followed by methanol in an ultrasonic bath. The cleaned and dried samples were then immersed in a prepared solution of 5 mol/L HNO_3 and 12 mol/L HF, at room temperature. Immediately after that, the wet samples were rinsed in water and dried. The roughness of the samples was measured by an Atomic Force Microscope (AFM) (NanoScope IV). The Si (100) surfaces after chemical etching were checked by X ray Photoelectron Spectroscopy (XPS). No chemical contamination was detected on the etched surfaces, after proper cleaning and drying. The chemically etched as well as the virgin Si samples were sputtered in a low energy ion beam system described elsewhere [65]. All the samples were bombarded by 16.7 keV O_2^+ at an angle of 60^0 with respect to the surface normal. The ion fluence was varied from 2×10^{16} to 1.1×10^{19} atoms/cm^2. The developed surface patterns were examined by the AFM and the quantitative analysis, e.g., the measurements of amplitude, wavelength and correlation length, was performed as described earlier [25,50].

Figs. 5.5 [(b1), (c1), (d1), (e1) and (f1)] show the morphology of chemically etched Si surfaces, while Figs. 5.5 [(b2), (c2), (d2), (e2) and (f2)] illustrate the corresponding surface patterns after ion sputtering at fluence 6×10^{17} atoms/cm^2. For comparison, the morphologies of the unetched Si (100) surface before and after sputtering at the same fluence, are shown in Figure5.5 [(a1) and (a2)]. The results show that the ripple topography developed after sputtering are dissimilar for various initial roughness. Figure 5.5 (g) shows the changes of ripple amplitude, wavelength and correlation length with the initial values of surface roughness. The ripple amplitude is taken as the measured surface roughness of the bombarding samples. Since the initial roughness values are different, the roughness developed after ion bombardment will obviously be different. The ion induced roughness, σ is calculated from the final roughness, σ_f and the chemical roughness, σ_i using the relation:

$\sigma = \sqrt{\sigma_f^2 - \sigma_i^2}$. It is seen from Figure 5-5 (g) that the ripple amplitude grows faster up to

the initial roughness value 7.6 nm, followed by a slower growth rate at higher initial roughness values. It is also seen from the same figure that with increase of surface roughness, the ripple wavelength and correlation length, gradually increase and finally saturate.

To investigate the fluence dependent structure formation on initially rough surfaces, we bombarded the flat Si (roughness 0.1 nm) and the etched Si of roughness 7 ± 2 nm, 9 ± 2 nm and 28 ± 2 nm, respectively, at various ion fluences. Figs. 5.6 [(a)–(g)] show some typical AFM images for the bombarded Si samples with initial roughness 7 ± 2 nm. The ripple structures start to form at fluence of 3×10^{16} atoms/cm^2 only; while for the initial flat Si (100) surface, the threshold fluence for ripple formation is $\approx 3 \times 10^{17}$ atoms/cm^2 (Figure 5.6 (a1)). If ion sputtering is continued on both the initially flat and 7 ± 2 nm rough surfaces, the ripples grow with fluence, but at high fluence the ripples starts to disintegrate leading to kinetic roughening of the surface [52].

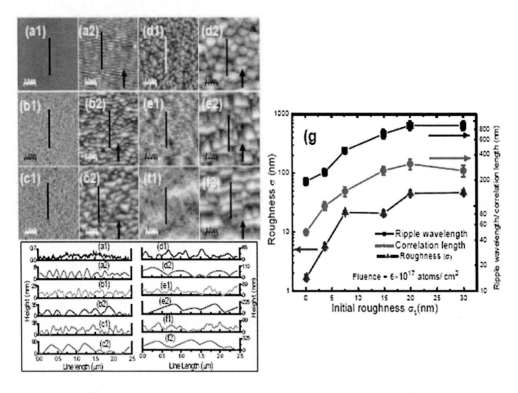

Figure 5.5. (a1) Flat Si (100) of rms roughness 0.1 nm. Chemically generated different initial rough Si surfaces of rms roughness, (b1) 3.7 nm (c1) 7.6 nm (d1) 14.9 nm (e1) 20 nm, and (f1) 31 nm. (a2), (b2), (c2), (d2), (e2) and (f2) represent the corresponding AFM topographies after 16.7 keV O2+ bombardment at fluence 6×1017 atoms/cm2 of (a1), (b1), (c1), (d1), (e1), and (f1) respectively; the surface profile corresponding to the marked line for each AFM images is shown in the lower panel and the arrows indicate the beam direction. (g) ion induced roughness (σ), ripple wavelength and correlation length as a function of initial surface roughness (σ_i). (Ref. [64] copyright (2008) by American Institute of Physics).

Their dynamics were reported before for the same ion beam parameters [50]. It is interesting to note, that the kinetic roughening starts around the fluence 1.4×10^{18} atoms/ cm^2 for the flat surface (Figure 5.6 (f1)), while it is 4×10^{17} atoms/cm^2 for the 7 ± 2 nm rough surface.

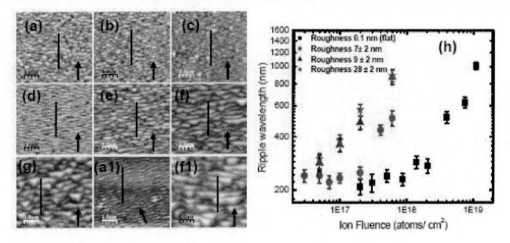

Figure 5.6. AFM topographies of 16.7 keV O$_2^+$ ion bombarded Si of initial roughness 7 ± 2 nm at fluences (a) 3×10^{16} atoms/cm^2 (b) 5×10^{16} atoms/cm^2 (c) 7×10^{16} atoms/cm^2 (d) 1×10^{17} atoms/cm^2 (e) 2×10^{17} atoms/cm^2 (f) 4×10^{17} atoms/cm^2 and (g) 6×10^{17} atoms/cm^2. Morphology of the flat Si (100) surface after bombardment at (a1) 3×10^{17} atoms/cm^2 (first appearance of ripples) and (f1) 1.4×10^{18} atoms/cm^2 (beginning of kinetic roughening); (h) ripple wavelength vs. ion fluence for flat and different initially rough Si surfaces. (Ref. [64] copyright (2008) by American Institute of Physics).

Figure 5.6(h) shows the variation of ripple wavelength with ion fluence for flat and initially rough surfaces, respectively. For the flat surface, the wavelength does not change with the fluence at lower ion fluence regime following the BH theory. For the 7 ± 2 nm rough surface, the identical initial ripple wavelength invariance is also observed, but the ripple starts to develop at lower ion fluence than that for the flat surface. However, for higher initial rough surfaces e.g., 9 ± 2 nm and 28 ± 2 nm, invariance of ripple wavelength is not observed; instead of, the wavelength show an increase from the beginning of ion bombardment (Figure 5.6(h)).

The BH model [8] is based on Sigmund's sputtering theory [7], assuming an ellipsoidal shape of the collision cascade. If the surface has local curvature, more energy from the collision cascades reaches to the valleys than the hills and therefore, the preferential sputtering of the valleys generates instability. In addition to the sputtering induced instability, thermal diffusion is also considered, which is responsible for the smoothening of the surface during bombardment.

It is obvious that to initiate the curvature dependent instability, the presence of local surface curvature is essential. Therefore, for an initial flat surface and fixed angle of ion incidence, no modulated structures could be expected. But experiments with initial flat surface produces ripple structures. BH assumed an initial perturbation, present on the surface, and sputtering increases the amplitude of the perturbation, but the origin of perturbation was not clearly mentioned. Cuerno, et al. [51] introduced a noise term in the nonlinear continuum equation to consider the random arrival of the ions, but the effect of the noise term on the surface morphology was not emphasized. Khang et al. [18] did not consider the noise term, instead of they assumed an initially rough surface for simulations of ion-induced holes and dots formation.

In case of a flat surface, the ion beam itself generates the initial random rough surface. It has been proposed that the stochastic nature of incident ions and non overlapping character of collision cascades, in the interaction time scale ($\sim 10^{13}$ s) forms discrete and random vacancies and adatoms on the surface at low ion fluence [57,66]. The nature of randomness and in-homogeneity is also observed in single ion impact experiments [3]. The ion fluence, required to generate the minimum roughness on the surface, depends on the specific ion target combination, preferential sputtering, reactive sputtering, and impurities present on the surface. Once the surface flatness is destroyed, the curvature dependent sputtering starts and the shape of the surface structure depends on the various ion beam parameters and diffusion processes. The present experiment shows that the creation of initial rough surface by chemical way helps the ion beam to skip of the process of surface roughening for local curvature development. As the local curvature is readily present on the surface, the BH curvature dependence sputtering takes place from the very beginning of ion bombardment and ripples are observed at relatively lower ion fluences.

For long time ion bombardment, kinetic roughening and saturation of ripple amplitude were predicted by the nonlinear extension of the linear BH theory [51,52]. Experimentally, the nonlinear effect has been reported in the case of Ar^+ bombarded Si (100) [53] and graphite (HOPG) [54] surfaces. We also reported earlier [50] the kinetic roughening in the case O_2^+ bombarded flat Si(100) for long time ion bombardment. For the case of 7 ± 2 nm initial rough surface, the observation of kinetic roughening [Figure 5.6(f)] and the increase of ripple wavelength with ion fluence [Figure 5.6(h)] indicate that the nonlinear effects starts at moderate ion fluence compared to that of flat surface. The initial invariance of ripple wavelength with ion fluence for both flat and 7 ± 2 nm rough surfaces (Figure 5.6(h)), is in qualitative agreement with the BH linear theory which predicts the ripple wavelength to be independent of ion fluence. In the case of higher initial rough surfaces (9 ± 2 nm and 28 ± 2nm), the increase of ripple wavelength from the beginning of ion bombardment (Figure 5.6(h)), indicates that the nonlinear effects start at the early stages of ion bombardment.

The rotation of ripple structures along the ion beam direction for very high fluence ion bombardment has also been predicted by Park et al. [52]. But to achieve very high fluence ($\sim 1 \times 10^{19}$ atoms/cm^2), high current ion beam system or exceptionally long time of ion bombardment is required. Recently, Brown et al. [67] reported the rotation of ripple at elevated temperature with Ar^+ ion bombardment on Si(111) at 4.8×10^{19} ions/cm^2. At room temperature we observed rotated structures along the ion beam direction at fluence $\sim 1 \times 10^{19}$ atoms/cm^2, but in the case of initial rough surfaces (Figure 5.5 (e2), (f2)), such structures are observed only at 6×10^{17}atoms/cm^2. This allows us to produce rotated structures at easily attainable fluence, just by introducing high initial roughness by the chemical process.

SUMMARY

The surface morphology induced by near normal ion beam sputtering of polycrystalline thin films shows dot structures whereas at oblique angle it exhibits rough surfaces of self-affine scaling behavior. Grazing ion beam sputtering can induce ripple structures on thin metallic films. Such ripples are found to be quite stable at ambient conditions. It is noted that, independent of the initial morphology of the surface, the ripples in metallic films start to generate at ion fluences as low as 10^{15} ions/cm^2 which is roughly two orders of magnitude smaller than that for the ripples formed on Si surfaces.

Ion sputtering technique produces nanoclusters in a controllable manner, and that these clusters exhibit electronic size effects. The combination of keV ion sputtering and alkali-metal ion scattering provides a unique method for producing and probing nanomaterials.

In case of Si, ripple structures are formed at oblique angle oxygen ion bombardment. At the beginning the ripple amplitude grows exponentially with the sputter time, while at the late stages the ripple structure dissociates and the surface becomes faceted. The wavelength of the ripples shows a linear increase with the incident projectile energy.

The combination of chemical etching and physical sputtering is likely to have a good potential for the fabrication of nanostructures in a simple but cost and time effective way. It is observed that surface roughness enhances the initial perturbation, which aids to form the ion induced regular nanostructures at an ion fluence typically one to two orders of magnitude less than that are required to produce the same structures on an initially flat surface. This observation opens up the scope for further theoretical and experimental work to understand the effect of initial surface roughness on ion induced nanostructure formation.

Selective oxidation of nano ripples by oxygen bombardment is also shown and the preferential sputtering of oxidized part by multi charge Ar ion is presented. This opens up the scope of selective etching of surfaces in nanometer scale and a new way of nano structure formation by ion beams.

ACKNOWLEDGMENTS

The author is highly grateful to Prof. D. Ghose, Prof. T. K. Chini, Prof. S. R. Bhattacharya, Prof. J. A. Yarmoff and Prof. A. Chakrabarti for their constant support and encouragement.

REFERENCES

[1]   M. V. Ramana Murty, Surf. Sci. **500**, 523 (2002).

[2]   M. A. Makeev and A. L. Barabasi, Appl.Phys. Lett. **71**, 2800 (1997).

[3]   U. Valbusa, C. Boragno, and F. B. d. Mongeot, J. Phys.:Condens. Matter **14**, 8153 (2002).

[4]   M. Navez, C. Sella, and D. Chaperot, C. R. Acad. Sci. Paris 254 240 (1962).

[5]   D. Ghose and S. B. Karmohapatro, in:Advances in Electronics and Electron Physics, Ed. P. Hawak (Academic Press, New York) **79**, 73 (1990).

[6]   A.-L. Barabasi and H. E. Stanley, Fractal Concepts in Surface Growth (Cambridge University Press, Cambridge, England) (1995).

[7]   P. Sigmund, Phys. Rev. **184**, 383 (1969).

[8]   R. M. Bradley and J. M. E. Harper, J. Vac. Sci. Technol. A **6**, 2390 (1988).

[9]   M. A. Makeev, R. Cuerno, and A.-L. Barabasi, Nucl. Instrum. and Meth. B **197**, 185 (2002).

[10] E. A. Eklund, R. Bruinsma, R. J, and R. S. Williams, Phys. Rev. Lett. **67**, 1759 (1991).

[11] M. Karder, G. Parisi, and Y.-C. Zhang, Phys. Rev. Lett. **56** 889 (1986).

[12] I. Koponen, M. Hautala, and O.-P. Siev, Phys.Rev. Lett. **78**, 2612 (1997).

[13] F. A. Stevie, P. M. Kara, D. S. Simons, and P. Chi, J. Vac, Sci.Tech. A **6** 76 (1988).

[14] Wittmack, J. Vac, Sci.Tech. A 8, 2246 (1990).

[15] A. Karen, Y. Nakagawa, M. Hatada, K. Okuno, F. Soeda, and A. Ishitani, Surf.Interf. Anal. 23 506 (1995).

[16] J. Erlebacher, M. J. Aziz, E. Chason, M. B. Sinclair, and J. A. Floro, Phys. Rev. Lett 82, 2330 (1999).

[17] S. Hebenicht, W. Bolse, K. P. Lieb, K. Reimann, and U. Geyer, Phys. Rev. B 60, R2200 (1999).

[18] B. Kahng, H. Jeong, and A. L. Barabasi, Appl. Phys. Lett. 78, 805 (2001).

[19] S. Facsko, T. Dekorsy, C.Koerdt, C.Trappe, H. Kurz, A. Vogt, and H. L. Hartnagel, Science 285 (1999).

[20] S. Rusponi, C. Boragno, and U. Valbusa, Phys Rev. Lett. 78, 2795 (1997).

[21] P. Karmakar and D. Ghose, Nucl. Intr. and Meth. B 222, 477 (2004).

[22] P. Karmakar and D. Ghose, Surf. Sci. 554, L101 (2004).

[23] J. P. Wilcoxon and B. L. Abrams, Chem. Soc. Rev 35, 1162 (2006).

[24] M. S. Chen and D. W. Goodman, Catalysis Today 111, 22 (2006).

[25] Y.-P. Zhao, G.-C. Wang, and T.-M. Lu, *Characterization of Amorphous and Crystalline Rough Surface: Principles and Applications* (Academic Press, San Diego, 2001).

[26] T. Karabacak, Y.-P. Zhao, G.-C. Wang, and T.-M. Lu, Phys. Rev. B 64, 085323 (2001).

[27] U. Valbusa, C. Boragno, and F. B. d. Mongeot, Materials Science and Engineering C 23, 201 (2003).

[28] G. Costantini, Thesis, University of Genova, December (1999).

[29] G. Costantini, S. Rusponi, F. B. d. Mongeot, C. Boragno, and U. Valbusa, J. Phys.: Condens. Matter 13, 5875 (2001).

[30] J. H. Jeffries, J.-K. Zuo, and M. M. Craig, Phys. Rev. Lett. 76, 4931 (1996).

[31] S. Wei, B. Li, T. Fujimoto, and I. Kojima, Phys. Rev. B 58, 3605 (1998).

[32] S. M. Rossnagel and R. S. Robinson, J. Vac. Sci. Technol. 20, 195 (1982).

[33] G. Carter, J. Phys. D: Appl. Phys. 34, R1 (2001).

[34] G. K. Wehner, Appl. Phys. Lett. 43, 366 (1983).

[35] G. Carter and V. Vishnyakov, Phys. Rev. B 54, 17647 (1996).

[36] Z. F. Ziegler, IBM Research, SRIM-2000.40 (PC version), Yorktown Heights, NY (1999).

[37] J. Kim, D. G. Cahill, and R. S. A. P. R. B, Phys. Rev. B 67 (2003) 045404. 67, 045404 (2003).

[38] S. Facsko, H. Kurz, and T. Dekorsy, Phys. Rev. B 63, 165329 (2001).

[39] J. J. Vajo, R. E. Doty, and E.-H. Cirlin, J. Vac. Sci. Technol. A 14, 2709 (1996).

[40] P. Karmakar, G. F. Liu, Z. Sroubek, and J. A. Yarmoff, Phys. Rev. Lett. 98, 215502 (2007).

[41] H. C. Chen, C. M. Huang, K. F. Liao, S. W. Lee, C. H. Hsu, and L. J. Chen, Nucl. Instrum. and Meth. B 237, 465 (2005).

[42] R.Krishna, V. Baranwal, Y. S. Katharria, D. Kabiraj, A. Tripathi, F. Singh, S. A. Khan, A. C. Panday, and D. Kanjilal, Nucl. Instrum. and Meth. B 244, 78 (2006).

[43] W. B. Fan, L. J. Qi, H. T. Sun, Y. Y. Zhao, and M. Lu, Nanotechnology 17, 1878 (2006).

[44] G. F. Liu, Z. Sroubek, and J. A. Yarmoff, Phys. Rev. Lett 92, 216801 (2004).

[45] A. R. Canario and V. A. Esaulov, J. Chem. Phys. 124, 224710 (2006).

[46] A. R. Canario, T. Kravchuk, and V. A. Esaulov, New J. Phys. 8, 227 (2006).

[47] H. Hovel and I. Barke, Prog. Surf. Sci. 81, 53 (2006).

[48] L. D. Landau and E. M. Lifshitz, (Pergamon, New York 1960).

[49] K. Elst and W. Vandervorst, J. Vac. Sci. Technol. A 12, 3205 (1994).

[50] P. Karmakar and D. Ghose, Nucl. Instr. And Meth. B 230, 539 (2005).

[51] R. Cuerno and A.-L. Barabási, Phys. Rev. Lett. 74, 4746 (1995).

[52] S. Park, B. Kahng, and A. L. Barabasi, Phys. Rev. Lett. 83, 3486 (1999).

[53] J. Erlebacher, M. J. Aziz, E. Chason, M. B. Sinclair, and J. A. Floro, J. Vac. Sci. Technol. A 18, 115 (2000).

[54] S. Habenicht, Phys. Rev. B 63, 125419 (2001).

[55] Q. M. Hudspeth, K. P. Nagle, Y.-P. Zhao, T. Karabacak, C. V. Nguyen, M. Meyyappan, G.-C. Wang, and T.-M. Lu, Surf. Sci. 515, 453 (2002).

[56] J. Aue and J. T. M. D. Hosson, Appl. Phys. Lett. 71, 1347 (1997).

[57] P. Karmakar, G. F. Liu, and J. A. Yarmoff, Phys. Rev. B 76, 193410 (2007).

[58] P. Karmakar, S. Bhattacharjee, V. Naik, A. K. Sinha, and A. Chakrabarti, J. Phys. Cond. Matt. 22, 175005 (2010).

[59] Y. Homma, A. Takano, and Y. Higashi, Appl. Surf. Sci. 203-204, 35 (2003).

[60] B. Gautier, B. Fares, G. Prudon, and J.-C. Dupuy, Appl. Surf. Sci. 231-232, 136 (2004).

[61] D. Ghose, P. Karmakar, and E. Parilis, Nucl. Instr. and Meth. in Phys. Res. B 212, 420 (2003).

[62] M. Tona, S. Takahashi, K. Nagata, N. Yoshiyasu, C. Yamada, N. Nakamura, S. Ohtani, and M. Sakurai, Appl. Phys. Lett. 87, 224102 (2005).

[63] G. Ozaydin, A. S. O¨zcan, Y. Wang, K. F. Ludwig, H. Zhao, R.L.Headrick, and D. P. Siddons, Appl. Phys. Lett. 87, 163104 (2005).

[64] P. Karmakar, S. A. Mollick, D. Ghose, and A. Chakrabarti, Applied Physics Letters 93, 103102 (2008).

[65] P. Karmakar and D. Ghose, Nucl. Instr. and Meth. B 212, 358 (2003).

[66] W. Möller, *Fundamentals of Ion-Surface Interaction*, lecture notes found at http://www.fz-rossendorf.de/FWI.

[67] A.-D. Brown, J. Erlebacher, W.-L. Chan, and E. Chason, Phy. Rev. Lett. 95, 056101 (2005).

In: Synthesis and Engineering of Nanostructures...   ISBN 978-1-62100-261-1
Editors: Devesh Kumar Avasthi & Jean Claude Pivin   © 2012 Nova Science Publishers, Inc

Chapter 7

X-RAY SCATTERING STUDIES OF NANODOT PATTERN FORMATION ON SEMICONDUCTOR SURFACES BY LOW ENERGY ION BEAM SPUTTERING

O. Plantevin[1], R. Gago[2], L. Vázquez[2], A. Biermanns[3], D. Carbone[4] and T.H. Metzger[4]

[1] Univ Paris-Sud, Centre de Spectrométrie Nucléaire et de Spectrométrie de Masse, CNRS, UMR 8609, 91405 Orsay, France
[2] Instituto de Ciencia de Materiales de Madrid, Consejo Superior de Investigaciones Científicas, E-28049 Madrid, Spain
[3] Universität Siegen, Festkörperphysik, D-57068 Siegen, Germany
[4] European Synchrotron Radiation Facility, BP220 38043 Grenoble Cedex, France

ABSTRACT

We show the capability of in-situ and ex-situ grazing-incidence small angle X-ray scattering (GISAXS) and diffraction (GID) techniques, using synchrotron radiation, to study the formation of self-organized nanodot patterns on semiconductor targets by ion beam sputtering (IBS). Particularly, surface nanopatterns of short-range hexagonal arrays of nanodots (as observed by atomic force microscopy imaging) were produced on Si(001) and GaSb(001) using low-energy (below or around 1 keV) Ar+ IBS under normal incidence. As an illustrative example of ex-situ application, we present the influence of the surface temperature on the pattern formation on Si(001), where the combination of GID and GISAXS allows to separate between amorphous and crystalline contributions. The ion-induced amorphization and progressive loss of the nanodot pattern with increasing temperature are discussed. In the case of in-situ formation, the authors illustrate real-time monitoring of the process for GaSb(001) surfaces, using GISAXS and a specially designed IBS chamber. Here, pattern coarsening and stabilization is discussed as a function of the ion energy. These results have technological implications, regarding the control over the pattern characteristics and also provide relevant information to the theoretical understanding of pattern formation by IBS

1. INTRODUCTION

Low-energy ion beam sputtering (IBS) has proven to be a very flexible method for the production of ordered, uniform structures with sizes down to 10 nm, on the surface of metals, semiconductors and insulators[1,2]. In particular for semiconductors, hexagonal arrays of nanodots are produced at normal incident ion irradiation, whereas at off-normal incidence very regular ripple patterns are formed.

The pattern formation mechanism by IBS is explained as a result of the interplay between the ion-induced sputtering and surface relaxation processes. A successful theoretical approach to describe the surface instability related to the pattern formation is based on continuum models, where the surface height evolution is described by partial differential equations [3]. The first proposal was launched by Bradley and Harper (BH)[4], which accounts for ripple formation under off-normal incidence and the transition of the ripple orientation from perpendicular to parallel to the projected beam for incidence angles above a critical value with respect to the surface normal. Several extensions of the BH model have been proposed to cover other experimental observations, such as pattern stabilization for long sputtering times[5], nanodot formation for the isotropic case[6], and more recently the observation of ordering[7,8] and coarsening. This theoretical effort needs accurate experimental information about the pattern temporal evolution to contrast, extend, and validate the different proposed equations. The temporal evolution of nanodot patterns has been addressed for GaSb [9,10], InP [11] and Si [12] substrates by *ex-situ* imaging methods. In this work, both *ex-situ* and *in-situ* grazing incidence X-ray scattering studies using synchrotron radiation are presented. The *in-situ* studies were performed with the use of a specially designed sputtering chamber [13,14] which allows following the dynamics of the nanostructuring process in real-time.

2. GRAZING-INCIDENCE X-RAY SCATTERING TECHNIQUES

Grazing-incidence small-angle X-ray scattering (GISAXS) and grazing-incidence diffraction (GID) techniques can be applied to get relevant information on the shape, size, strain and chemical composition of semiconductor nanostructures [15]. The grazing-incidence configuration is aimed at sampling the near-surface region. The pattern formation and characteristics are derived from the presence of satellite peaks in the diffuse scattering appearing around the reflected and diffracted peaks in the GISAXS and GID scans respectively. A schematic of the experimental set-up for both techniques is presented in figure 1. The observation of satellite peaks are related to the emerging of correlated roughness over the surface and the selection of a specific wavelength out of the fluctuations due to the pattern formation. The position and width of the GISAXS and GID peaks provide complementary information about the characteristic wavelength (λ) or mean inter-dot distance, and correlation length (ξ) of the ordered domains, respectively, of the nano-patterns. Particularly, λ is derived from the $Q_{max}=2\pi/\lambda$ relation whereas the peak width is approximately inversely proportional to the correlation length in a short-range order (SRO) scenario [16]. Finally, simultaneous GID and GISAXS scans allow discriminating the contribution from the nanostructure crystalline core (if present).

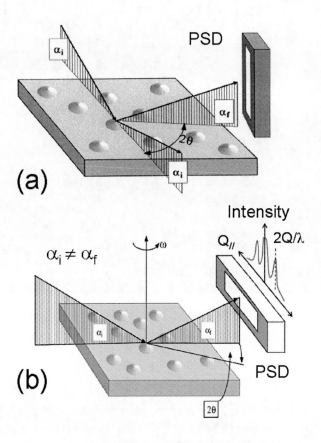

Figure 1. GID (a) and GISAXS (b) X-ray scattering configurations (adapted from Ref. 15).

3. EXPERIMENTAL DETAILS

3.1 Self-Organized Nanopattern Production

The Si(001) substrates were sputtered *ex-situ* with 1 keV Ar$^+$ ions in the temperature range 300-625 K, with an ion current density fixed at ~240 μA/cm^2 for 10 min, such that the surface morphology has reached a stationary state.

In addition, the GaSb(001) samples were sputtered in a compact high vacuum chamber (base pressure of 10^{-7} mbar) mounted in the centre of the goniometer. The chamber is equipped with a Kaufman ion gun and a 360° Be window to allow *in-situ* x-ray scattering experiments, as shown in figure 2. The samples were irradiated under normal incidence at Ar$^+$ energies of 300, 700 and 1200 eV. The ion current density was set at ~100 μA/cm^2, except for the low energy value, which was approximately the half. The sputtering was done at room temperature, although temperatures between 50-80°C were reached at the sample surface due to ion bombardment.

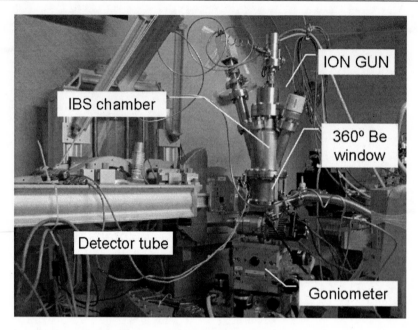

Figure 2. Picture of the IBS experimental set-up for in-situ X-ray scattering measurements during pattern formation.

3.2 Pattern Characterization

GISAXS and GID measurements were performed at the beamline ID01 of the European Synchrotron Radiation Facility (ESRF) in Grenoble (France) The experiments were done at an X-ray wavelength of 1.54 Å (E=8 keV) and an incidence angle of α_i=0.25° (0.2°) for GaSb (Si) surfaces, slightly below the critical angle for total reflection, to enhance the scattered signal. The GISAXS scans were recorded with a linear position sensitive detector (PSD), placed 1 meter away from the sample position, at an exit angle of α_f=0.25° (0.3° for Si) and perpendicular to the sample surface. The intensity is integrated along the detector in a range of exit angle (α_f) of about 2° above the sample surface. For Si(001) surfaces, GID scans were also recorded around the (220) Bragg reflection. In the case of *in-situ* pattern formation on GaSb(001), erosion and GISAXS measurement periods were done sequentially.

Complementary to X-ray scattering techniques, the patterns were imaged *ex-situ* using atomic force microscopy (AFM) in tapping mode with silicon cantilevers. In the case of Si surfaces, high-resolution transmission electron microscopy (HR-TEM) was also performed on cross-sectional specimens (not shown here).

4 - EXPERIMENTAL OBSERVATIONS AND DISCUSSION

4.1 Temperature Dependence of Nanopattern Formation on Si(001)

Figure 3 shows an atomic force microscopy (AFM) image from an IBS pattern produced on a Si(001) surface after 10 min of sputtering at 375 K.

Figure 3. Left: AFM image (1x1 µm^2) of a nanodot (height 6-7nm) pattern produced by IBS on Si(001) surfaces after 10 min sputtering at 375 K. Right: Autocorrelation image showing the hexagonal arrangement.

This pattern corresponds to the saturation temporal regime. The surface pattern, as previously observed, consists of short-range ordered hexagonal arrays of nanodots, with a lenticular shape of 40-50nm width and 5-6 nm height.

The GISAXS and GID results from IBS patterns, produced at different temperatures, are displayed in Figure 4 and Figure 5, respectively. Here, the combination of both techniques allows comparing the relative contributions of the amorphous and crystalline volumes of the surface nanostructures. Radial GID scans are also sensitive to the presence of strain in the near surface region. The direct comparison of GID and GISAXS spectra shows that the nanodots are mostly crystalline at low temperatures (< 400 K). The correlation peak position gives the average inter-dot distance and the peak width is related to the degree of ordering. Contrary to theoretical studies from continuum models, which predict an increase of the pattern wavelength with temperature, AFM and X-ray methods reveal a decrease in the interdot distance (higher dot density). Also, the loss of correlation between the crystalline cores at 475 K indicates an increase of the amorphous volume contribution with temperature which, in light of AFM data, can be understood by a progressive decrease of the dot height. Finally, there is an emerging strain near the surface (Figure 5), which may affect diffusion processes.

Compiling all the experimental findings in this work [17], the production of Si nanodots by IBS as a function of the substrate temperature can be described as follows. In the low-temperature range, below 400 K, the pattern is not significantly affected by temperature and the interdot distance remains constant at about 50 nm. Within the 425 – 500 K range, both the characteristic length and average height of the dot pattern decrease with temperature. This behavior continues up to 525 K, where an abrupt change of the surface morphology takes place. Still, a sort of dot morphology is present with dot height slightly larger than the crystalline dot core, as supported by the HR-TEM (not shown here). The disappearance of the correlation peaks in GID at lower temperature (475 K) than in GISAXS (550 K) indicates a reduced crystalline volume in this range, and a relative increase of the contribution coming from the top-most amorphous layer.

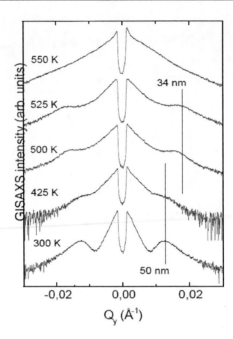

Figure 4.GISAXS scans obtained from Si(001) substrates sputtered with 1 keV Ar[+] ions for 10 min at 300 K, 425 K, 500 K, 525 K and 550 K (from Ref. 17, Copyright (2006) American Physical Society).

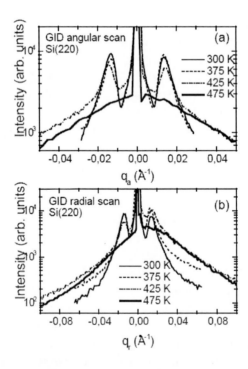

Figure 5. GID measurements around the (220) in-plane Bragg peak in (a) angular and (b) radial directions from Si(001) substrates bombarded under normal incidence by 1 keV Ar[+] ions for 10 minutes at 300 K (thin solid line), 375 K (dashed line), 425 K (dashed-dotted line) and 475 K (thick solid line) (from Ref. 17, Copyright (2006) American Physical Society).

When the target temperature is further increased to 550 K, the dot pattern completely vanishes, as shown by the top curve on Figure 4, corresponding to diffuse scattering from a rough surface without any particular feature. In this regime, the surface morphology becomes flat and dot-less as assessed by HR-TEM and AFM.

4.2 *In-Situ* Study of Nanopattern Formation on Gasb(001)

The power of high-brilliance synchrotron radiation allows us to follow *in-situ* the surface morphology evolution during the IBS by means of GISAXS[18]. As already discussed, in the short-range order (SRO) scenario, the appearance of the correlation peaks reveals the pattern formation threshold (versus time, or fluence) and the surface morphology evolution can be followed by monitoring the changes in the peak features (position and width).

Figure 6(a) shows the time evolution of a GISAXS spectrum, measured sequentially during ion bombardment at 700 eV. The evolution of the spectra shows that the pattern formation occurs at the first minute of ion beam sputtering. Also, a clear coarsening of the pattern (increase in λ with time) is evidenced by the shift of the correlation peak to lower Q values. Finally, the increase in the intensity and width of the correlation peak reveals the enhancement of ξ driven by the self-organization process. For quantification of λ and ξ, the GISAXS scans have been fitted with IsGISAXS, using the 2D hexagonal paracrystal model [19]. A typical fit is shown in Figure 6(b) for the pattern obtained after 60 min of sputtering at 300 eV, where only one side of the symmetric GISAXS curve is displayed. The fitting results for λ and the normalized correlation length (ξ/λ) are plotted in panels (a) and (b) of Figure 7, respectively.

The same trend is found for different ion energies, i.e. the pattern appears after a short irradiation time (few minutes), and is followed by an increase, i.e. coarsening, of λ until reaching a saturation value that scales with ion energy. The observation of coarsening is relevant since, although coarsening has been reported in ripple formation by IBS [20], the results for nanodot patterns on semiconductor surfaces are somehow controversial [21,22]. We have reported a similar coarsening behavior on nanodot pattern formation on Si [23]. Here, the results show the same evidence of coarsening for GaSb nanodot patterns, as first reported by Facsko *et al.*[9,10] The increase is quite small (15 %), but it can be resolved unambiguously. It is interesting to note that this coarsening mechanism is accounted for only by a recently proposed hydrodynamic model for pattern formation during IBS [8]. Another interesting feature extracted from Figure 7(a) is the slower temporal evolution in the pattern formation for the lower energy. The temporal evolution of the correlation length as obtained from the short-range order 2D paracrystal model is plotted in Figure 7(b), for the three different ion energies. The results show an increase of the correlation length (note that $\square$ value is normalized to λ) for the three energies. Except at 300 eV, the degree of order reaches a saturation value. The ordering enhancement with time has been previously observed qualitatively for GaSb, InP and Si patterns by means of AFM, and only quantified by GID for Si nanodot patterns [24].

The slower time evolution and the achievement of a higher degree of ordering at lower ion energy represent relevant findings in our study, both fundamental and applied. Here, the sputtering rate (SR) is nearly four-fold at 1200 eV, with respect to 300 eV, as derived from the calculated sputtering yield by the SRIM[24] code and the measured sample current density. In analogy with the reported trends in Ref. 22, faster time evolution is induced at higher SR, i.e. higher ion energy, while the lower SR results in larger correlation length.

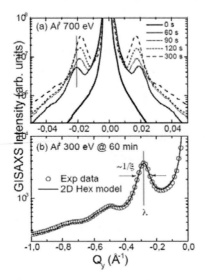

Figure 6. (a) GISAXS scans showing the temporal evolution of nanodot pattern formation on GaSb(001) by IBS under 700 eV Ar+. (b) Fit of the GISAXS intensity (GaSb sputtered at 300 eV for 60 min) to the 2D hexagonal paracrystal model (from Ref. 18, Reprinted with permission from, Plantevin, O.; Gago, R.; Vázquez, L.; Biermanns, A.; Metzger, T.H. *Appl. Phys. Lett.* 2007, vol 91, 113105. Copyright [2007], American Institute of Physics).

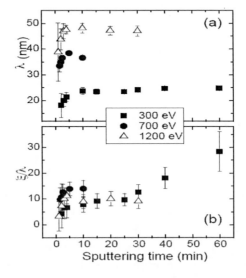

Figure 7. Temporal evolution of the (a) wavelength λ and (b) normalized correlation length ξ/λ for nanodot patterns induced on GaSb(001) surfaces at different ion energies (from Ref. 18, Reprinted with permission from, Plantevin, O.; Gago, R.; Vázquez, L.; Biermanns, A.; Metzger, T.H. *Appl. Phys. Lett.* 2007, vol 91, 113105. Copyright [2007], American Institute of Physics).

CONCLUSION

We have shown the benefits and application of *ex-situ* and *in-situ* GISAXS and GID measurements to study the formation of nanopatterns on semiconductor surfaces by IBS. For this, we have presented two illustrative examples. On one hand, we have studied *ex-situ* nanodot pattern production on Si(001), at different irradiation temperatures, allowing control over the nanodot morphology and pattern characteristics. On the other hand, we have presented *in-situ* and real-time monitoring of nanodot pattern formation and evolution on GaSb(001) surfaces under low-energy IBS. Both studies comprise technological implications regarding the control over the pattern characteristics and also provide relevant information to the theoretical understanding of pattern formation by IBS.

Regarding the influence of temperature on the nanodot pattern formation on Si(001), three different temperature regimes are observed. This has been determined by the unique combination of GISAXS and GID techniques. First, the pattern remains unaltered for target temperatures below 400 K, with the dot volume mostly crystalline. Second, there is a progressive decrease in the dot height for an increase in the temperature from 400 K up to 500 K, which implies a higher contribution of the amorphous surface layer on the dot morphology. At the same time, there is an increase in the compressive strain within the crystalline core of the dots, as temperature increases. Finally, for temperatures above 550 K the nanostructures disappear and the surface becomes featureless and flat.

In the case of GaSb(001), we have found that the pattern appears after only a few minutes of irradiation and, then, coarsens with time until the wavelength reaches a saturation value. This behavior has been observed in the 300-1200 eV range, finding that the saturation value scales with ion energy. An ordering enhancement is induced after prolonged irradiation, and the larger correlation length is obtained for the lower ion energy. Finally, the pattern time evolution is also slower (higher cross-over time for the saturation regime) at lower ion energy. The former trend is attributed to the influence of the sputtering rate on the pattern formation.

ACKNOWLEDGMENTS

The authors like to thank S. Facsko, R. Cuerno, J. García-Muñoz, M. Castro for fruitful discussions. The technical support at the ESRF from L. Petit and H. Dzajouli is also greatly appreciated. This work was partially supported by Grants No. FIS2006-12253-C06-02 and 03 and CSD2008-0023 (MEC, Spain) and CCG08-CSIC/MAT-3457 (CAM, Spain). The authors also acknowledge the financial support by the ESRF.

REFERENCES

[1]   Valbusa, U.; Boragno, C. ; Buatier de Mongeot, F. *J. Phys.: Condens. Matter* 2002, vol, 14, p 8153.

[2]   Chan, W.L.; Chason, E. *J. Appl. Phys.* 2007, vol 101, 121301.

[3]   Makeev, M.A.; Cuerno, R.; Barabási, A.L. *Nucl. Instr. Meth. Phys. B* 2002, vol 197, 185.

[4]   Bradley R.M.; Harper, J.M.E. *J. Vac. Sci. Technol.* 1988, vol A 6, 2390.

[5]   Cuerno, R.; Barabási, A.-L., *Phys. Rev. Lett.* 1995, vol 74, 4746.

[6]   Kahng, B.; Jeong, H.; Barabási, A.-L *Appl. Phys. Lett.* 2001, vol 78, 805.

[7]   Facsko, S.; Bobek, T.; Stahl, A.; Kurz, H.; Dekorsy, T. *Phys. Rev. B* 2004, vol 69, 153412; Vogel, S.; Linz, S.J. *Phys. Rev. B* 2005, vol 72, 35416.

[8]   Castro, M.; Cuerno, R.; Vázquez, L.; Gago, R. *Phys. Rev. Lett.* 2005, vol 94, 16102 ; Muñoz-García, J.; Castro, M.; Cuerno, R. *Phys. Rev. Lett.* 2006, vol 96, 86101.

[9]   Facsko, S.; Dekorsy, T.; Koerdt, C. ; Trappe, C. ; Kurz, H. ; Vogt, A. ; Hartnagel, H.L. *Science* 1999, vol 285, 1551.

[10]   Bobek, T.; Facsko, S.; Kurz, H.; Dekorsy, T.; Xu, M.; Teichert, C. *Phys. Rev. B* 2003, vol 68, 85324.

[11]   Frost, F. ; Ziberi, B. ; Höche, T. ; Rauschenbach, B. *Nucl. Instr. and Meth. in Phys. Res. B* 2004, vol 216, 9.

[12]   Gago, R.; Vázquez, L.; Cuerno, R.; Varela, M.; Ballesteros, C.; Albella, J.M. *Appl. Phys. Lett.* 2001, vol 78, 3316.

[13]   Carbone, D.; Plantevin, O.; Gago, R.; Mocuta, C.; Bikondoa, O.; Alija, A.; Petit, L.; Djazouli, H.; Metzger, T.H. *J. Synchr. Rad.* 2008, vol 15, 414.

[14]   Carbone, D.; Biermanns, A.; Ziberi, B.; Frost, F.; Plantevin, O.; Pietsch, U.; Metzger, T.H. *J. Phys. Cond. Matt.* 2009, vol 21, 224007.

[15]   Stangl, J.; Holy,V.; Bauer, G. *Rev. Mod. Phys.* 2004, vol 76, 725.

[16]   Holy, V.; Pietsch, U.; Baumbach, T. *High-Resolution X-Ray Scattering from Thin Films and Multilayers* ; Springer-Verlag: Berlin, GE 1999.

[17]   Gago, R.; Vázquez, L.; Plantevin, O.; Sánchez-García, J.A.; Varela, M.; Ballesteros, M.C.; Albella, J.M.; Metzger, T.H. *Phys. Rev. B* 2006, vol 73, 155414.

[18]   Plantevin, O.; Gago, R.; Vázquez, L.; Biermanns, A.; Metzger, T.H. *Appl. Phys. Lett.* 2007, vol 91, 113105.

[19]   Lazzari, R. *J. Appl. Cryst.* 2002, vol 35, 406.

[20]   Habenicht, S.; Lieb, K.P. *Phys. Rev. B* 2002, vol 65, 115327.

[21]   Ziberi, B.; Frost, F.; Höche, Th.; Rauschenbach, B. *Phys. Rev. B* 2005, vol 72, 235310.

[22]   Tan, S. K. ; Wee, A. T. S. *J. Vac. Sci. Technol. B* 2006, vol 24, 1444.

[23]   Gago, R.; Vázquez, L.; Plantevin, O.; Metzger, T.H.; Muñoz-García, J.; Cuerno, R.; Castro, M. *Appl. Phys. Lett.* 2006, vol 89, 1.

[24]   Ziegler, J.F.; Biersack, J.P.; Littmark, U. *The Stopping and Range of Ions in Solids* ; Pergamon: New York, US, 1985.

B. SYNTHESIS OF BURIED NANOSTRUCTURES BY ION IMPLANTATION PROCESS

In: Synthesis and Engineering of Nanostructures…   ISBN 978-1-62100-261-1
Editors: Devesh Kumar Avasthi & Jean Claude Pivin   © 2012 Nova Science Publishers, Inc

Chapter 8

CONTROLLING IRRADIATION-INDUCED QUANTUM DOT SYNTHESIS

Harry Bernas and Roch Espiau de Lamaëstre[1]

CSNSM-CNRS, Université Paris-Sud 11, Orsay, France

ABSTRACT

The purpose of this chapter is to stress two important, insufficiently considered features that occur when attempting to synthesize quantum dots by ion irradiation or implantation in insulators or wide-gap semiconductors. These are (i) the conditions under which the nanocluster (NC) size and size distribution may be controlled, and (ii) the fact that charge effects and, correspondingly, chemistry (redox effects) play a major role in quantum dot synthesis.

1. INTRODUCTION

The electronic properties of materials are all related to some characteristic lengths, whose scales depend on which property is considered. Examples are the Fermi wavelength or the electron mean free path for conductivity, the Debye wavelength for phonons, the dipolar interaction distance for electromagnetic interactions, the pair correlation length for superconductivity, etc..., all of which vary typically from ~ 0.1 to several tens of nanometers. Much of nanoscience involve attempts to analyze what happens when the physical size of the sample shrinks down to the characteristic length scale of one or another of its basic physical properties. This applies exactly to nanocrystals (NCs): their electrical, optical, magnetic or mechanical properties are radically affected by their size and shape, by the symmetry of their environment and by their coupling (chemical bonds, radiation...) to the latter. Why is size control important? Figure 1 shows an example - the photoluminescence emission of a sample containing many supposedly identical quantum dots, over which different apertures have

---

[1]   present address, CEA-MINATEC, Grenoble, France.

allowed the detection of emission by a single dot or by an assembly of dots (in varying numbers).

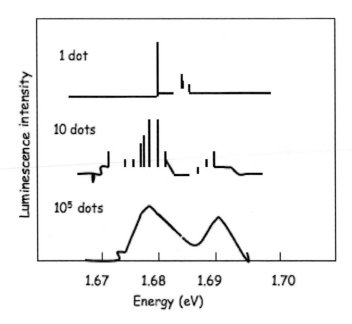

Figure 1. Photoluminescence spectra from quantum dots excited and detected via apertures in a mask with dimensions 0.2mm to 25mm. Schematically adapted from D. Gammon et al., Phys. Rev. Lett. 76, 3005 (1996).

It is clearly seen that, in spite of the care in preparing the sample, the dots are not quite identical: their shape and size (and possibly bonding to the environment) varies very slightly, and this suffices to induce significant shifts in emission energy and intensity from one to another.

The consequences, in cases where NCs are prepared by ion irradiation or implantation, of these rather elementary remarks are perhaps not sufficiently taken into account. Attempts are made to synthesize metallic or semiconducting nanocrystals in, say, a semiconducting or insulating medium by "brute force" ion implantation, i.e., forcing supersaturation of a solute at temperatures low enough to avoid unmixing, and then obtaining a second phase by progressively annealing at increasing temperatures. They are based on the idea that one may somehow extend thermodynamics textbook physics to extreme conditions in which miscibility can go down to zero, the solute profile is nonuniform, nonequilibrium defects play a (sometimes major) role, etc. This extension rests on many approximations and requires precautions, of course. The following are two examples among many.

The first example stems directly from the remark above: it is the importance of controlling the nanocluster (NC) size and size distribution, and the corresponding conditions for such control. The second example involves a different perspective: it is the major importance of charge effects and the corresponding role of chemistry (redox effects) in quantum dot synthesis. Both features have often been underrated or ignored – I will argue that they are crucial when attempting to synthesize quantum dots by ion irradiation or implantation in insulators or wide-gap semiconductors.

2. WHAT DETERMINES THE NC RADIUS AND SIZE DISTRIBUTION?

We are all jealous of chemists who know how to prepare NCs of all sorts and sizes by colloidal or sol-gel chemistry, with very narrow size distributions (typically a few %). When studying intrinsic NC properties, the NC population is left in solution, and the native properties are preserved. Problems may, or not, arise when they are to be inserted in a solid state matrix. A typical example [1] concerns FePt NCs, of major interest for ultrahigh density magnetic recording media. Beautiful ordered arrays of the B2 (cubic) phase are obtained via colloidal chemistry; unfortunately, the useful phase is $L1_0$, obtained by a high temperature annealing treatment that destroys the organic host, leading to NC coalescence and disordering the array. Inclusion of these NCs in hosts such as Si, the III-V compounds, or silica and glasses involves complexities that chemists' ingenuity has sometimes solved (e.g., in some waveguide glasses), or left to physics-based techniques (e.g., in the case of Si NCs in silica), but which practically always lead to more or less drastic modifications in the NC size distribution. Let us approach this problem in a rather general way, and attempt to discern a useful strategy.

In order to predict and control the NC average size and size distributions, we ideally require (1) a full description of nucleation processes, and of growth processes; (2) to avoid overlap of nucleation and growth (since this obviously broadens the size distribution); (3) a full description of coarsening (mass transport from small particles to their larger counterparts), i.e., of the particle size distribution's time evolution from an arbitrary initial distribution. In colloidal chemistry, these conditions are often realized; not so in solids, where solubility, possible reactions of the NC element(s) with host components, clustering or coalescence all may occur. Also, nucleation differs widely depending on the nature of the material in which the NCs are to be grown. In metals and many semiconductors, it may often depend on quasi-equilibrium thermodynamics and on diffusion, whereas in insulators and some semiconductors the primary aggregation process also depends on the charge state properties (i.e., the chemistry) of moving species, including electrons and holes (see below). Growth processes are correspondingly also very different. Hence, multiple mechanisms may occur and interfere, leading to difficulties in predicting and controlling NC populations and size distributions.

Standard quasi-equilibrium thermodynamics nucleation and growth provide terms of reference. Although it is by no means ideal for obtaining narrow size distributions, this theory has the advantage of being predictive in simple cases. A generalization was given by Binder [2] in terms of coupled rate equations. It provides a framework to evaluate conditions for the control of a NC population's evolution: it allows us to discern whether a study of the NC population moments' time and/or temperature evolution in some of the more common NC nucleation and growth cases provides information on the corresponding mechanisms.

2.1 Nucleation

In order to grow NCs, we generally focus on the low solute concentration/volume fraction part of a phase diagram, where unmixing occurs by metastable decomposition. Clusters form due to species mobility and chemical affinity (bond energies); some monomers eventually form small aggregates that can *grow or dissolve (see §2)* depending on their free energy. The driving force towards stability then induces growth by capture of surrounding monomers (thus justifying a rate-equation approach as in chemistry), and later at the expense of surrounding precipitates (coarsening). Microscopically, the initial phase separation is described by (i) near-neighbor bond energies and (ii) differing energy barriers for B and A atomic jumps as they diffuse and interact. These parameters determine the diffusion coefficients and the solubility. As a cluster grows from 2, 3,... to n atoms, its energy changes relative to the surrounding solution, modifying its stability and internal and interface structure. The thermodynamics of binary systems provides an initial approach to the origin and main parameters determining the unmixing phase evolution that leads to NC formation in solids as well as liquids or on surfaces. It is far from the whole story, but provides a guideline.

NC nucleation is generally by no means an irreversible process smoothly evolving from a diatom to a several hundred- or thousand-fold configuration. Subtle quasi-equilibrium thermodynamics nucleation theories [3-5] have been developed in order to approximate most of the kinetics. They provide us with an adequate description of how concentration fluctuations lead to incipient nucleation as long as atoms are free to move. Hence the importance of combining kinetics with thermodynamics. The very first steps of NC nucleation, the NCs' composition and structure at this early stage determine their ultimate evolution via their free energy (stability) and their reactivity with their surroundings. Diffusion is a prerequisite to monomer interaction. In order to obtain, after growth, as narrow a size distribution as possible, the initial NC population size distribution should itself be narrow - ideally, *all nuclei should be formed simultaneously*. This obviously depends on the nucleation speed, hence on an adequate combination of fast NC component diffusion, a large NC formation enthalpy and free energy (the latter determining its stability). The ultimate NC density and average size, as well as the size distribution, all depend on how well this criterion is met. Now in quasi-equilibrium thermodynamics conditions, a significant fraction of NCs is still undergoing formation as others grow - an effect that broadens the NC size distribution significantly. This may sometimes be circumvented, but efficiency is always limited by the phase diagram and diffusion properties. The effort to find tricks leading to a narrow, controlled initial NC population is one of the main reasons for developing techniques in which NCs are formed under far-from-thermodynamic equilibrium conditions.

2.2 Growth and Coarsening

Can we predict a NC growth law? If there is no creation or destruction of NCs, quasiequilibrium thermodynamics allows us to write a conservation equation during growth, f(R, t) being the density distribution in size space:

$$\partial f/\partial t + \partial/\partial R (f.dR/dt) = 0 \qquad\qquad (1),$$

Where the term in parentheses is the flux density in size space. This equation says that at all times t, the number of NCs whose radius is around a (growing) value R is conserved. From this, we may predict a size distribution, if all of three conditions are met: (1) the total NC mass is conserved (this is generally verified), (2) the number density of NCs is conserved (also verified), and (3) we have information on the NC growth rate law dR/dt – a criterion that is very rarely satisfied. A notable exception is Ostwald ripening, in which the existence of a self-similar size distribution during growth leads to the well-known Lifshitz-Slyozov-Wagner (LSW) [6] analytical treatment. Assuming the latter, we may write the cluster evolution in size and time space as

$$\frac{dn_l(t)}{dt} + \frac{d}{dl}J_l = 0$$ (2),

Where the cluster current in the size representation consists of two terms: (i) a thermodynamically driven drift component that leads the system towards its miminum free energy. This is

$$J_{der} = -\frac{\partial}{\partial l}\left(\frac{\Delta F_l}{k_B T}\right)R_l n_l(t)$$ (3);

(ii) a diffusion component describing the contribution of fluctuations to the nucleation and growth process. This contribution is

$$J_{diff} = R_l \frac{\partial}{\partial l} n_l(t)$$ (4),

and always tends to *broaden* the size distribution.

In the long-term (asymptotic) LSW size distribution [6], the mean radius R_c is the scaling length – when the radius is normalized by Rc, the size distribution's shape is invariant in time. It does contain some information about the system's precipitation physics. An example [7] is shown in Figure 2. Here, the entire nuclei population was first synthesized by ion irradiation (analogous to the first stage of the photographic process, see below) and then all nuclei grew simultaneously under a thermal anneal. The conditions of this experiment were very close to LSW approximation conditions, and the resulting late-stage growth size distribution is in excellent agreement with the LSW prediction.

Although the agreement in Figure 2 apparently validates the assumptions regarding the system's long-term evolution, can one work backwards and say anything at all about the earlier nucleation and growth mechanisms from the post-coarsening size distribution? This is generally not true. For example, the long-term LSW solution is obtained whether or not there is an energy barrier for nucleation (spinodal or metastable decomposition). Other cases are worse, as shown now. In the case of the LSW distribution, changes in the shape of the size distribution were related to differences in the aggregation process. This is by no means general, as demonstrated by the example of lognormal size distributions. The lognormal distribution function reads

$$f(r) = \frac{1}{r\ln(\sigma)\sqrt{2\pi}}exp\left(-\frac{\ln^2(r/\mu)}{2\ln^2(\sigma)}\right)$$ (5)

Where σ is the geometric standard deviation and μ the geometric average. Both are dimensionless.

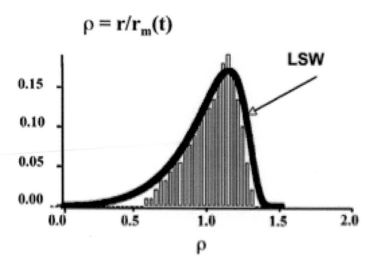

Figure 2. Comparison of experimental size distribution for Cu NCs in glass, as obtained via irradiation and annealing [from ref. 7, copyright (2001) American Physical Society] with the predictions of [6] . The average radius rm in this case was about 4 nm.

Experimental results on NC size distributions after more or less complex, nonequilibrium synthesis techniques (notably including ion implantation) often display such shapes, which are often noted but not discussed. Could they possibly provide any information on operative mechanisms? The answer is interesting, albeit totally negative.As for the LSW distribution, this asymptotic size distribution shape is independent of the initial nucleation conditions. This was demonstrated theoretically [8]. In fact, lognormal distributions are ubiquitous. One was even found when measuring the height distribution of British infantry soldiers in the late 19th century. It does not tell us much about the birth and growth conditions of these unfortunate young men.

In order to estimate whether any information is obtainable at all, we examine the problem in terms of information theory. The amount of information on a distribution f is given by its entropy, defined by

$$S = \int f \ln f \tag{6}$$

For example, the entropy of a normalized Gaussian is

$$S_g = \ln(\sigma\sqrt{2\pi e}) \tag{7}$$

Entropy grows as the size distribution width increases, confirming the intuition that the broader the distribution, the less controlled the growth process. According to an information theory principle [9], entropy is maximized at equilibrium (true here, since we consider long-term behavior), under general constraints that are, for nucleation and growth, the matter conservation equation:

$$\int_0^\infty ln_l(t)dl = cste$$

(8)

and the size distribution's evolution equation given above,

$$\frac{dn_l(t)}{dt} + \frac{d}{dl}J_l = 0$$

(9)

These equations fully determine the system's evolution.

It was shown [11] that the distribution function obtained under the sole constraint of matter conservation is simply

$$\tilde{n} = e^{-v},$$

(10),

which closely approximates the large-size tail of the lognormal size distribution in the case [10] of NC syntheses with complex growth mechanisms (Figure 3). Whereas the shape after LSW ripening at least partially reflected features due to the evolution of the initial nanocrystal population, the existence of the above long-term size distribution in a NC population shows that all memory of its evolution mechanisms has been lost, due to a combination of different – and possibly interfering - nucleation and growth processes. The apparently "lognormal" shape of the distribution only signals matter conservation. Its occurrence at the outcome of a NC synthesis experiment tells us that the nucleation and growth processes were just too complex to control in that experiment.

How then can we narrow the NC size distribution? Late stage growth is mainly controlled by (i) the sample dimensionality, (ii) matter conservation and (iii) basic quasiequilibrium or nonequilibrium thermodynamics, including entropy. It is usually unrelated to early nucleation and growth – there is clearly, very generally, a memory loss in this regard. After long-term coarsening, the size distribution most often does NOT depend on nucleation. For example, attempts to form an ordered NC array via a nucleation process are generally doomed to fail when growth reaches its late, equilibrium stage (e.g., by annealing). Thus in the absence of cage-building organic chemistry techniques, NC size distribution control is reachable by (1) separating nucleation and growth, which are totally different processes, and (2) remaining in the early nucleation and growth regimes, so as to reduce the entropy. A privileged means to do this is via nonequilibrium thermodynamics and, specifically, experimental techniques involving radiation and athermal energy deposition.

3. ROLE OF CHEMISTRY IN BEAM-INDUCED NC NUCLEATION AND GROWTH

Ion implantation generally produces a compositional change - it is now well-established [12] [13] that a simple quasiequilibrium thermodynamical "binary mixture" picture is not sufficient (or even often relevant) here.

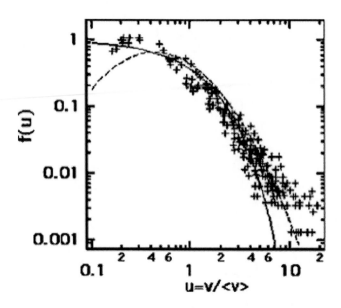

Figure 3. Plot of u, the reduced volume's probability density, adapted from Ref 10. Crosses: experimental data for semiconductor PbS, PbSe, CdSe, and PbTe NCs grown by sequential implantation of components into pure silica and long-term annealing. In spite of differences in preparation, in average sizes and depth distributions, all fit the universal curve corresponding to the maximum entropy distribution e−u, determined only by the constraint of volume conservation. Dashed line is the best fit of experimental data (for u >1) to the reduced lognormal distribution µ=1: the latter only deviates from the former when NC sizes are extremely small. A "lognormal"distribution provides no information at all on the NC evolution.

Irradiation-assisted or -induced precipitation is one source. Another, often surprisingly neglected by the ion beam community, dominates in insulators and wide-gap semiconductors: charge (electron and hole) injection effects. Simply stated, defects and chemical species may have more than a single charge state, and *reaching equilibrium between charge states is a relatively long-term and reversible process*. Thus, in addition to phase diagram considerations, we must include the electron and hole populations, the defect populations, the (ionic and/or neutral) chemical species, as well as the laws of carrier and species transport. This leads us to consider the effects of redox properties on nucleation. We argue that ion beams, as other (UV, electron) irradiation beams, induce effects that are basically similar to the photographic process analyzed by Mott and Gurney [14]. Consider Figure 4. Light (energy) impacts on a AgBr NC, inducing the formation of electron-hole pairs. Three possibilities occur, only one of which (A) leads to the formation of a Ag^0 monomer that diffuses rapidly and remains stable by trapping at the surface. In turn, this monomer can trap others that are similarly produced, and growth (cluster formation) follows. The other processes either lead to Ag^+ (B), which remains in solution, or to recombination (C). From this schematic, it is clear that one cannot avoid considering the possibilities of reverse reactions, that convert neutrals back to ions for example: the final equilibrium state depends on the energy deposition efficiency, but also on host-dependent properties such as charge stability mechanisms (e.g., stabilization by defects, or the relative stability of different-sized aggergates, whether or not they are charged, etc.). In the photographic process, so-called developers are introduced.

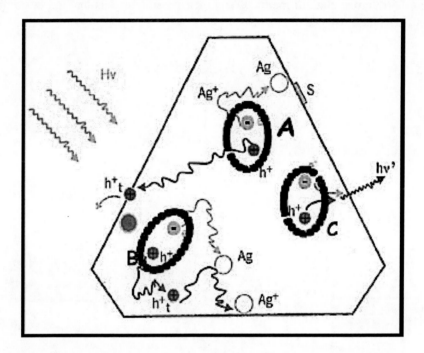

Figure 4. Initial stage of photographic process, according to the description of Ref. 14. See text.

They are electron donors, whose role is basically to bias the electron/hole population in favour of the former so as to enhance Ag monomer (or charged Ag aggregate) neutralization and hence precipitation.

We have shown [15], by comparing gamma- and MeV ion irradiation-induced formation of Ag NCs in glass via UV spectroscopy and ESR experiments, that under ion irradiation, the beam's deposited energy density (DED) affects both the electron and hole density as well as the species' mobility. The resulting NC formation probability also depends on (i) the metal atom or ion's charge state, (ii) the stability of this charge state, and (iii) the monomer or aggregate diffusivity. All these quantities depend, in turn, on the temperature and on the redox potential in a given host. Thus, the DED is one among a series of parameters affecting the clustering efficiency. Specifically, gamma irradiation mostly leads to trapped holes, i.e., to the formation of an oxidising medium that tends to favour Ag^+ formation, in solution. MeV ion irradiation (corresponding to 10^4 larger DED) on the other hand, favours electron trap formation, hence a reducing medium that enhances NC formation. This is summarized by a "phase diagram" in Figure 5.

CONCLUSION

It is probably clear that this chapter is an attempt to put ion beam NC synthesis in a broader perspective, relating to other, more classical synthesis techniques. The fact that ion beam NC synthesis involves nonequilibrium thermodynamics does not mean "indifference towards thermodynamics", and quite general laws from the latter provide useful guidelines for designing new synthesis technique and evaluating their limits. The other point we make, regarding a fairly broad class of materials and their possible use, is that ion beam physicists should not forget the existence of chemistry.

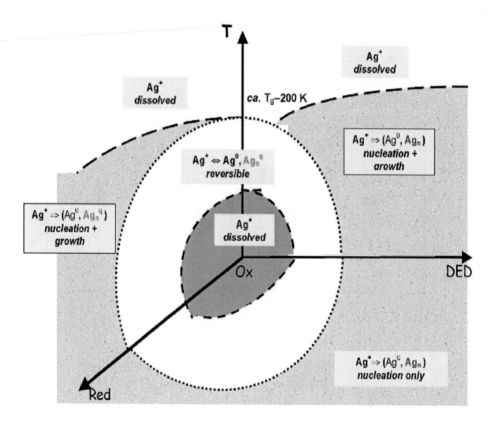

Figure 5. "Phase diagram" showing the effects of standard chemical redox (Red) properties entailing Ag NC precipitation in glass - in the (T, Red) plane, versus the effect of different deposited energy densities DED - in the (T, DED) plane. The possibility of combining redox and DED effects facilitates novel NC formation conditions. (Adapted from Ref. 15).

This holds particularly when irradiation-induced charges are not too short-lived and may affect the host's redox properties via time- and temperature-dependent charge equilibrium and via the formation of defects acting as elecron or hole sources. We have shown [16] that such redox properties may actually be used to control NC synthesis by manipulating the charge balance in a host, biasing it via the irradiation-induced deposited energy density. This has allowed controlled formation of PbS NCs in glass, and a study [17] of their optical properties.

ACKNOWLEDGMENTS

Our work on these topics benefited greatly from the contributions of Hélène Béa (now at University of Genevà), J. Belloni and J.L. Marignier (LCP-University of Orsay), B. Boizot (LSI-Palaiseau), F. Jomard (LPSC-Meudon), O. Kaitasov (CSNSM- University of Orsay), J. Majimel (University of Bordeaux), and D. Pacifici, F. Priolo, G. Franzo (University of Catania).

REFERENCES

[1]   Sun, S. ; Murray, C. B. ; Weller, D.; Folks, L. and Moser, A. Science 2000, 287, 1989.

[2]   Binder, K. *Phys. Rev. B* 1977, 15, 4425

[3]   Wagner, R.; Kampmann, R. and Vorhees, P. W. Chapter 5 in *Phase Transformations in Materials* ed. G. Kostorz, Wiley-VCH (2001)

[4]   Binder, K.; and Fratzl, P.; Chapter 6 in *Phase Transformations in Materials* ed. G. Kostorz, Wiley-VCH (2001)

[5]   Cahn, J. W.; and Hilliard, J. E. *J. Chem. Phys.* 1958, 28, 258; Cahn, J. W. and Hilliard, J. E. *J. Chem. Phys.* 1959, 31, 688; Cook, H. E. Acta Met. 1970, 18, 297.

[6]   Lifshitz, I.M. and Slyozov, V.V. *J. Phys. Chem. Solids* 1961, 19, 35; Wagner, C. *Z. Elektrochemie* 1961, *65*, 581.

[7]   Valentin, E.; Bernas, H.; Ricolleau, C. and Creuzet, F. *Phys. Rev. Lett.* 2001, *86,* 99

[8]   Hidy, G.M. *J. Colloid. Sci.* 1965, *20*,123

[9]   Jaynes, E.T. *Phys. Rev.* 1957, *108*, 171

[10] Lamaestre, R. E. de and Bernas, H. *Phys. Rev. B* 2006, *73*, 125317.

[11] Rosen, J.M. *J. Colloid Interface Sci.* 1984, *99*, 9

[12] Martin, G. and Bellon, P. *Solid State Phys.* 1997, *50*, 189.

[13] Averback, R.S. and Bellon, P. *Materials Science with Ion Beams*, ed. H. Bernas, Springer 2009.

[14] Gurney, R. W. and Mott, N. F. *Proc. Roy. Soc. A* 1938, *164,* 151

[15] Lamaestre, R. E. de; Béa, H.; Bernas, H.; Belloni, J. and Marignier, J. L. *Phys. Rev. B* 2007, *76,* 205431 and refs. Therein.

[16] Lamaestre, R.E. de and Bernas, H. *J.Appl.Phys.* 2005, *98,* 104310

[17] Lamaestre, R.Espiau de.; Pacifici, D.; Bernas, H.; Priolo, F. and Franzo, G. *Appl. Phys. Lett.* 2006, *88*, 181115

In: Synthesis and Engineering of Nanostructures...   ISBN 978-1-62100-261-1
Editors: Devesh Kumar Avasthi & Jean Claude Pivin   © 2012 Nova Science Publishers, Inc

Chapter 9

SYNTHESIS AND PACKAGING OF NANOCRYSTALS BY ULTRA LOW ENERGY ION IMPLANTATION FOR APPLICATIONS IN ELECTRONICS, OPTICS AND PLASMONICS

Alain Claverie[1], Caroline Bonafos, Robert Carles, Sylvie Schamm-Chardon, Arnaud Arbouet, Vincent Paillard and Gérard Benassayag

CEMES-CNRS and University of Toulouse, nMat Group, 29 rue Jeanne Marvig, 31055 Toulouse, France

ABSTRACT

Ultra low energy ion implantation is a flexible and fully Si CMOS compatible technique to fabricate 2D arrays of nanocrystals of controlled size and density, buried in dielectrics and at a tuneable distance from the surface. Si nanocrystals, fabricated by this technique, have been used to store charges and integrated into CMOS based devices, to improve the performances of the floating gate (flash) memories. Recently, planes of Ag nanocrystals have been produced following the same route, foreseeing the possibility to fabricate "SERS-ready" substrates.

It is the goal of this chapter to review the main materials science aspects of the fabrication of 2D arrays of nanocrystals of controllable sizes in dielectric layers and at tuneable distances from their surfaces or from electrodes by using ultra low energy ion implantation. The basic rules for the selection of appropriate implant/matrix combinations, for the fine tuning of the depth-positioning and of the density of 2D arrays of NCs together with problems related to humidity penetration and solutions for optimized passivation of the NCs, are among the discussed topics.

---

[1]   Contact author: claverie@cemes.fr.

1. INTRODUCTION

Metallic and semiconducting nanocrystals (NCs) often exhibit different or enhanced physical properties compared to their bulk state. These properties can result from their ability to store or recombine carriers, the possibility to tune their band gap through their size, their large surface/volume ratio or their ability to localize electromagnetic fields. These NCs can be fabricated using a large variety of chemical and physical routes. However, for most of the applications, they need to be buried and ordered within a solid dielectric, localized with nanometer precision at controlled distances from the surface or from electrodes, and finally integrated into a more or less classical planar device, a MOS for example. In general, the fabrication and the subsequent integration/packaging of these nanocrystals are two different technological steps, which are rarely compatible, although the physical properties which are to be used dramatically depend on the final characteristics (quality) of the NCs/dielectric association. Process compatibility, reproducibility and reliability issues have often prevented the industry from integrating "nanos" inside their devices.

The ultra low energy (ULE) ion implantation, followed by annealing under controlled atmosphere, has appeared as a flexible and fully Si CMOS compatible technique to fabricate 2D arrays of nanocrystals of controlled size and density, buried in dielectrics, at a tuneable distance from the surface [1]. Si nanocrystals fabricated by this technique have been firstly used to store charges and integrated into CMOS based devices to improve the performances of the floating gate (flash) memories [2]. The performances of these electronic devices (write/erase and retention times) dramatically depend on the integrity of the dielectric layer after processing [3]. The same nanocrystals and almost the same architecture can be used to produce light from an all silicon device [4, 5]. In this case, the efficiency of the device mostly depends on the passivation of the NCs/dielectric interfaces [6, 7]. Recently, planes of Ag nanocrystals showing surface enhanced Raman scattering (SERS) have been fabricated using the same route, foreseeing the possibility to manipulate photonic signals [8].

It is the goal of this chapter to provide a review of the main materials science aspects of the fabrication of 2D arrays of nanocrystals in dielectric layers of controllable sizes and at tuneable distances from the dielectric surfaces or metallic electrodes by using ultra low energy implantation. The basic rules for the selection of appropriate implant/matrix combinations, for the fine tuning of the depth-positioning and of the density of 2D arrays of NCs, problems related to humidity penetration and solutions for optimized passivation of the NCs, are among the discussed topics. Finally, two possible applications will be presented, one already demonstrated at the industrial level, nanocrystal memories, and the other foreseen, SERS-ready substrates, which could be used for the detection of molecules.

2. THE ULE-IBS METHOD

2.1 The Classical IBS Method for the Fabrication of Nanocrystals

In the traditional ion beam synthesis (IBS) method, desired impurities are implanted at a few tens of keV into a dielectric matrix, then annealed at a temperature sufficient for the phase separation to occur. In general, one obtains a depth-distributed population of NCs centred at a depth close to the projected range of the ions. As a rule of thumb, impurity concentrations larger than 1-2%, at the projected range, are required to form isolated nanocrystals through nucleation and growth phenomena, while concentrations of more than 20% results in networks of connected particles obtained through the spinodal decomposition of the supersaturated matrix.

There are, however, a couple of characteristics the NCs/matrix should possess. Firstly, the impurity should not be miscible in the matrix. If the matrix has to keep its intrinsic properties, the solid solubility limit of the implanted impurities should be as small as possible. To obtain "stable" NCs buried in a "pure" dielectric, the binding energy of the impurity should be large within the NC phase and small in the matrix. The matrix should show only marginal chemical reactivity to the implanted species, so that the precipitation of a pure second phase is possible. In other words, all the reactions allowing the formation of the NCs phase should have a negative Gibbs free energy [9, 10]. Finally, a low diffusivity of the implanted species at room temperature, although not mandatory, will insure that the final sizes and densities of NCs will be controlled only by the thermal treatment following the implantation step. Thus, there are, in principle, a number of elements which can be implanted to form NCs, at least in SiO_2, such as Si, Ge, ..., Au, Ag, Ni, Co... Beyond SiO_2, the choice of matrices includes Si_3N_4, Al_2O_3, HfO_2, HfAlO, HfON,..., GdO_3 and other rare earth oxides.

In practical, the number of adequate NCs/matrix combinations is dramatically reduced due to different factors. For example, recent studies show that Ge redistributes and exodiffuses too much in SiO_2 during annealing for the reliable and robust fabrication of devices, using these NCs [11, 12]. Both Si and Ge implants result in the formation of NCs in Si_3N_4 [13].

In Al_2O_3, Si gets totally oxidized during annealing, while Ge does form NCs but produces an interfacial SiO_2 layer, at the initial Al_2O_3/Si interface [13]. HfO_2 is a terrible matrix for the synthesis of NCs by the ion implantation, as the implanted Si gets oxidized after implantation due to the hygroscopic properties of the matrix and/or humidity drive-in [14]. Moreover, this Si oxidation gives rise to the formation of an intermediate SiO_2 layer between the HfO_2 and the Si substrate. At the moment, different groups worldwide are exploring other implant/matrix combinations, which could allow the fabrication of NCs in different insulating/dielectric layers, using the IBS technique and with characteristics favourable to their integration into devices.

2.2 Advantages of the ULE-IBS Method

Modern CMOS technology already makes use of energies down to 0.5 keV to fabricate ultra shallow junctions in Si so that ultra low energy ion implantors are already commercially available. Few laboratories (among them CEMES/CNRS) have developed decelerator devices fitted to classical ion implantors and able to produce reasonably intense ion beams at energies in the keV range. The main advantage of the ULE-IBS method is evidenced in Figure 1, in the case of fabrication of Si NCs in SiO_2. Clearly, while the fabrication of NCs by the conventional IBS method results in the formation of a population of depth distributed NCs, the ULE technique results in the formation of a single plane of NCs, all located at a fixed distance from the surface.

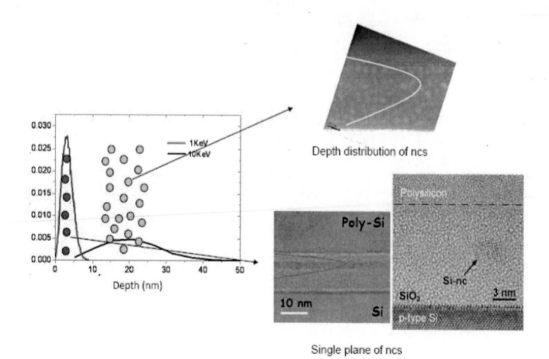

Figure 1. Comparison between typical populations of Si NCs fabricated by i) conventional IBS method at 10 keV (top) and, ii) using the ULE-IBS method at 1 keV (bottom). All TEM images are taken on cross sectional samples. Top TEM image, taken using energy filtered electrons, shows the depth-distribution of Si NCs within the SiO_2 matrix. The left bottom TEM image, taken under Fresnel conditions, shows a band of aligned NCs at a constant distance from the surface. The right bottom image, taken under high resolution conditions, shows an isolated Si NC buried in a thin SiO_2 layer.

3. DEPTH POSITIONING OF THE NCS LAYERS WITHIN THE MATRIX

Most of the physical properties of the NCs, which are to be exploited at the device level, dramatically depend on the distance between the NCs and the surface of the implanted layer. Thus, controlling and manipulating this distance is of great importance.

When the thickness of the dielectric layer is large compared to the maximum range of the ions, the depth of the NCs layer from the surface can be simply tuned by increasing the ion beam energy. This is illustrated by Figure 2, in the case of Ag NCs in SiO_2, taken from ref [15]. It is worth to note that Ag NCs are obtained during/after implantation and that the structure was not intentionally annealed, confirming the very high diffusivity of Ag during implantation.

However, the distance between the surface and the center of mass of the NC population can be tuned from 4 to 7 nm by increasing the beam energy from 0.6 to 3 keV. It is interesting to note that the predictions of the TRIM code are not very different from the actual results measured by TEM.

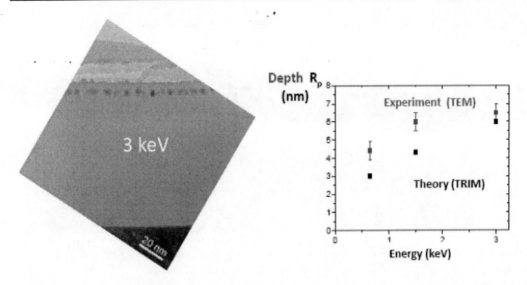

Figure 2. Left, cross sectional bright field TEM image of the band of aligned Ag nanocrystals formed by implanting Ag at 3 keV. Right, variations of the depth-position of the center of mass of the particles, as measured by TEM, and of the projected range of the Ag ions in pure silica, as calculated by TRIM.

These (small) discrepancies can be due to many factors, from stopping powers not calibrated for such low energy implants to sputtering and changes in matrix stoichiometry; both effects being very important, owing to the large doses required to form NCs. Such effects are now be accounted for by modern Monte Carlo simulators such as TRYDYN [16].

There are however applications for which the 2D array of NCs should be buried in a very thin insulating layer. This is the case when charges are to be injected from the top and/or from the bottom of this layer where the electrodes are located. In this case, the precise localization of the plane of NCs can be more difficult. For example, the implantation of Si at 1 keV and at a dose of 10^{16} cm^{-2} into 10 nm thick SiO_2 oxide, followed by annealing at 900°C for 30 min, under nitrogen ambient results in the formation of a band of NCs of about 2.5 nm in diameter and centered at a depth of about 3.5 nm below the surface. Under such conditions, the distance between the Si/SiO_2 interface and the NC layer (we will name it as the injection distance) is of about 8 nm. To reduce further this distance and to possibly allow the injection of charges from this interface towards the NCs by tunneling, a classical reflex is to increase the implantation energy of the ions [17]. Figure 3 shows the results of increasing the beam energy onto the location of the NCs band. Up to 3 keV, this attitude pays and the NCs band gets deeper in the SiO_2 layer i.e., closer and closer to the injecting interface down to 5 nm. However, when the beam energy is further increased, NCs are apparently not formed anymore. In contrast, the Si/SiO_2 interface gets rougher. ToF-SIMS analysis of the same layers shows that up to 3 keV energy, the Si ion implantation results in the formation of a well separated peak of Si concentration within the SiO_2 layer (Figure 4). In contrast, after a 5 keV implant, the implantation of Si mostly results in the broadening of the signal characteristics of the Si/SiO_2 interface. This broadening, in the form of an error-like function, is typical of the mixing of the interface. TRIDYN Monte Carlo simulations [16] of the ion implantation process, in such structure, confirm this finding [17].

When the ion beam energy is increased, ion beam mixing of the SiO_2/Si interface is so strong that the induced concentration profile overlaps with the Gaussian Si profile characteristics of the implanted ions. Under such conditions, where no local concentration maximum exists, NCs cannot be formed during annealing.

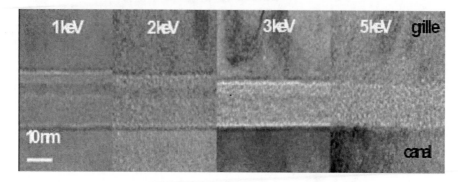

Figure 3. Set of XTEM images obtained under Fresnel contrast conditions showing the effect of increasing beam energy onto the depth position of a 2D array of NCs.

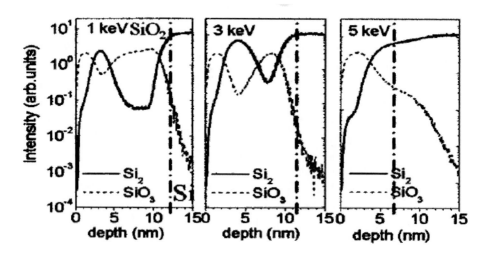

Figure 4. Set of ToF-SIMS profiles showing the progressive overlapping of the Si implant profiles by mixing at the interface when increasing beam energy.

Thus, for any given SiO_2 thickness, there exists a maximum energy above which it is no more possible to form a band of NCs, well separated from the Si/SiO_2 interface. This energy maximum can be estimated through computer simulations of the collisional processes involved during the slowing down of the incident ions [17].

To overcome this difficulty and fabricate NCs bands located closer to the channel of the future device, it is preferable to use ultra low energies, i.e. energies typically below 1 keV, and implant into thinner oxides. The result of such a reduction of the initial oxide thickness is reported in Figure 5. Working with a fixed energy of 1 keV, the injection distance can be reduced from 8 nm down to 2 nm by decreasing the initial thickness of the oxide layer from 10 nm to 5 nm. Both ToF-SIMS (Figure 6) and Monte Carlo simulations confirm that this possibility is due to the limited mixing of the SiO_2/Si interface under such conditions [17].

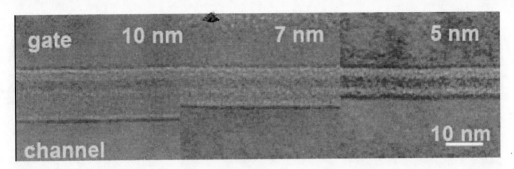

Figure 5. Set of XTEM images obtained under Fresnel contrast conditions showing the effect of decreasing the initial oxide thickness while implanting at a constant energy of 1 keV onto the depth positioning of a 2D array of NCs.

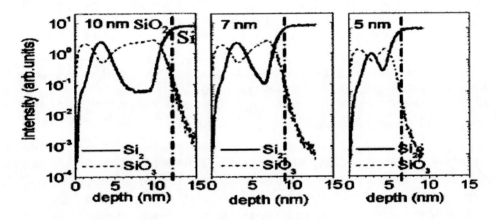

Figure 6. Set of ToF-SIMS profiles showing the progressive displacement of the Si implant profile towards the interface when decreasing the initial oxide thickness.

In summary, there always exists a compromise between beam energy and thickness of the oxide which renders possible to position the NCs band at a controlled distance from the surface or electrodes of the future device. This distance can be tuned down to 2 nm. This compromise can be optimized through computer simulations [16].

4. OPTIMIZATION OF THE NCs DENSITY

Optimizing the density of NCs in view of specific applications is often necessary. Figure 7 shows the effect of increasing the dose by a factor of 4, for implantation of 3 keV Ag ions into SiO_2. As seen from the images, increasing the dose results in an increase of both the density and of the mean size of the NCs. This clearly shows that the precipitation and growth process cannot be described by a simple Ostwald ripening mechanism in a dilute system for which the final size of the NCs should be independent on the initial concentration of the solute atoms [18]. Moreover, an estimation of the total volume occupied by the Ag NCs corresponds to less than half of the implanted dose that has precipitated in the form of NCs.

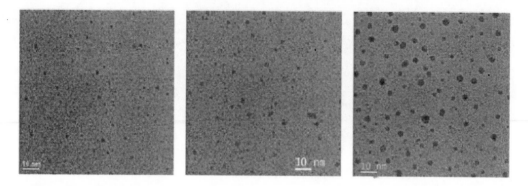

Figure 7. Set of PV TEM image showing the effect of increasing the Ag dose from 1.2 to 2.3 then to 4.7.1015 cm-2 (from left to right) at 3 keV on the characteristics of the NCs population.

This phenomenon is often observed, whatever the NC/matrix association, and is referred to as the "dose loss" problem. Different hypothesis can be proposed to account for this phenomenon but for the time being it has not been studied in detail for Ag in SiO_2.

In contrast, this problem has been extensively studied by our group, in the case of Si NCs into SiO_2 [19] and allows one to understand the complexity of the different phenomena which can be involved during the implantation/ annealing of such layers.

4.1 The "Dose Loss" Problem in Si Implanted SiO_2

Figure 8 shows the effect of implanting increasing doses of Si at 1 keV into 10 nm thick SiO_2 layers. After annealing at 900°C for 30 min, under nitrogen ambient, Si NCs can be observed only if the dose is larger than 5.10^{15} cm^{-2}. Above this dose, the NCs density increases with the dose until the particles apparently coalesce, forming a network of connected particles of elongated form parallel to the surface. In all cases, the quantitative analysis of the characteristics of the NCs populations shows that only a fraction of the implanted dose (up to 40%) has precipitated into NCs.

This apparent missing of a large fraction of the implanted dose has been confirmed by computer simulation (Kinetic Monte Carlo) of the nucleation and growth processes of the NCs [20]. Figure 9 shows the comparison between the characteristics of the NCs population predicted by the KMC simulation and those observed by TEM. It is remarkable that the KMC simulation well predicts the change from a population of isolated NCs, obtained through the nucleation and growth of a second phase from a supersaturated matrix, towards a network of connected particles, obtained through the spinodal decomposition of a highly supersaturated matrix. However, the dose discrepancies are striking. The KMC predicts much lower doses both for the minimum dose for the formation of NCs and for the percolation threshold.

4.2 Anomalous Swelling of the SiO_2 Layers

The last puzzling information was provided by the analysis of cross sectional TEM images of the evolution of the whole structure as a function of the implanted dose. Figure 10 shows that when increasing the implanted dose, as expected, the oxide layer becomes thicker.

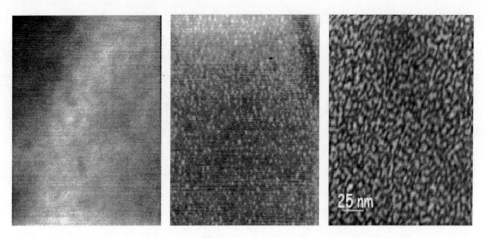

Figure 8. Set of energy filtered PVTEM images showing the effect of increasing the dose onto the morphology of the NCs populations. From left to right, 5.10^{15}cm^{-2}, 1.10^{16}cm^{-2} and 2.10^{16}cm^{-2}.

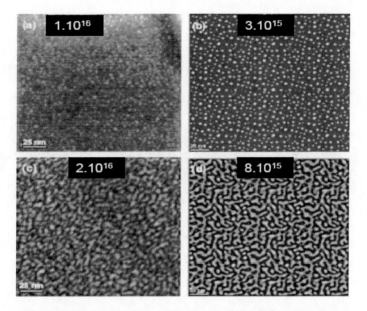

Figure 9. Comparison between XTEM observations (left) and KMC simulations (right) of the structure and morphology of NCs populations. Note the large dose discrepancies [from ref. 20, Reprinted with permission from Müller, T.; Bonafos , C.; Heinig , K.-H.; Tencé, M.; Coffin , H.; Cherkashin, N.; Ben Assayag, G.; Schamm, S.; Zanchi, G.; Colliex, C.; Möller, W.; Claverie , A. *Appl. Phys. Lett.* 2004, *85*, 2373. Copyright AIP (2004)].

Surprisingly, it becomes thicker mainly through the increase of the thickness of the injection oxide, i.e. in the oxide region located *below* the NCs population [21].

The comparison between the layer thicknesses observed before and after annealing shows that this "anomalous swelling" of the oxide layer occurs during or immediately after implantation and *not* during annealing (see Figure 11). Finally, we observed that the overall increase of the oxide layer could not be accounted for, only by the addition of matter due to the ion implantation (even when neglecting ion sputtering). In the example shown in Figure

11, the precipitation of all the implanted Si atoms should have resulted in an increase of 2.6 nm of the overall oxide layer thickness, much smaller than the 5.3 nm observed by TEM.

It is important to note that the same quantitative characteristics could be obtained on wafers implanted and stored at different places, in Europe and USA, and under different relative humidity contents.

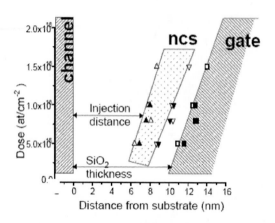

Figure 10. Schematics showing the increase of the injection oxide for increasing implanted doses.

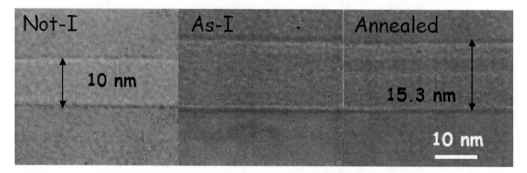

Figure 11. Set of XTEM images taken under Fresnel contrast conditions showing the swelling of the layer immediately after implantation. It does not change after annealing under N_2.

In summary, following implantation, a large part of the implanted Si atoms do not precipitate in the form of NCs. They apparently contribute to the growth of additional SiO_2 mostly in the region located between the NCs and the SiO_2/Si interface. Since this probable oxidation of implanted Si atoms naturally requires the availability of twice the same amount of oxygen atoms, it thus became crucial to investigate from where these atoms could come from.

5. HUMIDITY PENETRATION INTO IMPLANTED LAYERS

In a first series of experiments [22], 100 nm-thick SiO_2 layers were implanted with various ions (Si, Ge and Sn) at energies so that the projected range of the ions was kept constant at about 20 nm. After implantation, the wafers were stored in a clean room under

40% relative humidity. The depth-distribution of hydrogen atoms were obtained by Nuclear Reaction Analysis (NRA).

Figure 12 shows some of these results. It was observed that H concentrations as high as 10% could be found at depths down to twice the projected range of the ions i.e., in the region damaged by the ion beams. Moreover, this penetration of hydrogen atoms was found to increase with the energy losses provided by the implantations i.e., increased with the dose and the atomic mass of the incident particles [22]. During annealing, massive exodiffusion of hydrogen takes place.

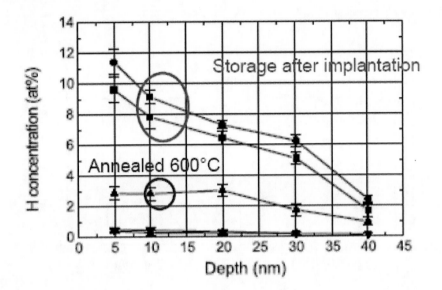

Figure 12. H depth profiles obtained by NRA on the SiO_2 layers implanted with Ge^+ ions [Reprinted from Schmidt , B.; et al. *Nucl. Instr. and Meth. in Phys. Res.* B 2002, *191*, 48222 Copyright (2002) by Elsevier].

We thus came with the hypothesis that following implantation, humidity could penetrate the layers, (the more damaged, the easier to penetrate) and react with part of the implanted species.

In order to further refine this scenario, layers of different thicknesses were implanted with 75 keV Si^+ ions at various doses and finally stored immediately after implantation into a small chamber containing a mixture of N_2 and $H_2^{18}O$ (< 40% relative humidity) [23, 19]. Parts of these wafers were eventually annealed at 900°C for 30 min under N_2. Then, the depth distributions of ^{18}O, H and OH in all these samples were obtained by ToF-SIMS. Selected results are shown in Figure 13. Clearly, ^{18}O is detected in high concentrations (up to several percents) immediately after exposure to $H_2^{18}O$. This oxygen does not redistribute during annealing. On the contrary, while both H and OH are detected after exposure to humidity, they disappear during annealing. We have noted that this penetration of water molecules increases with ion dose, i.e. the damage created by the Si^+ ions, up to some threshold, where it saturates. Interestingly, this phenomenon is almost independent on the time, during which the samples are exposed to humidity.

In summary, we have got a picture according to which, immediately after implantation, the heavily damaged SiO_2 layers absorb humidity. The water molecules are driven in the layers, dissociate and finally react with the implanted Si to form SiO_2. During annealing, further dissociation of OH takes place and finally most of the H atoms diffuse out to the surface. The penetration and final concentration of water molecules do not depend on the relative humidity in the atmosphere but are only limited by the degree of damage, i.e. the concentration of defects, in the SiO_2 matrix. Finally, KMC simulations based on the assumption that Si oxidation occurs much faster than precipitation, shows that this oxidation occurs preferentially in the region where the O concentration is initially larger than that of Si i.e. in the tail region of the implanted profile [24]. This phenomenon, thus results in an increase of the thickness of the oxide layer close to the deep Si/SiO_2 interface as experimentally observed.

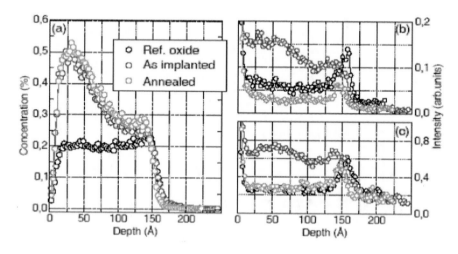

Figure 13. Set of ToF-SIMS profiles obtained after Si^+ irradiation of thin SiO_2 layers. Left, ^{18}O profile; bottom right, OH profile and top right, H profile. Note that the ^{18}O profile is unaffected by annealing (from ref [23]).

6. NCS PASSIVATION AND OXIDE HEALING

To take full advantage of the NC/matrix association, it may also be necessary that the NCs are well passivated, i.e. that neither dangling bonds nor defects are present at the NC/matrix interface. This is particularly important if the NCs are used to store or recombine charges, i.e. for memory or light emitting devices. The matrix should also be free of intrinsic and impurity related defects which could affect or deteriorate their dielectric and insulating properties.

For example, after annealing at typically 900°C for 30 min, the performances of Si-NC MOS capacitors are usually poor. The injection oxide is leaky and the available "flat band voltage shifts", i.e the memory windows available, are very limited [25]. These characteristics are caused by defects remaining in the oxide (mainly extra Si atoms) and by interfacial defects at the NC/SiO_2 interface. High temperature and long time annealing are of little effect since the diffusivity of Si in SiO_2 is extremely small [26, 27]. Thermal energy alone is not sufficient to allow the reconstruction of well-passivated Si NC/SiO_2 interfaces and the healing of the oxide layer. Alternatively, annealing under oxidizing ambient, i.e. using a mixture of

N_2 and O_2, has been found to be extremely efficient in restoring the oxide integrity as well as passivating the NCs [2] and recent NC MOS structures are fabricated by this route [28]. Figure 14 shows typical Raman and photoluminescence spectra, obtained on such structures depending on annealing conditions [25]. After annealing under oxidizing ambient, the background signal in the Raman spectra, usually assigned to non-crystalline silicon, disappear. In the meantime, the photoluminescence spectrum shows intense red emission ascribed to the well-passivated NCs.

However, the phenomena which control the overall oxidation of a structure consisting in a Si-rich SiO_2 layer, in which Si NCs are embedded, are not trivial. Figure 15 shows the result of an oxidizing annealing performed on a population of connected NCs, obtained after implantation into a 7 nm-thick SiO_2 layer of a relatively large dose of Si^+ at 1 keV.

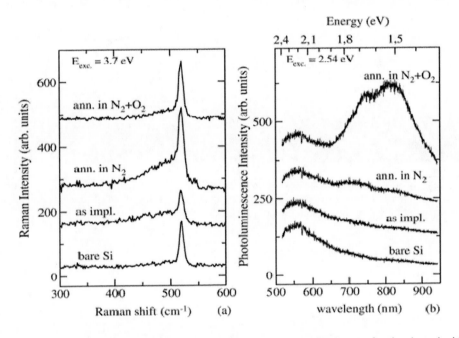

Figure 14. Raman (left) and photoluminescence (right) spectra obtained on wafers implanted with Si ions at 1 keV, depending on annealing conditions. Compare annealing under N_2 alone and N_2+O_2 [from ref. [from ref. 25, Reprinted with permission from Wellner, A.; et al. *J. Appl. Phys.* 2004,*96*, 2403.a Carrada , M. ; et al. *Appl. Phys. Lett.* 2005,*87*, 2519115Copyright AIP (2005)].

After a first annealing under N_2, the population consists of connected NCs which cover 35% of the surface. During annealing at 950°C under a mixture of N_2+O_2, the surface fraction occupied by the NCs rapidly decreases. At first, the elongated NCs get disconnected probably through the preferential oxidation of the grain boundaries they contain. This first step results in the formation of a population of isolated and well separated NCs and in the increase of the control (upper) and injection (lower) oxides. Finally, the densities and sizes of the NCs can be controlled through the annealing time. In the mean time, the injection oxide increases until all NCs have disappeared [26].

A careful investigation of this phenomenon has led to the conclusions that at first, when the surface fraction occupied by the NCs is large, the NCs form a diffusion barrier for

166   Alain Claverie, Caroline Bonafos, Robert Carles et al.

oxygen. The oxidation mostly affects the control oxide and the NCs but not the injection oxide. This results in the swelling of this control oxide. When the annealing time is larger however, and that the surface fraction occupied by the NCs is sufficiently small, oxygen atoms can penetrate through the NCs layer and oxidize the still Si-rich injection oxide and the Si substrate at its interface with the SiO_2 layer [29].

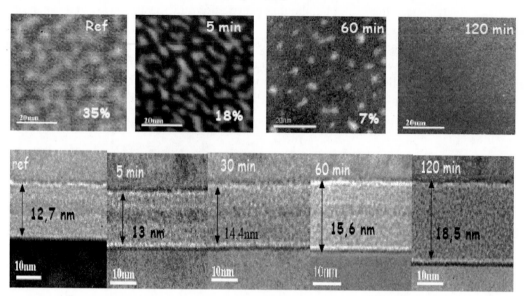

Figure 15. Top, set of PVTEM image showing the effect of annealing under oxidizing ambient onto the morphology of an initial network of connected nanocrystals. Bottom, set of XTEM image showing the concomitant evolution of the control and injection oxides.

7. APPLICATIONS

7.1 Nanocrystal Memory Devices

In a conventional floating-gate semiconductor memory device, a polycrystalline Si layer is buried in the gate oxide of a MOS transistor (Figure 16). If this layer, named the floating gate (FG) layer, is not charged, an adequate voltage applied on the gate results in a source/drain current. When this layer is charged, the potential from the gate is screened and no current flows from the source to the drain.

Whether the floating gate layer is charged or not defines the two states of the memory which can be read just by applying a given voltage to the gate. This layer can be charged and the memory "written" by injecting electrons or holes from the channel of the transistor. Alternatively, the memory can be erased by allowing the stored charges to come back to the channel or one of the doped regions of the device. The retention of the device, i.e. its ability to keep the charge within the FG layer directly depends on the thickness and integrity of the injection or tunnel oxide. This technology is currently limited by the possibility that all the charges stored in the polysilicon layer can leak towards the channel if only one conductive path exists in the injection oxide.

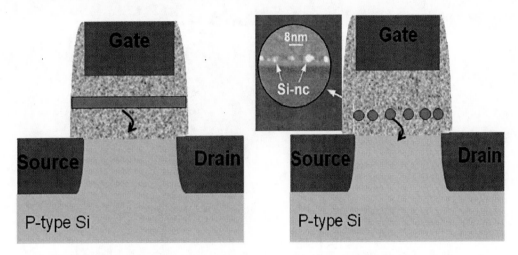

Figure 16. Schematics showing a conventional FG memory (left) to a NC-memory. The polysilicon layer is replaced by a band of NCs.

By exploiting the benefits (robustness and fault-tolerance) of a charge storage distribution, nanocrystal MOS memory devices, i.e. devices in which the FG layer is replaced by a single plane of NCs (Figure 16), offer an attractive alternative for overcoming the scaling limitations of conventional floating-gate semiconductor memories [30, 31]. For achieving reliable devices and avoiding fluctuations in device performance, not only the nanocrystal characteristics (e.g. size, density, interspacing) but also their location inside the gate dielectric, have to be well controlled. In particular, fine control of the thickness of the dielectric layer (the so-called injection oxide or tunnel oxide) separating the NCs and the substrate is absolutely required since a change of less than 1 nm dramatically affects the programming properties (write/erase times and voltages) and data retention of the devices. Moreover, good retention characteristics require that the oxide integrity is totally restored after the implantation/annealing process step.

Knowing how to meet these requirements, we have succeeded in fabricating, in an industrial environment, two types of memory devices we name EEPROM-like and RAM-like in correspondence to their overall characteristics [3, 31, 32]. The flexibility of the ULE-IBS technique is demonstrated by Figure 17. Indeed, it is important to note that the two different devices have been obtained only by slightly varying the implantation and annealing conditions but using the same initial transistor structure. In the first memory device (top, RAM-like)), the NCs are located at distance of 5 nm from the channel of the transistor which serves as the charging electrodes. Consequently, the NCs can be all charged after a short pulse of 10 µs at 7V.

A reasonable retention time of several hours is obtained. In the second device (bottom, EEPROM-like), the NCs are located at a larger distance from the channel (6.5 nm) and this is obtained by simply reducing the Si beam energy from 1.5 to 1. keV. Subtle changes of other parameters (dose, annealing scheme) are aimed at increasing the density of well passivated NCs. As a result, larger writing times, in the ms range, and higher voltage pulses at about 9 V are required to operate the device but retention times of more than 10 years can be obtained at 85°C, an ensemble of characteristics which compare favourably with existing non-volatile memory devices.

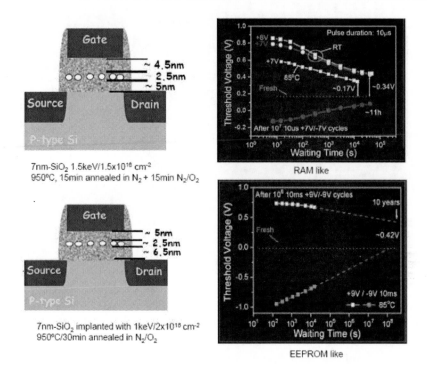

Figure 17. Two distinct devices can be fabricated by ULE-IBS on the same MOS platform by slightly changing the implantation and annealing conditions. Top, RAM-like device and bottom, EEPROM-like device. On the left, schematics of the structures and, on the right, retention characteristics of the real devices.

We believe these two complementary devices fabricated from the same starting platform, demonstrate the flexibility of the ULE-IBS method.

7.2 Plasmonic Nanostructures

Much effort has been recently devoted to the fabrication of substrates for surface-enhanced light emission or scattering by molecules or quantum dots [33, 34]. The most efficient metal for optical applications in the visible or near-infrared range is Ag.

A very critical parameter for potential applications based on enhanced optical fields or plasmon coupling is the "optical gap" between the surface of the Ag-ncs and the free SiO_2 surface on top of which nano-objects that emit or scatter light can be deposited.. It has been recently shown that by over coating nanotextured Ag surfaces with thin dielectric layers their plasmonic activity is preserved, allowing for SERS-based molecular detection [35, 36]. Moreover, the capping layer is also very effective in stabilizing the SERS substrate, make it more robust. The main difficulty is limiting the porosity of the over layer while maintaining the electromagnetic coupling: a good compromise was achieved with a silica thickness of about 7 nm [36].

With these results in mind, we have extended the ULE-IBS approach; we have developed for Si NCs in SiO_2 to synthesize planes of Ag nanocrystals buried at controlled distances from the free surface of a SiO_2 layer grown on Si (100) substrate. As confirmed by TEM measurements (see Figure 2), the optical gap can be adjusted in the nm range by simply tuning, in the keV range, the energy of implanted ions. For all conditions, the surface of wafer remains remarkably flat, at the nanoscale.

Furthermore, we were able to record their vibronic signature using resonant Raman-Brillouin spectroscopy [15]. For this, the 413 nm radiation of a Krypton laser was used to take benefit of resonance effects on inelastic scattering cross section. The laser beam was focused under Brewster incidence and the scattered light was collected through a confocal microscope objective. This "dark-field" geometry ensured a very high rejection level of the spurious scattered light in the low-frequency range. Moreover, the thickness of the silica layer has been chosen around 100 nm, to obtain a bilayer optical interference effect [37].

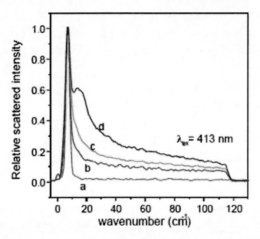

Figure 18. Low frequency Raman-Brilouin spectra of a set of implanted samples using the same kinetic energy (3 keV) and different doses, 5 (b), 10 (b) and 20 (c) atomic percent of Ag at maximum of the implanted profile. Spectrum (a) refers to a non-implanted sample.

Typical Raman spectra of a set of samples implanted at 3 keV for increasing Ag doses are reported in Figure 18 (b-d), in comparison with that of a non-implanted zone (a). On all these spectra, the Brillouin peak of the Si substrate is clearly observed at 6.5 cm^{-1}. On its high energy side the signature of the Ag-ncs develops as a broad band for the lowest doses (b and c) whereas, a well defined peak emerges for the highest dose (d). Owing to the optical amplification provided by the 100 nm thick SiO_2 layer and to the plasmon resonance condition, we have been able to record the vibrational signature of a very small amount of Ag, i.e. less than the volume occupied by an equivalent 1nm-thick continuous layer. Indeed, from the relative integrated intensities, one has estimated that the normalized polarizibility per Ag atom is more than 3 orders of magnitude higher than that of Si. By normalizing this signature with regard to the Brillouin intensity of the structure, one observes that the integrated intensity does increase quasi linearly with the total Ag amount.

CONCLUSION AND FUTURE DIRECTIONS

It has been the goal of this chapter to describe the main materials science aspects of the fabrication of 2D arrays of nanocrystals buried in SiO_2 layers and at tunable distances from the surface, by using the ULE-IBS technique. Different phenomena take place during and after ion implantation. In thin SiO_2 layers, ion beam mixing of the deep Si/SiO_2 interface can prevent the formation of NCs if the trade-off between beam energy and oxide thickness is not optimized. Following implantation, humidity penetrates the implanted layers and may react with the matrix and/or the implanted impurities. In addition to some "dose loss", this oxidation may result in larger than expected and asymmetrical growth of the matrix. Passivation of the NCs and restoration of the integrity of the SiO_2 layer can be achieved by annealing under slightly oxidizing conditions. During annealing under an oxidizing ambient, both the NCs and the deep SiO_2/Si interface can be oxidized and this again may result in a somehow asymmetrical growth of the oxide. All these phenomena play a role in defining the final characteristics of the structure, morphology, size, density and surface coverage of the nanocrystals as well as in their exact positioning with respect to the surface of the wafer and to the matrix/Si interface. The optimization of demonstrating devices based on the use of any given matrix/NCs association requires that an in-depth knowledge of these phenomena is gained prior to evaluation.

High performance NC memory devices with tunable characteristics have been fabricated following this route. Nanodevices showing single electron effects at room temperatures have been recently demonstrated [38, 39]. Finally, the characteristics of these NCs memories based on the Si/SiO_2 association are only limited by Physics, i.e. it is not possible to reduce the writing time without reducing the retention time as both characteristics depend on the probability of charge transfer through the injection oxide. Recent efforts aim at breaking this restrictive trade-off by synthesizing semiconducting or metallic NCs into "high k" dielectrics.

With respect to the fabrication of "plasmonic nanostructures", the main advantages offered by the ULE-IBS technique are both the protection of the particles from oxidation or contaminants adsorption, and the preservation of a perfectly flat surface, allowing further processing. By using an optically designed substrate, it offers the possibility of enhancing the coupling between photons and precisely localized plasmons and/or acoustical-like phonons. In particular, it can give a relevant response to most of the challenges, linked to the fabrication of efficient SERS substrates, namely: the control of the size and aspect ratio of nanostructures, the growth of the expected nanostructures onto specifically designed substrate geometry, and the integration of the fabrication process with other conventional micro-fabrication techniques. Finally its versatility offers some possibility in elucidating details of the mechanisms of SERS and the formation of the desired "hot spots" by modifying the density, the structure and the location of the active delta layer with regard to the surface.

REFERENCES

[1]   BenAssayag, G.; Bonafos, C.; Carrada, M.; Normand, P.; Tsoukalas, D.; and Claverie, A. *Appl. Phys. Lett.* 2003, *82,* 200.

[2]   Bonafos, C.; et al. *Solid State Electronics* 2005, *49,* 1734.

[3]   Normand, P.; Kapetanakis, E.; Dimitrakis, P.; Tsoukalas, D.; Beltsios, K.; Cherkashin, N.; Bonafos, C.; Coffin, H.; Benassayag, G. and Claverie, A. *Appl. Phys. Lett.* 2003, *83,* 168.

[4]   Carreras, J.; Bonafos, C.; Montserrat, J.; Dominguez, C.; Arbiol, J. and Garrido, B. *Nanotechnology* 2008, *19,* 205201.

[5]   Jambois, O.; Carreras, J.; Pérez-Rodríguez, A.; Garrido, B.; Bonafos, C.; Schamm, S.; Ben Assayag, G. *Appl. Phys. Lett.* 2007, *91*, 211105.

[6]   López, M.; Garrido, B.; García, C.; Pellegrino, P.; Pérez-Rodríguez, A.; Morante, J. R.; Bonafos, C.; Carrada, M. and Claverie, A. *Appl. Phys. Lett.* 2002, 80 (9), 1637-1639.

[7]   Garrido, B.; López, M.; García, C.; Pérez-Rodríguez, A.;. Morante, J. R.; Bonafos, C.; Carrada, M. and Claverie, A. *J. Appl. Phys.* 2002, *91*, 798-807.

[8]   Carles, R.; Farcău, C.; Bonafos, C.; Benassayag, G.; Pécassou, B. and Zwick, A. *Mater. Res. Soc. Symp. Proc.* 2009, *1182*, EE09-21.

[9]   Hosono; et al. *Nucl. Instr. and Meth. B*, 1994, *91*, 510-514.

[10] Chen.; et al. *IEEE Trans. Elec. Dev.* 2004, *V51*, 11, 1840.

[11] Beyer, V. and Borany J. V. *Phys. Rev. B* 2008, *77*, 014107.

[12] Kapetanakis, E.; Normand, P. and Holliger, P. *J. Appl. Phys.* 2008, *103*, 064515.

[13] Dimitrakis, P; Mouti, A; Bonafos, C; Schamm, S; BenAssayag, G; Ioannou-Sougleridis, V; Schmidt, B; Becker, J and Normand, P; *Microelectronic Engineering*, Nr. 86, 2009, 1838–1841.

[14] Fanciulli, M.; Perego, M.; Bonafos, C.; Mouti, A.; Schamm, S.; Ben Assayag, G. *Advances in Science and Technology* 2006, *51*, 156. and Bonafos, C.; private communication.

[15] Carles, R.; Farcău, C.; Bonafos, C.; Benassayag, G.; Pécassou, B.; and Zwick, A. *Nanotechnology*, 2009, *20*, 355305.

[16] Moller, W. and Eckstein, W.; *Nucl. Instrum. and Methods Phys. Res. B* 1984, *2*, 814.

[17] Bonafos, C.; Carrada, M.; Cherkashin, N.; Coffin, H.; Chassaing, D.; Ben Assayag G. and Claverie, A. *J. Appl. Phys.* 2004, *95*, 5696.

[18] Cherkashin, N.; Claverie, A.; Bonafos, C.; et al. *J. Appl. Phys.* 2007, 102 (2), 023520.

[19] Claverie, A.; et al. *Defect and Diffusion Forum* 2006, 258-260, 531-541,.

[20] Müller, T.; Bonafos , C.; Heinig , K.-H.; Tencé, M.; Coffin , H.; Cherkashin, N.; Ben Assayag, G.; Schamm, S.; Zanchi, G.; Colliex, C.; Möller, W.; Claverie , A. *Appl. Phys. Lett.* 2004, *85*, 2373.

[21] Carrada , M.; et al. *Mat. Sci. and Eng. B.* 2003, *101*, 204.

[22] Schmidt , B.; et al. *Nucl. Instr. and Meth. in Phys. Res. B* 2002, *191*, 482.

[23] Perrego, M.; and Fanciulli, M.; "ToF-SIMS study of $H_2^{18}O$ penetration in irradiated SiO_2 films" *NEON internal report* March 30 (2004). (www.cemes.fr/neon)

[24] Muller, T.; *PhD Thesis*, FZR-439 (Dresden), Nov. 2005.

[25] Wellner, A.; et al. *J. Appl. Phys.* 2004,*96*, 2403.a Carrada , M. ; et al. *Appl. Phys. Lett.* 2005,*87*, 2519115.

[26] Tsoukalas, D.; et al. *J. of Appl. Phys.* 2001,*89*, 7809.

[27] Mathiot, D.; et al. *J. of Appl. Phys.* 2003,*94*, 2136.

[28] Normand, P.; Kapetanakis, E.; Dimitrakis, P.; Tsoukalas, D.; Beltsios, K.; Cherkashin, N.; Bonafos, C.; Benassayag, G.; Coffin, H.; Claverie, A; Soncini, V.; Agarwal, A.; and Ameen, M. *Appl. Phys. Lett.* 2003, *83*, 168.

[29] Coffin, H.; Bonafos, C.; Schamm, S.; Carrada, M.; Cherkashin, N.; Ben Assayag, G.; Dimitrakis, P.; Normand, P.; Respaud, M.; and Claverie, A. *Mat. Sci. And Eng. B* 2005, *124*, 499-503.

[30] Tiwari, S.; Rana, F.; Hanafi, H. I.; Hartstein, A.; Crabbé, E. F. and Chan, K. *Appl. Phys. Lett.* 1996, *68*,1377.

[31] Normand, P.; Kapetanakis, E.; Dimitrakis, P.; Skarlatos, D.; Beltsios, K.; Tsoukalas, D.; Bonafos, C.; Ben Assayag, G.; Cherkashin, N.; Claverie, A.; et al. *Nucl. Inst. and Meth. in Phys. Res.B* 2004, *216*, 228.

[32] Dimitrakis, P.; Kapetanakis, E.; Tsoukalas, D.; Skarlatos, D.; Bonafos, C.; Ben Asssayag, G.; Claverie, A.; Perego, M.; Fanciulli, M.; Soncini, V.; Sotgiu, R.; Agarwal, A.; Ameen, M.; and Normand, P. *Solid-State Electron.* 2004, 48, 1511.

[33] Ko, H.; Singamaneni, S.; Tsukruk, V. V. *Small*, 2008, 4, 1576-1599.

[34] Lakowitz, J. R. *Plasmonics*, 2006, 1, 5-33.

[35] Zhang, X.; Zhao, J.; Whitney, A. V.; Elam, J. W.; Van Duyne, R. P. *J. Am. Chem. Soc.* 2006, 128, 10304-10309.

[36] Scholes, F. H.; Bendavid, A.; Glenn, F. L.; Critchley, M.; Davis, T. J.; Sexton, B. A. *J. Raman Spectrosc.*, 2008, 39, 673-678.

[37] Bacsa, W. S.; Lannin, J. S. *Appl. Phys. Lett.*, 1992, 61, 19-21.

[38] Schalchian, M.; Grisolia, J.; BenAssayag, G.; Coffin, H.; Atarodi, S. M. and Claverie, A. *Appl. Phys. Lett.* 2005, 86, 163111.

[39] BenAssayag, G.; Schalchian, M.; Grisolia, J.; Coffin, H.; Atarodi, S. M. and Claverie, A. *J. Vac. Sci. Technol B* 2005, 23(6), 2821.

In: Synthesis and Engineering of Nanostructures…
Editors: Devesh Kumar Avasthi & Jean Claude Pivin

ISBN 978-1-62100-261-1
© 2012 Nova Science Publishers, Inc

Chapter 10

.

NANOMETRIC BUBBLE FORMATION IN SIO₂ BY ION IMPLANTATION: INFLUENCE OF THE SUBSTRATE

E. Oliviero[1], B. Décamps[1], M.-O. Ruault[1], O. Kaitasov[1] and E. Ntsoenzok[2]*

[1]CSNSM, CNRS-IN2P3-Université Paris-Sud, Bât 108 - 91405 Orsay, France
[2]CEMHTI-CNRS, 3A, rue de la férollerie, 45071 Orléans, France

ABSTRACT:

Amorphous SiO_2 layers grown thermally and by chemical vapour deposition (CVD) were implanted at room temperature with Kr ions in an attempt to form bubbles in the oxide layer. Cross–sectional Transmission Electron Microscopy studies show that Kr implantation induces bubbles in both type of SiO_2. However, the bubble distribution and size depend strongly on the type of SiO_2. Moreover, in CVD silicon oxide the bubble distribution and size depend on the pre-implantation treatment, i.e. if densification is carried out or not. These results are discussed in the light of migration and coalescence mechanisms and surface diffusivity. The understanding of bubble and defect formation in SiO_2 should give rise to new techniques for modifying dielectric properties and may yield possibilities for low-k applications.

1. INTRODUCTION

Until now, SiO_2 having a dielectric constant of 3.9 has been used as a dielectric material for the interconnections in integrated circuit (IC) devices. But with the constant miniaturization of devices and thus the continual increase in the density of multilevel interconnections, a lower dielectric constant material is needed to minimize time delay $\tau = RC$ (where R is the resistance and C the capacity), power consumption and cross-talk [1]. The International Technology Roadmap for Semiconductors (ITRS) has projected that the dielectric constant of the material should fall below 2 by 2010 [2]. There are two possible approaches to achieve this. The first approach is to use new materials with lower k. The second one, very promising, is to decrease the effective dielectric constant by incorporating pores into the material [3]. Air has a dielectric constant of roughly 1.00059, thus increasing the layer porosity may be a solution to reduce the dielectric constant of the material. The pore structure and its distribution then have distinct influences on the basic physical properties of the material. While the reduction in k is desirable, there are also adverse effects such as deterioration of the mechanical properties as porosity increases. There is also the problem of moisture adsorption in the presence of pores at the surface [4]. Therefore, an ideal porous material would consist of a network of small pores embedded into material, with a regular size distribution. An appropriate technique to realize such a porous network within the dielectric is rare gas ion implantation.

It was shown that, ion implantation of heavy inert gases (such as Xe and Kr) in thermally grown SiO_2 leads to the formation of bubbles [5]. While the formation and growth mechanisms of cavities are relatively well understood in metals [6] and semiconductors [7], the creation and growth mechanisms of bubbles/cavities in SiO_2 is not yet understood and requires detailed analyses of the bubbles characteristics as well as considerations including the diffusivity of the gas atoms in SiO_2 and the nature of defects created by implantation. Conversely, in the case of SiO_2 the nucleation and growth of metallic/semiconductor nanoprecipitates has been extensively studied, while the formation and growth of cavities remain unexplored. For both type of nanostructures (bubbles and nanoprecipitates), no detailed study of their formation in the different types of SiO_2 has been conducted until now. Such a study is imperative since SiO_2 obtained by chemical vapour deposition (CVD) is still the dielectric material most frequently used in devices.

2. EXPERIMENTAL CONDITIONS

Thermal SiO_2 layers were grown by heating n-type silicon wafers to 1100°C in ambient air. The oxide layer formed had a thickness of 2.3 μm. CVD samples were obtained directly from ST Microelectronics. A 1.22 μm thick amorphous SiO_2 layer was deposited on an n-type silicon wafer. Densification of some of these samples was carried out by annealing them at 940°C for 1 hour. These samples will be referred to, as densified-CVD SiO_2. Their thickness was 1.19 μm. All different types of samples were implanted in a home-built Implanter for Research in Metallurgy and Astrophysics (IRMA) [8], at room temperature, with 220 keV Kr^+ ions at the same fluence of $5x10^{16}$ cm^{-2}. The implantation energy was chosen, according to Stopping and Range of Ions in Matter (SRIM) simulations [9], in order to have a mean projected range (R_p) of ~ 120 nm. Ion flux was kept as low as $1x10^{12}$ cm^{-2}s^{-1} in order to avoid any temperature increase during implantation. The as-implanted samples were characterized by cross-sectional Transmission Electron Microscopy (XTEM) using a Tecnai G^2 20 microscope operating at 200 kV. The samples were thinned in cross-section geometry by mechanical polishing using a tripod polisher to electron transparency. Specimens were imaged in underfocus and overfocus conditions to highlight the cavity edges with Fresnel contrast. In the following, "S" in the TEM images denotes the implanted surface of the sample.

3. CHARACTERIZATION OF NANO SIZE KR BUBBLES IN SIO$_2$

3.1. Thermal SiO$_2$

Fig 1a is a cross-sectional micrograph of 2.3 µm thermal SiO$_2$ that has been implanted with 220 keV Kr ions at a fluence of 5×10^{16} cm^{-2}. Nanostructures are located in a continuous and well-defined band. The band starts at about 80 nm from the free surface and its width is 160 nm. All the nanostructures observed were identified as bubbles/cavities since they exhibited characteristic Fresnel fringes at their interface with SiO$_2$: black for underfocus condition (Fig 1a) and white for overfocus conditions (Fig 1b) [10]. Moreover, it can be stated that they are Kr bubbles since Rutherford Backscattering Spectroscopy (RBS) measurements (not presented here) have demonstrated that all the implanted Kr is located within this band and is expected to be mainly located within the cavities. The size of the bubbles ranges from 4 to 30 nm with an average size of 12 nm (Fig 2). The size distribution within the band is quasi-homogeneous. The bubble area ratio as a function of depth clearly displays a "plateau" shape in contrast to the Kr distribution predicted by SRIM calculation [9] which exhibits a Gaussian profile with a peak located at 120-130 nm (Fig 3). This result is in agreement with RBS results (not shown here), which showed that the Kr profile exhibits a "plateau" instead of a peak. When both the theoretical damage and Kr depth distributions are plotted together with the bubble-area distribution in function of depth (Figure 3), it can be observed that the bubble extend preferentially on the deeper side of the Kr profile predicted by SRIM. The "plateau shape" corresponds to Kr diffusion within the implanted region and might be related to implantation-induced defects. A detailed study of a possible enhanced diffusion by "defects" due to irradiation is needed. This could be done by increasing either the Kr energy or the damage rate (dpa) or by irradiating within a in-situ TEM experiment.

It should be noted in Fig 1 that the bubbles are not completely spherical in shape, a few of them being rather elongated or presenting an irregular shape. Modification of the bubble shape and/or instability of the bubbles have been observed under an electron beam [5]. So care was taken to image zones of the bubble layer immediately when exposing them to the electron beam.

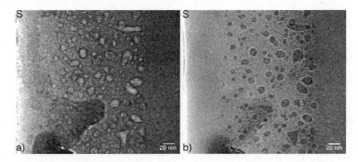

Figure 1. XTEM bright field images of as-implanted thermal SiO$_2$ with 220 keV Kr ions at a fluence of 5×10^{16} cm^{-2} in (a) underfocus and (b) overfocus conditions.

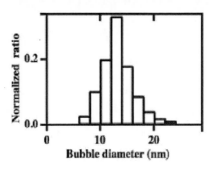

Figure 2. Size profile of bubbles created by 220 keV Kr at a fluence of 5×10^{16} cm^{-2} in 2.3 µm thermal SiO$_2$. Normalized with the total number of the nanostructures present in the layer.

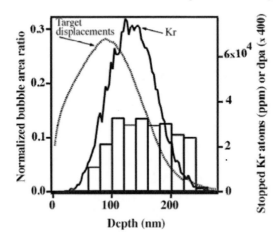

Figure 3. Bubble area ratio as a function of depth for 220 keV Kr at a fluence of 5×10^{16} cm^{-2} in 2.3 µm thermal SiO$_2$. Normalized with the total area of all the nanostructures present in the layer.

3.2. CVD SiO$_2$

A cross-sectional image obtained after 220 keV Kr implantation to a fluence of 5×10^{16} cm^{-2} into 1.22 µm CVD SiO$_2$ is presented in Fig 4. Clearly, the microstructure of the damaged layer is different to that obtained in thermal SiO$_2$ with the same implantation conditions (Fig 1). A continuous band of bubbles is formed at 50 nm from the implanted surface but the width of the band is now 250 nm. More striking is the bubble size that now ranges from 4 to 120 nm with a mean size of 17 nm. The size distribution within the band is not homogeneous. Larger bubbles are located at the centre of the band that corresponds to the region of maximum Kr concentration calculated by SRIM simulations (Fig 5). The band can thus be divided into three layers: a layer containing a mixture of larger bubbles and a few smaller bubbles at the centre, surrounded by two layers of smaller bubbles. Again, it should be noted that the bubbles are not completely spherical in shape, a few of them being elongated. It seems that the bubble density is higher in the deeper layer containing small bubbles. However, this effect could be due to the cross section preparation, which leads to an increase in thickness from about 20 nm at the free surface up to around 50 nm at the end of the layer (i.e. at 300 nm from the surface).

As mentioned for thermal SiO_2, modification of bubble shape and instability of the bubbles under the electron beam has been also observed. The effects are stronger and quicker in CVD SiO_2. Further work is needed to clearly understand these phenomena. In the image (Fig 4) again, great care was taken to image the bubble layer immediately when exposed to the electron beam.

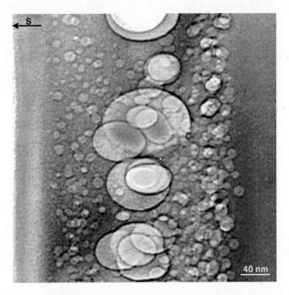

Figure 4. An underfocused XTEM bright field image of as-implanted CVD SiO_2 with 220 keV Kr ions at a fluence of 5×10^{16} cm^{-2}.

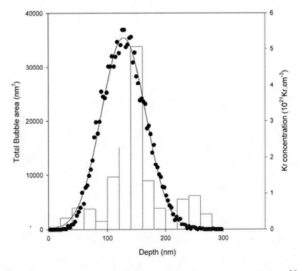

Figure 5. Bubble area as a function of depth for 220 keV Kr at a fluence of 5×10^{16} cm^{-2} in 1.22 μm CVD SiO_2.

3.3. Densified SiO$_2$

Fig 6 shows the microstructure of the damaged layer after 220 keV Kr implantation at a fluence of 5×10^{16} cm^{-2} into 1.19 µm densified-CVD SiO$_2$. Clearly, the densification had a strong effect on the bubble formation. A continuous band of bubbles is observed at 40 nm from the implanted surface and extends over 160 nm. The bubble size ranges from 4 to 24 nm with a mean size of 11 nm. Again, it should be noted that the bubbles are not completely spherical in shape, a few of them being elongated. The size distribution within the band is quasi-homogeneous and a plateau is again observed (Fig 7). The effect of the electron beam has been also observed. Bubble formation by Kr implantation in densified-CVD SiO$_2$ is somewhat similar to that in thermal SiO$_2$.

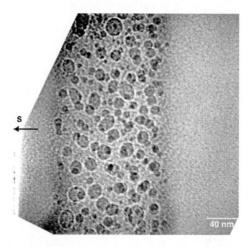

Figure 6. Underfocused XTEM bright field image of as-implanted densified-CVD SiO$_2$ with 220 keV Kr ions at a fluence of 5×10^{16} cm^{-2}.

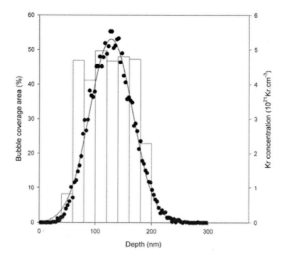

Figure 7. Bubble area ratio as a function of depth 220 keV Kr at a fluence of 5×10^{16} cm^{-2} in 1.19 µm densified-CVD SiO$_2$.

3.4 Discussion

The formation of bubbles in amorphous materials seems to be quite different from that in crystalline materials. It is well known that inert gas implantations into crystalline materials such as Si [11], SiC [12], GaN [13] leads to the formation of tiny bubbles of 1–3 nm in size. Recently, it was shown that He implantation in amorphous silicon leads to the formation of significantly larger bubbles compared to those observed in crystalline Si under identical implantation conditions [14]. Bubble mobility in Si almost certainly results from surface migration processes. The migration of atoms at the bubble surface leads to a stochastic displacement of the centre of mass of the bubble and leads to a Brownian motion with smaller cavities moving more rapidly than larger ones [14]. Changes in the surface diffusivity can affect the ability of bubbles to migrate and coalesce. In amorphous silicon it was shown that the activation energy for surface diffusion could be as low as 0.35–0.45 eV [14]. Assuming that the surface diffusivity is even lower in amorphous SiO$_2$, this would allow bubble coarsening to occur directly during implantation, explaining the observation of much larger bubbles following Kr implantation into SiO$_2$. Small bubbles could be mobile at room temperature (and thus during the implantation) and so will grow by thermally induced motion and coalescence as well as by any radiation-induced processes. In addition, this would explain the rather non-spherical aspect of the bubbles. This would be the result of the recent coalescence of spherical bubbles as claimed in He implanted silicon, where the observations of elongated voids were considered to be consistent with recent coalescence [7]. In CVD SiO$_2$, the density is lower than in thermal SiO$_2$ and therefore it can be assumed qualitatively that the activation energy for surface diffusivity is lower. Moreover the material offers more space for the larger bubbles to be accommodated. This leads to the observed layer of larger bubbles. This effect is lost when densification is carried out prior to implantation.

In order to have a better understanding of these effects, in-situ experiments on a TEM coupled to an ion accelerator are necessary to detect any bubble motion during implantation. Moreover, the stability of bubbles under electron/ion beam could be also investigated. This will be done on the dual-beam TEM of the JANNuS facility at Orsay [15].

4. CONCLUSION

Kr implantations into SiO$_2$ for low-k interconnections applications have been investigated by means of TEM studies. Different behaviours have been observed for the different types of SiO$_2$ used. It was shown that bubble formation could strongly depend on the surface diffusivity that would be linked to the density of the implanted material. Bubble instability under the electron beam has been mentioned. Further work is needed to enrich the understanding of these phenomena using an in-situ TEM coupled to ion accelerators.

ACKNOWLEDGMENTS

This work was funded by ANR French organization through the contract "Nanocafon" : NT05-2-42001

REFERENCES

[1]   Maex, K.; Baklanov, M.R.; Shamiryan, D.; Iacopi, K; Brongersma, S.H.; Yanovitskaya, Z.S. *J. Appl Phys* 2003, 93, 8793-8841.

[2]   *Process integration, devices and structures in International Technology Roadmap for Semiconductors* (Semiconductor Industry Association publisher, 2007), available at http://www.itrs.

[3]   Jain, A.; Rogojevic, S.; Ponoth, S.; Agarwal, N.; Matthew, I.; Gill, W.N.; Persans, P.; Tomozawa, M.; Plawsky, J.L.; Simonyi, E. *Thin solid Film* 2001, 398-399, 513-522.

[4]   Chang,C.L.; Huang, T.J. *Mat Sci and Eng B* 2003, 98, 45-53.

[5]   Oliviero, E.; Ruault, M.-O; Décamps, B.; Fotuna, F.; Ntsoenzok, E.; Kaïtasov, O.; Collin, S.; *Micropor Mesopor Mat* 2010, 132, 163-173.

[6]   Donnelly,S.E.; Evans, J.H.; *Fundamental Aspects of Inert Gases in Solids*, 219, Plenum, New York, 1991.

[7]   Evans, J.H. *Nucl Instr and Meth B* 2002, 196, 125-134.

[8]   For details of the ion implantation system see: http://semiramis.in2p3.fr

[9]   Ziegler, J.F.; Biersack, J.P.; Littmark, U. *The Stopping and Range of Ions in Solids*, Pergamon, New York, 1985.

[10]   Loretto, M.H.; Smallman, R.E. *Defect Analysis in Electron Microscopy*, Chapman and Hall, London, 1975.

[11]   Raineri, V.; Fallica, P.G; Percolla, G.; Battaglia, A.; Barbagallo, M.; Campisano, S.U. *J. Appl Phys* 1995, 78 , 3727-3735.

[12]   Oliviero, E.; David, M.L.; Beaufort M.F.; Nomgaudyte, J.; Pranevicius, L.; Declémy, A.; Barbot, J.F. *J Appl Phys* 2002, 91, 1179-1186.

[13]   Barbot, J.F.; Pailloux, F.; David, M.L.; Pizzagalli, L.; Oliviero, E.; Lucas, G. *J Appl Phys* 2008, 104, 43526-1-43526-7.

[14]   Beaufort, M.F.; Pizzagalli, L.;Gandy, A.S.; Oliviero, E.; Eyidi, D.; Donnelly, S.E. *J Appl Phys* 2008, 104, 94905-1-94905-7.

[15]   http://jannus.in2p3.fr

In: Synthesis and Engineering of Nanostructures...   ISBN 978-1-62100-261-1
Editors: Devesh Kumar Avasthi & Jean Claude Pivin   © 2012 Nova Science Publishers, Inc

Chapter 11

HIGH RESOLUTION TRANSMISSION ELECTRON MICROSCOPY STUDIES OF ION BEAM INDUCED MODIFICATIONS IN GOLD NANOSTRUCTURES ON SILICON: SPUTTERING AND ENHANCED DIFFUSION

P. V. Satyam[1], J. Ghatak[2], Umananda M. Bhatta, B. Satpati[3] and A. Rath

Institute of Physics, Sachivalaya Marg, Bhubaneswar, 751005, India

ABSTRACT

In this paper, we review our recent work on ion – solid interaction, in particular, ion interaction with nanostructures in ballistic regime of ion stopping. The transmission electron microscopy (TEM) is a powerful and unique characterization tool to study atomic structure of various irradiated specimen. We also present a brief overview on the functioning and the use of high resolution transmission electron microscopy (HRTEM) in understanding the ion beam induced effects. Modifications occurring at surfaces and interfaces will be presented using planar and cross-sectional TEM methods. The growth of nanoparticles correlated to sputtering phenomena of uniform and non-uniform films along with the sputtered nanoparticles size and their size distribution at various incident ion beam parameters, will be reported. Systematic investigations of the enhancement of gold atoms diffusion in silicon, in particular, the role of incident ion flux for 1.5 MeV gold ions will be presented.

Keywords: *Ion irradiation, nanoislands, Strain, HRTEM, Asymmetric X-ray Bragg reflection*

---

[1] Corresponding Author: satyam@iopb.res.in.

[2] Present Address: Dept of Material Science and Engineering, National Cheng Kung University, Tainan, Taiwan.

[3] Present Address: Institute of Minerals and Materials Technology, Bhubaneswar, INDIA.

INTRODUCTION

Energetic ions, photons (x-rays) and electrons have been extensively used to study the structural aspects of materials. The scattering process, involving the energetic light ions (keV to MeV), such as proton and helium ions, is based on Rutherford scattering and nuclear reactions. Most of the structural investigations using ion beams as probes exploit Rutherford scattering in random and channeled direction (RBS/Channeling) typically with 1 – 2 MeV alpha particles. Using RBS method, one usually determines the "mass" of the target material and while using channeling methods (i.e., RBS with channeling geometry) would be used to determine the atomic locations in the lattice. These methods are used to study depth profiles and composition analysis of thin films in non-destructive methods. Though, channeling is used to study the "crystalline nature" of the target material, no atomic structure is easily available. For determining the atomic structure that has long range ordering (without information on local structures), one typically uses keV x-rays in a scattering process, involving elastic and in-elastic x-rays. Most popular among the x-ray methods is "x-ray diffraction" methods, exploiting the Bragg law to determine the inter-planar spacing of the target material that have long – range order. There are many types of x-ray scattering methods, such as, powder diffraction, single crystal diffraction, small angle scattering, reflectometry/ standing waves, grazing incidence-in-plane diffraction, etc. The x-ray methods are non-destructive in nature, work in reciprocal space and invoke long-range order and hence no real space imaging at atomic level is possible. The *real space microscopic structural* study, in particular the atomic structure of thin films and buried layers can be obtained by using high resolution TEM (HRTEM) method [1 – 4]. In the following, we give a brief introduction on the various experimental issues related to HRTEM.

Transmission Electron Microscopy (TEM):

There are several techniques that use energetic electrons to study structures both in real space (imaging) and reciprocal space (scattering). Some of these are low energy electron diffraction (LEED), reflection high energy electron diffraction (RHEED), scanning electron microscopy (SEM), transmission electron microscopy (TEM), etc. In electron microscopy (SEM and TEM), one exploits the short wavelength of energetic electrons to overcome the Rayleigh criteria [1]. Due to the short wavelengths (for example relativistic corrected wavelength of electrons for 200 keV is about 0.0025 nm) of these electrons, it is much easier to carry out a real space imaging with sub-Angstrom resolution. The main problem in imaging with the fast electrons is getting "good lenses" for focusing optics. Due to the problems of spherical aberration and chromatic aberrations, though the wavelength is much less than 0.01 nm, practically the resolution of the TEM is much above 0.01 nm (for example for a 200 keV electron microscope, with a spherical aberration coefficient of 0.5 mm, the point to point resolution of a typical TEM is about 0.19 nm). It is well known that one can make defect free lenses for the visible light, whereas, it is almost impossible to make defect-free electron lenses. In the new regime of sub-Angstram electron microscopy, correctors for imaging lenses and probe lenses are employed to achieve a resolution of ≈ 0.006 nm [4].

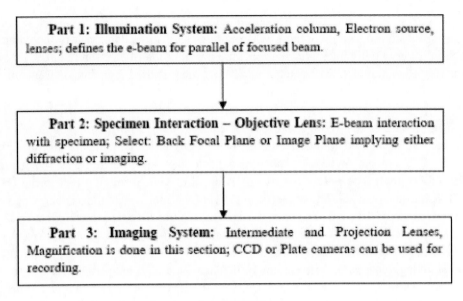

Figure 1. A schematic flow chart of various parts of TEM.

An electron microscope is a type of microscope that uses energetic electrons (few 10 keV to few MeV), to illuminate a specimen. Any electron microscope can be divided in to three typical sections, as depicted in Figure 1: (a) illumination system (b) specimen interaction – objective lens and (c) imaging systems. The following schematic flow diagram mentions the various functions in each section. In the illumination section (Part 1), an electrostatic lens in the form of Wehnelt cup is used after the filament to converge the maximum number of emitted electrons. This is the first of many lenses that follow (in a Jeol 2010 systems, there are about 17 lenses presents in total). The Wehnelt cup is the only electrostatic lens that is generally used in a conventional TEM. The remaining lenses are all electro-magnetic lenses. Illumination section consists of electron source, acceleration column and condenser lenses. Usually thermionic gun (W, LaB_6) or field emission gun (FEG) has been used as an electron source. Except the cost, in major respects (cross over, brightness, intensity and lifetime) FEG is better than thermionic gun. A high voltage is generated in a separated power supply unit using Cockcroft-Walton technique and is coupled to the acceleration column. Following the acceleration column, condenser lens system is available. Using different size of condenser aperture, one can change the illuminated area on the specimen. After this stage, specimen is used to insert either from the side or from the top. In the Part 2, the specimen is placed between the pole pieces of the objective lens. Often, the top of the Objective lens pole piece acts as mini condenser lens and will be used as part of illumination system. Just below the sample (2 – 5 mm), lower portion of objective lens (OL) is situated. In some cases, objective lens will have only one part, and in that case, it is followed after the specimen. After the objective lens, objective aperture and selected area diffraction aperture are placed (in Part 2). The combination of intermediate and projector lenses do the image magnification (Part 3). Finally, the magnified image forms at phosphor screen. To record the image or diffraction pattern, photographic film and/or charge coupled device (CCD) can be used (Part 3). The simplest digital cameras simply use a computer based video system, directed at a phosphor screen. These have limitations due to low light level from a phosphor screen and their video standard resolution. Much more sophisticated CCDs are also available which can measure the light from screen, but in this case, the light is channeled onto the CCD by block of optical fiber. Using image processing system, CCD outputs can also be combined to the computer. As electron is very highly interacting particle, the transmission of electron requires very high vacuum. In the column of TEM, vacuum of $\approx 1 \times 10^{-8}$ mbar is used to maintain. The column is often pumped with a sputter ion pump (SIP).

The TEM observations, presented in this report have been carried out using JEOL 2010 TEM operating at 200 keV (corresponding λ is equal to 0.0025 nm) [5]. Figure 2 shows the microscope, we have used for the results shown in this article [5]. In the machine photo, sections 1, 2, 3 are put in boxes that correspond to the same functions as schematically depicted in Figure 1. The pole piece of OL is an ultra high resolution pole piece (UHR-URP22) with a spherical aberration coefficient (C_s) of 0.5 mm which allows achieving point-to-point resolution of 0.19 nm. The images were recorded in TV rate camera (Gatan 622 SC) with video image processor (Gatan 750) and recently acquired Oriaus (Gatan 832) CCD [6]. The new CCD has the ability to record high resolution images at 25 frames per second and helps in studying dynamic phenomena, in particular with a high temperature TEM specimen holder. In our system, we also have a low temperature (up to -170° C) and a high temperature stages are available. In the high temperature holder, the temperature can be varied from room temperature (RT) to 1000° C.

In TEM, one needs to understand the specimen – electron interaction process. This involves either elastic or in-elastic processes. There are many processes that result after an electron interacts with a material and one can detect the following signals: secondary electrons, auger electrons, characteristic x-rays, in-coherent elastically backscattered electrons, forward scattered electrons (elastic and in-elastic), large angle – coherent elastic electron and incoherent elastic electrons, etc. Diffracted beams from crystal structures would be observed at very low forward angles (for example less than 1 degree for 200 keV electrons), due to smaller wavelengths) in transmission geometry. The conventional TEM image formation for thick specimen is very similar to the projector principle. In this case, an incoherent particle model can describe the interaction of the electrons with the specimen. Specimen show variation in thickness and density, so the electrons will lose more energy when transmits through the thicker and denser regions which will appear as darker objects. Same way, the thinner and rarer regions will appear as brighter objects. This is called thickness contrast imaging. Contrast in TEM also depends upon the crystalline nature of the specimen (diffraction contrast). However, for thin specimen at high magnifications (resulting lattice resolutions), this description fails because the wave nature of the electrons is then predominant. If the specimen is thin enough and crystalline, then elastic scattering is usually coherent and these electrons are now contributed to the image formation. After the exit of electron (elastically transmitted coherent electron beams), the diffraction spots and image are used to form at back-focal plane and image plane of OL. The diffraction pattern is nothing but the fast Fourier transformation (FFT) of the wave function of electron at the back focal plane of OL. One more time FFT of this wave function at back focal plane of OL, gives the high resolution (HR) lattice imaging. The HR image will form due to interference between the direct and diffracted beams, depending on the phase difference between these two. The beams diffracted at large angles can be cut down by the objective aperture. The resolution and the details of image formation are governed by the contrast transfer function (CTF).

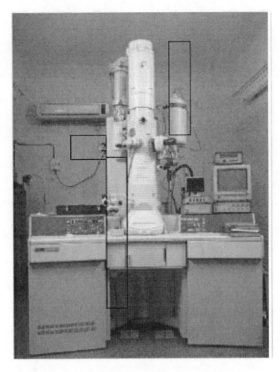

Figure 2. Jeol 2010 (200 keV) ultra high resolution TEM, LaB6 filament. 1, 2, 3 shown in boxes correspond to the respective parts as described by Figure 1.

The CTF depends on microscope parameters such as λ, C_s, chromatic aberration coefficient (C_c), defocus, width of defocus, stabilities in high voltage, OL lens current etc.

Uses of Electron Microscopy:

(A) Determination of Size and Size Distributions:

TEM provides a real space imaging of the various particles/structures due to the contrast arising from the mass-thickness variations. The microscope is calibrated at various magnifications, using standards: (a) at low magnifications (less that 10k magnification) gratings and (b) at very high magnifications, graphitized carbon specimen with a lattice spacing of 0.343 nm is used. Some times lattice spacing from gold nano-particles is also used as standard. Once, the magnification is calibrated, images are collected at various magnifications depending on sizes of structures under study. The key is that a large number of images of particles/structures need to be collected so as to draw a histogram. Following this, histogram is fit to an appropriate distribution functions (like Gaussian or Log-Normal, etc) and average size and error are determined.

(B) Determination of Crystalline Structure: Value of "D", Inter-Planar Spacing

A schematic diagram showing the geometry of diffraction pattern formation and may consider the much simpler ray diagram shown in Figure 2. This is necessary to get the crystallographic information about the specimen.

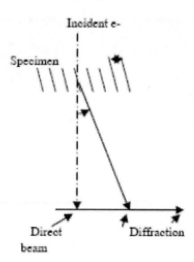

Figure 3. A schematic diagram showing the geometry of diffraction pattern formation.

A beam of electrons impinges on a crystalline specimen. Some of the electrons will pass through the specimen without interaction (direct beam) and heat the phosphor screen which is at a distance L (camera length) from specimen. Other electrons are diffracted through an angle 2θ by the crystal planes of spacing d, and hit the phosphor screen at a distance R, from the direct beam. According to Bragg's law of diffraction, the diffracted beam follows the relation $2d \sin \theta = \lambda$ which can be simplified for the small angle diffraction as $\lambda d = 2\theta$. From the trigonometric relation (again for the small angle approximation) we can write $R/L = 2\theta$. Combining these two, we find $d = \lambda L/R$. We use Image J software for the purpose of determining the values of "R" in diffraction pattern or lattice spacing from high resolution images [7]. Also, Gatan Microscopy Suite (or equivalent) can be used [6]. As the L and λ are constant for the instrument, the quantity $L\lambda$ is called camera constant. If we know the camera constant, then we can determine d simply by measuring R on the pattern. It is to be noted that L is not a physical distance between the specimen and screen, but is a notional distance which can be changed by the microscopist. Now to measure d from DP and lattice spacing from HR image, we need to measure R from DP and the distance between two consecutive fringes from HR image. Image J software helps to measure this more accurately by plotting the line profile of either diffraction spots or lattice fringes. The use of Image J for the DP and HR image has shown in Figure 4. The figure 4(a) and (b) are the DP and corresponding line profile of diffraction spots of same planes. Now the distance between two peaks will give R. For the HR image, the line profile should be perpendicular to the fringes. The lattice fringes and the corresponding line profile have been shown in figure 4(c) and (d), respectively. The d-spacing is now the distance between two peaks (or dips). It is better to take the fringes into account as much as possible in the line profile plotting to reduce the statistical error. The width of the peak also contributes to the error. So the better lattice image gives a narrower peak which will give the d-spacing with relatively less error. The analysis of particle size distribution can also be analyzed with this software.

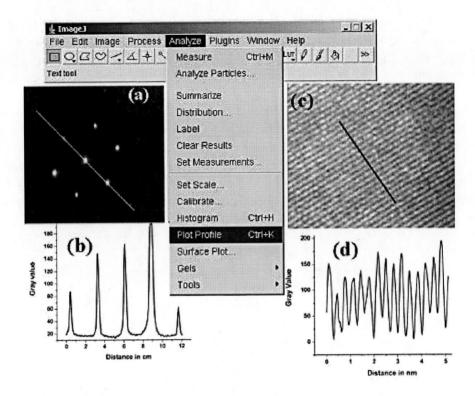

Figure 4. The use of Image J software: (a) and (b) are the diffraction pattern and corresponding line profile; (c) and (d) are the TEM lattice image and the corresponding line profile.

Sample Preparation

The sample preparation is the most crucial part of the TEM characterization. As the electrons transmit through the specimen, the specimen has to thin down to the electron transparency ($\approx$100 nm) for conventional TEM and even lesser $\approx$ 10 nm)for HRTEM. There are two types of samples to be prepared depending on the interest of study. The cross-sectional TEM (XTEM) sample is required to probe the interface and/or bulk solid, while the planar TEM specimen preparation is required to probe the surface morphology. For both the cases mechanical thinning followed by ion milling is required. For any TEM, the specimen should be 3 mm disc and that is why for both the cases, before thinning and ion milling, one need to make the specimen in that shape. The mechanical thinning starts with a rough emery paper with larger grit size and ends with an emery paper with finer grit size in South Bay technology (SBT), made lapping and polishing system (LPS) (model 910). Then the specimen again is thinned and polished by diamond paste and alumina suspension in Gatan made dimple grinder (DG) system (model 656). In this process, the edge remains thicker but center part becomes dimpled. After that specimen must be ion milled until the electron transparency is achieved. This is done with the Gatan made precision ion polishing systems (PIPS) (model 691). During PIPS, 3–5 keV Ar ion beam used to sputter the material from the specimen in grazing incidence ($4°–7°$). In figure 5 (a), the procedure of planar specimen is depicted pictorially. First of all, one needs to cut main sample into 3 mm discs using ultrasonic disc cutter. Then the disc is thinned down to ≈100 μm using LPS and further dimpled and polished to a final thickness of 30–50 μm using DG. The electron transparency was achieved in PIPS. In Figure 5(b), the procedure of XTEM specimen is depicted pictorially. First of all, one needs to cut main sample into two rectangular pieces of size 2.5×3 mm² each using SBT made Abrasive Slurry saw (model 850). Then the pieces are glued face to face (desired surface should face each other) using Gatan G1 epoxy and again glued the pieces with two silicon dummy pieces with similar dimension, as shown in figure 5(b). Now the assembly becomes 2×2.5×3 mm³ (assuming the entire piece is 0.5 mm thick). Then this was put in stainless steel cylinder with inner and out diameters are 2.5 and 3 mm. Then we made a 1 mm slice out of it, using SBT made Low speed diamond wheel Saw (model 650) and repeated the procedure as required for planar specimen. But in this case one needs to perform those steps for both side excluding only dimpling for one side.

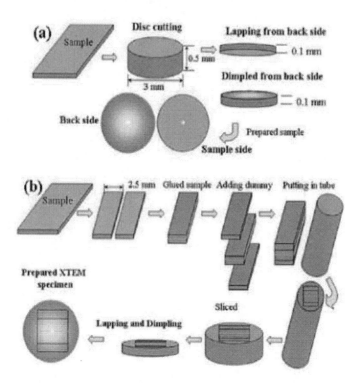

Figure 5. A schematic diagram of the procedure of (a) planar and (b) cross-sectional sample preparation for TEM.

Ion – Solid **Interactions at** *Nanoscale* **Regime:**

Understanding structure – property relationship of nanostructures can facilitate many important applications in various fields of advanced technology. The semiconductors, particularly Si, thin films on Si, doping and modifications of properties of Si with energetic ions, have been extensively studied. Nanostructures of variety of semiconductors, prepared by chemical methods are also being studied by large groups and have been finding enormous applications in various fields of industry due to their unique properties. Understanding the structure of these nanomaterials has become an interesting area of research activity, as the structural properties get modified due to its low-dimensionality and due to the quantum confinement effects. The energetic ions have been used from doping to change the electrical properties semiconductors, synthesizing new structures, coating thin films, mixing immiscible layers and for characterizing the materials. The process of ion-irradiation is an athermal or non-equilibrium thermal process and hence the properties of nanostructures could be tailored, which are otherwise difficult or not feasible by conventional methods. For example, ion induced shape changes have been reported. For these ion induced modification studies, the ion energies ranging from hundreds of eV to MeV, with various projectile ions, have been used.

When an energetic ion impinges on a solid material, many interesting phenomena can occur, like sputtering of target material, surface and interface morphological changes, etc [8]. Until now, not much effort has been given on involved mechanisms to understand various processes during an energetic ion interaction with nanoparticles or embedded nanostructures. All the spike models involve a confined region where the energy or pressure or temperature arising because of ion impact is confined to nanometer zones. It requires a systematic study on ion irradiation with a control on separating nuclear regime and electronic energy loss regimes and under various irradiation parameters like fluence, dose-rate (flux), substrate temperature, and geometry. While the phenomena at surface and interfaces are yet to be properly understood, the ion-solid interaction for the case isolated nanoislands has become an important topic [9 – 12]. For example, in the case of ion-nanosolid interaction, sputtering, burrowing and wetting are competitive mechanisms for nanoparticles that are immiscible with the substrate to undergo smoothing reactions [10].

In this paper, we review the effects of ion irradiation to modify nanostructures that are deposited on surfaces. Gold ions of energy 1.5 MeV have been used to bombard Au nanostructures grown on silicon substrate. Our result show (i) higher probability of crater formation, (ii) larger particle size and its coverage, and (iii) enhanced sputtering yield when compared with bombardment of continuous films of Au on Si substrate [13 – 15]. The average sputtered particle size and areal coverage was determined from transmission electron microscopy (TEM) measurements where as the amount of gold on the substrate has been found by Rutherford backscattering spectrometry (RBS). The other important aspects of ion-induced effects on nanostructures: (i) effect of energy/thermal spike confinement causing nano-scale ion beam mixing and formation of nanoscale gold silicide structures (this might provide a route to fabricate embedded nanostructures) (ii) absence of this behavior in case of continuous Au film on silicon for low flux irradiation [16]. But at high flux, irradiation effects change drastically for the same systems [17 – 19]. We report enhanced diffusion of gold atoms from gold films of various thicknesses (that are deposited on Si) due to 1.5 MeV Au^{2+} ion impacts under high flux conditions [18]. The maximum depths of mass transport have been found to be 95, 160 and 13 nm for the cases of 5.3, 10.9 and 27.5 nm thick gold films, respectively, at a fluence of 1×10^{14} ions cm^{-2}. Interestingly, at a higher fluence of 1×10^{15} ions cm^{-2}, gold atoms from the 27.5 thick films are transported to a maximum depth of 265 nm in the substrate. The enhanced diffusion for various film thicknesses is consistent with the recoil profiles of Au atoms into Si, which are obtained using SRIM simulations [20]. These results have been explained on the basis of the ion-beam-induced flux-dependent amorphous nature of the substrate, and transient beam-induced temperature effects. This work also confirms the absence of ion-induced spike confinement effects that might arise from the morphological nature of the isolated nanostructures.

Experimental Methods

For the work reported here, Au films of about $\approx$ 1.95, 4.7, 5.3, 10.9 and 27.5 nm thickness were deposited at room temperature by thermal evaporation under high-vacuum conditions onto Si(100) substrates. A $\approx$ 2 nm thick native oxide was present on Si(111) substrates. The substrates were cleaned with deionized water followed by rinsing in methanol and acetone prior to deposition. The thickness of each Au film was determined using Rutherford backscattering spectrometry (RBS) measurements and using simulations [21, 22]. During the simulations, the density of bulk Au was used to obtain the thickness values. The high flux irradiations were carried out with 1.5 MeV Au^{2+} ions and with an ion flux 6.3×10^{12} ions cm^{-2} s^{-1} (corresponding to a current density of 2.0 μA cm^{-2}). The lower flux irradiations were carried out with 1.5 MeV Au^{2+} ions and with an ion flux 1.3×10^{11} ions cm^{-2} s^{-1}. During the irradiation, the substrates were kept at room temperature. The fluences were varied from 1 $\times 10^{14}$ to 1×10^{15} ions cm^{-2}. The substrates were oriented 5° off normal to the incident beam to suppress the channeling effects. The RBS measurements were carried out with 2.5 MeV He^{+} ions at normal incidence. It is important to note that the projected ranges (determined using SRIM simulation) of 1.5 MeV Au^{2+} ions in Au and Si are $\approx$96 and 320 nm, respectively [20]. This implies that the impinging gold ions would penetrate deep into the Si substrate, much more than the average height of the Au layers for all cases. The maximum depth of diffusion of gold atoms in silicon was found to be 265 nm on the basis of TEM measurements [18]. Hence the mass transport that was observed is not from the impinging ions. A $\approx$2.0 nm thick native oxide layer was present on the substrate surface prior to these depositions. The irradiation has been carried out with 1.5 MeV Au^{2+} ions (at Ion Beam Laboratory, Institute of Physics, Bhubaneswar) at various impact angles and a raster scanning has been used for uniform irradiation. High flux irradiations were carried out using the 1.7 MV accelerator at IGCAR, Kalpakkam. The Rutherford backscattering spectrometry measurements were carried out with 1.35 MeV and 2.0 MeV He^{2+} ions.

RESULTS AND DISCUSSIONS:

(I) Sputtering from AU Nanostructures:

Sputtering by ions beams can be used to control fabrication of nanostructures: could be nanoparticles, clusters or nano-thin films. Sputtering phenomena is basically particle ejection from a target due to an energetic ion/atom bombardment. The sputtering yield is defined as the number atoms ejected per one impinging ion. Figure 6(a) and (b) show schematic representation of the sputtering from uniform and non-uniform thin films.

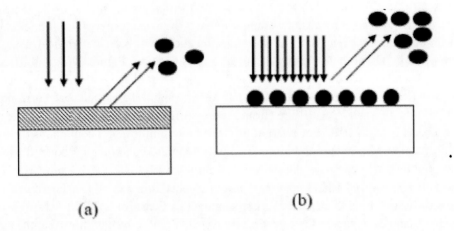

Figure 6. Schematic representation of sputtering process using energetic ion beams: (a) Nano-particles (clusters) ejected from continuous, uniform thin films (b) Sputter particles ejection from nano-disperse (non – uniform) films on a substrate.

Sputtering from isolated islands corresponds to non-uniform thin film case and continuous and thick film case corresponds to uniform film case. The particle size, size distribution, areal coverage and other structural aspects are determined using transmission electron microscopy measurements (high resolution TEM). The sputtering yield is determined by using the Rutherford backscattering spectrometry method.

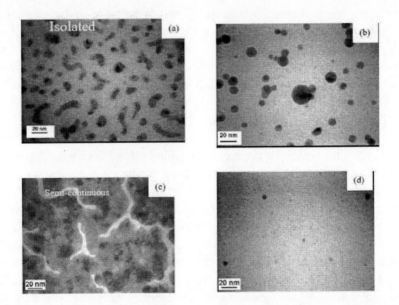

Figure 7. TEM micrographs for (a) as-deposited 1.95 nm thick Au film on silicon substrate (sample A) (b) as-deposited 4.5 nm thick Au film on silicon substrate (sample B) (c) sputtered particles collected from sample A, irradiated with 1.5 MeV Au ions to a fluence of 1×10^{14} ions cm^{-2} (d) sputtered particles collected from sample B, irradiated with 1.5 MeV Au ions to a fluence of 1×10^{14} ions cm^{-2} [From Ref. 15, Copyright (2003) by Elsevier].

Figure 7(a) and (b) show bright field planar TEM micrographs for (a) as-deposited 1.95 nm thick Au film on silicon substrate (sample A) and (b) as-deposited 4.7 nm thick Au film on silicon substrate (sample B). The effective thickness has been determined using RBS measurements by taking bulk density of Au into consideration. Figures 7(c) and (d) shown sputtered particles collected from sample A and sample B, irradiated with 1.5 MeV Au ions to a fluence of 1×10^{14} ions cm^{-2}, respectively. The average sputtered particle size corresponding to the 1.95 thick film is 12.3 ± 0.1 nm (from Figure 7(c)) with normalized island coverage on the catcher foil being $\approx 19\%$. For a target that was more uniform and continuous (schematic Figure 6(c) and TEM micrograph Figure 7(b)), under similar condition as above, the average sputtered (particle size corresponding to the 4.5 nm thick film is 2.3 ± 0.1 nm (from Figure 7(d)) and the normalized island coverage on the catcher foil was $\approx 4\%$. For much higher thickness of Au (21.4 nm thick), the average sputtered particle size is 2.95 ± 0.1 nm, with the normalized island coverage on the catcher foil being 1%. These results show that the average sputtered particle size obtained from the ion bombardment of isolated – nanoislands, if found to be much larger for continuous films. More details can be obtained from the reference [15].

Figures 8(a) and (c) shows the TEM micrograph of sputtered Au particles, collected on catcher grid at fluxes of 6.3×10^{11} and 6.3×10^{12} ions cm^{-2} s^{-1}, respectively, at a fluence of 1×10^{15} ions cm^{-2},. Fig 8(b) and (d) are the corresponding size distribution of sample (a) and (c) respectively. The average particle size was found to be 8.9 ± 1.9 nm for low flux irradiation conditions (6.3×10^{11} ions cm^{-2} s^{-1}) and 3.3 ± 1.9 nm and 9.8 ± 1.3 nm under high flux (6.3×10^{12} ions cm^{-2} s^{-1}) irradiation conditions. Interestingly, a bimodal distribution has been found, in case of irradiation with 6.3×10^{12} ions cm^{-2} s^{-1} (Figure 8(d)). At lower fluences, but with high flux, the sputtered particle size found to be more (data not shown). This is because the sputtered particle size depends on the substrate conditions. It is to be noted that the width of the distribution is minimum in case of irradiation with 6.3×10^{12} ions cm^{-2} s^{-1} [19].

Enhanced Diffusion in Substrate under High Flux Conditions:

The study of diffusion of noble metals in crystalline silicon has been actively pursued due to various technological applications and associated fundamental issues. As the electronic device size shrinking to nanometer regime, a better understanding of the effect of material interfaces at nanoscale regime on atomic processes is necessary. Gold is widely used in electronic devices to control the base minority-carrier life time due to its ability to act as a recombination centre when dissolved in silicon [23]. In the fabrication of such devices, gold is introduced into silicon wafers by high temperature diffusion process following vacuum evaporation of metallic gold on the surfaces. It is also well known that gold thin films act as contact layers in many systems for electronic measurements. Hence, the diffusion of gold atoms in crystalline silicon play important role. Two mechanisms, namely, "Frank-Turnbull" mechanism [24] and "kick-out" mechanism [25] have been used to explain the gold atoms diffusion in crystalline silicon. In case of amorphous silicon, the Au diffusion was explained in terms of direct diffusion in which the diffusing Au atoms are temporarily trapped by different kind of vacancy-liked effect [26, 27].

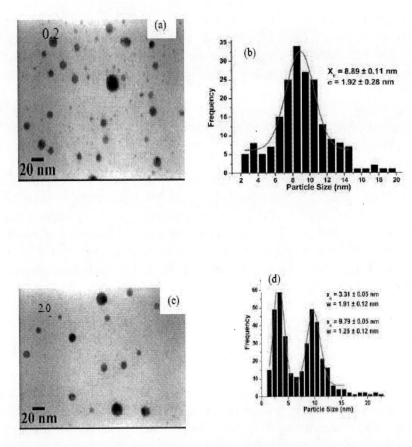

Figure 8. Flux dependent sputtering from ion irradiation from nanostructures: (a) shows the TEM micrograph of sputtered Au particles collected on catcher grid at fluxes of 0.2 μA cm^{-2} at a fluence of 1x10^{15} ions cm^{-2} (b) corresponding sputtered particle size distribution of (a); and (b) shows the TEM micrograph of sputtered Au particles collected on catcher grid at fluxes of 2.0 μA cm^{-2} at a fluence of 1x10^{15} ions cm^{-2} (b) corresponding sputtered particle size distribution of (c) [from Ref. 19, Reprinted from Ghatak, J.; Sundaravel, B.; Nair, K.G.M.; Satyam, P. V. *Journal of Physics D: Applied Physics* 2008, 41, 165302, Copyright (2008), Institute of Physics].

In general, at high enough temperatures, the amorphous silicon recrystallizes and hence it would be difficult to study of the diffusion of gold atoms in *a*–Si at these high temperatures. Past investigations of Au-implanted silicon have suggested that the gold segregation as a result of its being expelled from the recrystallized amorphous layer during thermal and ion beam annealing [28, 29]. It has been experimentally shown that the Au solid-solubility [30] and diffusivity [31, 32] in crystalline silicon (*c*-Si) is *lower* than that in amorphous silicon (*a*-Si). In the study of precipitation of implanted atoms, both the segregation and diffusion of gold atoms has been found to play role. When the implanted Au concentration exceeds the local solubility, Au precipitates were expelled from the matrix resulting segregation into densely defect regions and the diffusing Au reaches a dislocation-node where it exceeds the local threshold for precipitation and the Au therefore precipitates [33].

At low flux (1.3x10^{11} ions cm^{-2} s^{-1}), previously, it was observed that ion beam mixing (IBM) occurs for Au nanostructures deposited on Si after irradiation with 1.5 MeV Au^{2+} at a fluence of 1x10^{14} ions cm^{-2} with an impact angle of 60^{0}. It is to be noted that, at lower impact angle IBM did not observe at same irradiation condition [16]. Figure 9(a) corresponds to the high resolution cross-sectional TEM image of pristine Au nanostructured thin film, deposited on Si. ≈2 nm native oxide is clearly revealed. Figure 9(b) and (c) correspond to the low magnification (Figure (b)) and high resolution (Figure (c)) TEM images of the irradiated (condition as mentioned above) system.

At higher fluxes (6.3×10^{12} ions cm^{-2} s^{-1}), we have observed the variation of sputtered particle size and their size distributions. At these high flux values, a direct observation of dramatic mass transport due to 1.5 MeV Au^{2+} ion impact has been observed from isolated Au nanostructures (with an average size ~ 7.6 nm and height ~ 6.9 nm) deposited on Si (111) substrate. Irradiations were carried out under high flux (3.2×10^{10} to 6.3×10^{12} ions cm^{-2} s^{-1}) conditions. The nanostructures were formed as a result of non-wetting nature of thin gold film of thickness ≈ 2.0 nm on the native oxide covered surface. The XTEM measurements showed maximum mass transport into the substrate extending upto a distance of about 60 nm, much beyond the size of the nanostructures, present on the surface (the mass transport has been attributed to the radiation enhanced diffusion) [17]. The unusual mass transport was also found to be associated with the formation of gold silicide nanoalloys at sub-surfaces [18].

In this work, we present the enhanced mass transport from various thicknesses of gold films, deposited on silicon, under high flux conditions. The variation in thickness for gold films results in variation in the surface morphology. In as-deposited systems, for thin films (for ~ 5.3 nm thick gold films) isolated gold nanostructures were observed while for thick films (10.9 and 27.5 nm thick films) uniform and continuous layers were observed. In our previous work, on low flux irradiation experiments, while explaining the enhanced crater formation from nanostructures, we had proposed a possibility of ion-induced energy spike in the nanostructures, that is arising due to the spatially confined structures [16].

Figures in 10(a) and (b) are the bright field XTEM images of pristine 5.3 and 10.9 nm Au on Si (111) substrates. For the pristine film of thickness 5.3 nm, XTEM images show large isolated nanostructures, as shown in Figure 10 (a), while for the film thickness of 10.9 nm, the uniformity and the coverage area of gold nanostructures increases.

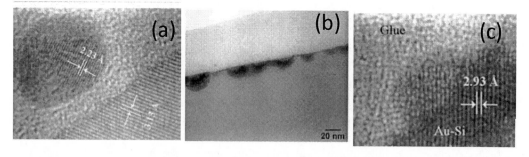

Figure 9. (a) corresponds to the high resolution cross-sectional TEM image of pristine Au nanostructured thin film deposited on Si. (b) and (c) correspond to the low magnification and high resolution TEM images of the irradiated system. Irradiation has been carried out with 1.5 MeV Au^{2+} at a fluence of 1×10^{14} ions cm^{-2} with an impact angle of 60 degree (from ref. 16, Reprinted with kind permission from Satpati, B.; Satyam, P.V.; Som, T. and Dev, B.N. *J. Appl. Phys* 2004, 96, 5212; *Appl. Phys. A* 2004, 79, 447, Copyright [2004], Springer Publishing.).

The irradiation effects at a fluence of 1×10^{14} ions cm^{-2} with flux 6.3×10^{12} ions cm^{-2} s^{-1} are shown in Figures 10(c) and (d) for 5.3 and 10.9 nm gold on Si(111) samples, respectively.

For these two cases, enhanced diffusion has been observed from the top gold layer into the Si substrate. In the case of 5.3 nm Au/Si system, the maximum depth for Au atoms diffused in to Si substrates has been found to be ~ 95 nm, whereas, the maximum transported depth of 160 nm has been found for 10.9 nm Au/Si systems (Figure 10(d)). That means the irradiation effects in 10.9 nm thick Au on Si system shows the more mass transport into Si than both the 2.0 nm and 5.3 nm thick gold films cases. The contrast that is seen in the bright field images (Figure 10(c) and (d)) has been attributed to the contribution from the diffused gold atoms (i.e. presence of gold atoms at larger depth in the interfacial region). These observations reveal that the amount of mass transport (and maximum depth) increases with the increase of top Au layer thickness, ruling out the confinement effects that are due to size of the nanostructures. Figure 10(e) corresponds to the selected area electron diffraction (SAED) pattern taken from the implanted region (circular region of Figure 10(d)) of 10.9 nm Au on Si system and this confirms the amorphization of the Si substrate at this fluence. This is also the same with the irradiated system of 5.3 nm thick film case. Hence, the diffusion that has been observed is attributed to the amorphous nature of silicon substrate. Interestingly, even if the gold atoms were present at the interface, and if the defect concentration of the substrate is not sufficient to drive the diffusion process, then the mass transport would be limited. This aspect would be discussed in the following. Figure 10(f) is taken from the rectangular region (near surface) of Figure 10(d), for irradiated 10.9 nm Au/Si system. The selected region show crystalline in nature with the lattice spacing corresponding to 0.304 ± 0.005 nm. This indicates the formation of Au_5Si_2 phase. The gold silicide phase formation indicates that the mass transport is associated with the thermal reaction. More details about the silicide formation have been reported elsewhere [17, 34].

The role of the crystalline nature of the substrate for the enhanced diffusion of gold atoms is evident from the mass transport studies of a thicker gold film (of thickness 27.5 nm thick on silicon). Figure 11(a) depicts the bright field XTEM micrographs for pristine Au film thickness of 27.5 nm. The TEM measurements show that the morphology of the Au film is continuous, unlike the thinner films case (5.3 and 10.9 nm thick). Figures 11(b) and (c) are the XTEM micrographs of the irradiated 27.5 nm Au/Si systems with a beam flux $6.3x10^{12}$ ions cm^{-2} s^{-1} at fluence $1x10^{14}$ and $1x10^{15}$ ions cm^{-2} respectively. Interestingly, for the case of 27.5 nm Au/Si system, we have observed a mass transport up to a maximum depth of only ~13 nm (see figure 2(b)) at a fluence $1x10^{14}$ ions cm^{-2}. It is to be noted that, at this fluence ($1x10^{14}$ ions cm^{-2}) and flux ($6.3x10^{12}$ ions cm^{-2} s^{-1}), a large mass transport was observed in thinner films (5.3 and 10.9 nm thick Au/Si systems). The mass transport has been increased dramatically upto 265 nm for this case at fluence $1x10^{15}$ ions cm^{-2} as shown in figure 11(c). The inset of figure 11(c) is the SAED from the implanted region of the substrate and indicates that the substrate up to projected range is completely amorphous. The lattice spacing of high resolution TEM image taken from the rectangular region of figure 11(c) again indicates the formation of Au-Si alloy, as mentioned earlier for figure 10(f). From the high-resolution XTEM measurements for all the above-mentioned samples, we conclude that high flux MeV ion irradiation leads to alloy formation for various thickness of Au films on Si, which was absent during the irradiation at low flux ($1.3x10^{11}$ ions cm^{-2} s^{-1}) conditions [16].

As the mass transport in case of 27.5 nm sample is small at a fluence $1x10^{14}$ ions cm^{-2}, to confirm Au transportation into Si, XTEM and RBS measurements on aqua rezia (HNO_3 : HCL = 1:3) treated irradiated sample were carried out. After irradiation, we have etched the top Au layer with aqua rezia which is known to etch pure Au. Figure 11(d) is the BF XTEM of the aqua rezia treated sample that was irradiated at a fluence of 1×10^{14} ions cm^{-2}.

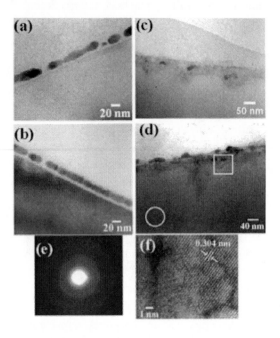

Figure 10. Cross-sectional bright field TEM micrographs for pristine Au/Si systems: (a) 5.3 nm and (b) 10.9 nm Au/Si system. In all the samples ≈ 2.0 nm native oxide is present. (c) and (d) correspond to the irradiated 5.3 nm and 10.9 nm Au/Si systems respectively. In all samples, irradiations were carried out with 1.5 MeV Au^{2+} ions at a fluence of 1×10^{14} ions cm^{-2} with a flux 6.3×10^{12} ions cm^{-2} s^{-1}. (e) The SAED pattern shows the amorphous nature of the implanted region of the substrate. (f) The high resolution cross sectional bright field TEM image of rectangular region of figure (d) (from ref. 18, Reprinted with permission from Ghatak, J.; Sundaravel, B.; Nair, K. G. M. and Satyam, P. V. *J. Phys.: Condens. Matter* 2008, 20, 485008. Copyright [2008], IOP Publishing).

This confirms the absence of Au on the surface and the presence of Au-Si alloy embedded in Si (it is to be noted that the aqua rezia does not etch gold silicide). Figure 11(e) is the RBS spectra for pristine, as–irradiated and aqua rezia etched samples. RBS measurements have been carried out using 1.35 MeV He^+ ions. For the sake of visualization, only Au signal for aqua rezia treated sample has been magnified (multiplied by a factor of 10). From the spectra, it is evident that there is presence of Au, even after aqua rezia treatment as well. The shift of Si edge to higher energy and the shift of Au edge to lower energy confirm the presence of Au embedded in to the Si, rather presence of Au layer on Si surface. This is in agreement with XTEM measurements.

The XTEM measurements in the case of 5.3 and 10.9 nm Au/Si system show the average film thickness of about 15.0 and 17.5 nm respectively. The nuclear energy loss and the electronic energy loss for 1.5 MeV Au ions in Au are 9.5 keV/nm and 2.5 keV/nm, respectively [16]. The total energy loss in 15.0 nm Au target (5.3 nm Au/Si systems) by 1.5 MeV Au ions is 180 keV which comes out to be less than the energy required for the Au atoms to reach the depth of 95 nm inside Si (300 keV) [20]. Hence, the TRIM simulation cannot explain the mass transport happens in 5.3 nm Au/Si system and so as the case with other thicknesses. The mass transportation to a depth of 13 nm for high flux and low fluence

$(1 \times 10^{14}$ ions cm^{-2}) can be considered as recoil or ballastically mixed events. From the present and earlier experimental results [17, 18], it appears that recoil of Au atoms from the top Au layer is highly influenced by the ion beam flux and the substrate amorphization and, at constant fluence, there exist a critical flux below which recoil is not noticeable.

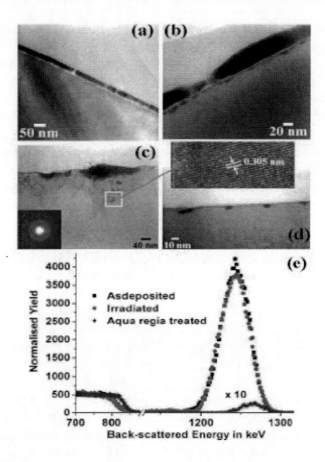

Figure 11: (a) The XTEM micrograph of pristine 27.5 nm Au/Si. (b) and (c) are the XTEM micrographs of 27.5 nm Au/Si after irradiated at a fluence of 1×10^{14} and 1×10^{15} ions cm^{-2} respectively. Inset of figure (c) depicts the SAED pattern after irradiation from the implanted region of the Si substrate. The high resolution XTEM image was taken from the rectangular region of figure (f) which is shown by arrow mark. (d) The XTEM micrograph of aqua rezia etched irradiated sample while the fluence was 1×10^{14} ions cm^{-2}. (e) The RBS spectra of irradiated 27.5 nm Au/Si systems before and after aqua rezia treatment. All the irradiations were carried out with 1.5 MeV Au^{2+} ions at a constant flux of 6.3×10^{12} ions cm^{-2} s^{-1} (from ref. 18, Reprinted with permission from Ghatak, J.; Sundaravel, B.; Nair, K. G. M. and Satyam, P. V. *J. Phys.: Condens. Matter* 2008, 20, 485008. Copyright [2008], IOP Publishing).

The incident beam flux can affect diffusion in two ways: amorphization and wafer temperature. It is known that in semiconductors, defect concentration increases with the increase of ion flux, which causes the amorphization faster (at lower fluence with higher flux) [35]. That means at a given temperature, with higher flux, lower fluence is needed to achieve amorphization, whereas with lower flux, the defect concentration has to be compensated with higher fluence [36]. From the previous flux dependent study, the amorphization has been observed at fluence 6×10^{13} ions cm^{-2} with ion flux 6.3×10^{12} ions cm^{-2} s^{-1} [17], which is less compared to the earlier observations [37] and hence we may infer that the higher flux leads to the faster amorphization in the present case also. This is so, as the displacements production (vacancy-interstitial pair) rate is proportional to the incident ion flux [38]. In the present experimental condition, beam heating is also a crucial factor for the mass transport as it mediates through diffusion. We have estimated the wafer temperature during irradiation [17], using the experimentally verified prescription given by Nakata [39]. For the flux 6.3×10^{12} ions cm^{-2} s^{-1}, the temperature rises due to fluences 1×10^{14} (irradiation time ~15 sec) and 1×10^{15} ions cm^{-2} (~150 sec) are 1150 and 1155 K, respectively. These estimates are useful for obtaining possible temperature rise. In future, we plan to study to measure the sample temperature using an appropriate sensor.

One can divide the diffusion in to two regimes: temperature dependent (thermal diffusion) and temperature independent (radiation enhanced diffusion). In the temperature dependent regime, thermal diffusivity is proportional to the substrate temperature. There is a critical temperature (T_c) exists, above which the radiation enhanced diffusion (RED) will be significant [40]. It is to be noted that $T_c = 422$ K for Au-Si case [41] which is less than the wafer temperature during irradiation due to beam heating and hence the phenomenon is strongly influenced by RED of recoiled Au atoms. Now the temperature of the wafer is high enough even when the substrate is partially amorphous (low flux irradiation or irradiation in higher thickness film) but the diffusivity of Au in a-Si is more than that of c-Si [31, 32]. This is due to the excess displacements created due to higher beam flux, guide the recoiled Au atoms to migrate in the substrate as a substitutional (kick-out mechanism) [25] and create rapid diffusion paths. Hence, during irradiation, as soon as the amorphization takes place in Si substrate, the diffusivity of recoiled Au atoms increases drastically. The transport atoms may be roughly estimated from a diffusion length of marker layer model, due to ballistic cascade mixing [42]. Considering the values of diffusivity D_{cas} ~ 700 nm^2 sec^{-1} at T ~1000K [31], average deposited energy $F_D(x) = 1761$ eV nm^{-1} [20], the transported depth comes out to be ~ 250 nm which is fairly matches with our observed transported depth and justifies the consideration of diffusion phenomenon associated with the mass transport. The difference in transported depth for different film thickness will be discussed in the following section.

From the results for various thicknesses of Au films, it is clear that the distributed depth of Au atoms is not similar for all the systems. In figure 12, we have plotted the TRIM simulation [20] of Au recoil distribution of 2.0, 5.0, 10.0 and 27.5 nm system, due to 1.5 MeV Au at normal incidence. In the inset of Figure 12, the zoomed recoil distribution of Au only into the Si for all above-mentioned Au film thickness is shown. It is clear from the figure that the amount of Au into Si (number of recoiled Au atoms per unit length (depth) of Si) is more in higher film thickness. So, if the available number of recoiled Au atoms is more to be diffused, then the volume of redistributed region will be more (as the stoichiometry of mixed regions remain Au_5Si_2) and hence the transportation depth also will be more. But one has to take the amorphization into account. For the same energetic ion beam, there will be different onset fluence for complete amorphization of Si substrates with Au films of different thicknesses. This is due to the fact that, with thicker film, nuclear energy loss inside the film will be more and hence higher fluence is needed for complete amorphization of the Si substrate. Hence, there will be a definite difference in defect concentration for different thicknesses of film at same fluence. As we have already discussed that diffusion is very much influenced by the nature of the substrate (in terms of defect concentration in the substrate). Similar conclusion is also available from the experiment of Ehrhard et. al, with a thick Au layer deposited on c-Si, a-Si and partially a-Si [27]. It was clearly shown in these experiments that Au diffusion from top Au layer is more in a-Si than in c-Si and any intermediate crystalline layer (that is partially a-Si) will suppress the effect. Hence, the depth of mass transport or diffusion region is more at fluence 1×10^{15} ions cm^{-2} than that of 1×10^{14} ions cm^{-2} in case of 27.5 nm Au/Si systems.

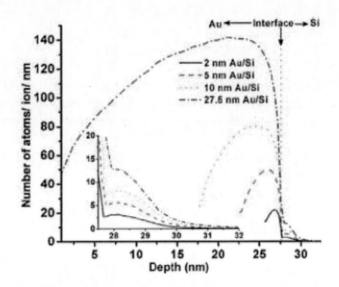

Figure 12. SRIM profile for Au recoil distribution due to 1.5 MeV Au ions. The Au thickness have been used in the simulation are 2, 5, 10 and 27.5 nm. Inset corresponds to the zoomed recoil distribution of Au only into the Si for all above mentioned of Au films (from ref. 18, Reprinted with permission from Ghatak, J.; Sundaravel, B.; Nair, K. G. M. and Satyam, P. V. *J. Phys.: Condens. Matter* 2008, 20, 485008. Copyright [2008], IOP Publishing).

We, therefore, propose the following mechanism to understand the enhanced diffusion of gold in silicon: (i) collision cascades drive gold atoms from the film into the substrate through ballistic mixing and recoil implantation processes. (ii) This is followed by amorphization in the substrate that occurs at lower fluence at high flux condition. (iii) The effective wafer temperature due to incident beam power, drives the mass transport (enhanced diffusion occurring for gold atoms in a-Si system).

CONCLUSIONS

The energetic ion beams found to show interesting observations for the case of ion – nanostructure compared to ion – bulk solid systems. A large sputtering was observed for the nanostructured thin films case while this being absent in uniform films at lower flux irradiations. We demonstrated the unusual mass transport for various thicknesses of Au films starting from nanoislands (5.3 nm Au/Si) to thick continuous film (27.5 nm Au/Si) due to MeV Au ion bombardment. The transported depth is found to be more for higher thickness of Au film, for example, about 265 nm for 27.5 nm Au/Si. Amount of recoiled Au atoms from the top Au layer is found to be more for higher thickness Au film and are consistent with the

TRIM simulation. Mass transport in all the samples starting with nanoislands to continuous thick layer suggests that the thermal spike confinement is insignificant in this issue when the substrate temperature is sufficiently high during high beam flux irradiation. High ion beam flux causes the faster amorphization and the rise in wafer temperature which help in faster diffusion of the recoiled Au atoms. Ion beam mixing can be achieved in thick continuous film also in case of Au-Si systems at high flux which was completely absent in earlier observations at low beam flux.

ACKNOWLEDGMENTS

We thank B. N. Dev, T. Som, B. Sundaravel and K. G. M. Nair for their valuable suggestions and help in the above works. We also would like to thank staff at IOP accelerator, IGCAR accelerator and IUAC accelerator for their co-operation during the ion irradiation effects.

REFERENCES

[1]   Williams, D. B.; Carter, C. Barry; *Transmission Electron Microscopy* Vol. I-IV (Plenum Press, New York, 1996).

[2]   Spence, J. C. H.; *High-resolution Electron Microscopy* (Oxford University Press 2003), 3rd Ed.

[3]   Fultz, B. and Howe, J. *Transmission Electron Microscopy and Diffractometry of Materials*, Springer 2005, 2nd Ed.

[4]   Batson, E.; Dellby, N.; Krivanek, O. L. *Nature* 2002, *418,* 61. Nellist, P. D.; Chisholm, M. F.; Dellby, N.; Krivanek, O. L.; Murfitt, M. F.; Szilagyi, Z. S.; Lupini, A. R.; Borisevich, A.; Sides, W. H. J.; Pennycook, S. J. *Science* 2004, 305, 5691.

[5]   M/S Jeol Ltd., Japan (www.jeol.com)

[6]   M/S Gatan Inc., USA (www.gatan.com)

[7]   It is a freeware available at http://rsbweb.nih.gov/ij/. A more detail documentation is available at http://www.macbiophotonics.ca/imagej/.

[8]   Nastasi M. and Mayer, J. W. *Ion implantation and synthesis of materials, Springer-Verlag* 2006 and references there in.

[9]   Dillen, T. van; Polman, A.; Fukarek, W. and Blaaderen, A. van; *App. Phys. Lett.* 2001, 78, 910.

[10]   Zhong, Y.; Ashkenazy, Y.; Albe, K. and Averback, R. S. *J. Appl. Phys.* 2003, 94, 4432.

[11]   Heining, K. –H.; Muller, T.; Schmidt, B.; Strobel, M. amd Moller, W. *Appl. Phys. A: Mater. Sci. Process. A* 2003, 77, 17.

[12]   Mantl, S. *Mater. Sci. Rep.* 1992, 8, 1.

[13]   Satyam, P. V.; Kamila, J.; Mohapatra, S.; Satpati, B.; Goswami, D. K.; Dev, B. N.; Cook, R. E.; Assoufid, L.; Wang, J. and Mishra, N. C. *J. App. Phys.* 2003, 93, 6399.

[14]   Satpati, B.; Goswami, D. K.; Vaishnav, U. D.; Som, T.; Dev, B. N. and Satyam, P. V. *Nucl. Instr. Meth. Phys. Res. B* 2003, 212, 157.

[15] Satpati, B.; Goswami, D. K.; Roy, S.; Som, T.; Dev , B. N. and Satyam, P. V. *Nucl. Instr. Meth. Phys. Res. B* 2003, 212, 332.

[16] Satpati, B.; Satyam, P.V.; Som, T. and Dev, B.N. *J. Appl. Phys* 2004, 96, 5212; *Appl. Phys. A* 2004, 79, 447.

[17] Ghatak, J.; Bhatta, U.M.; Sundaravel, B.; Nair, K.G.M.; Liou, Sz-C.; Chen, Cheng-Hsuan; Wang, Yuh-Lin; Satyam, P.V. *Nanotechnology* 2008, 19, 325602.

[18] Ghatak, J.; Sundaravel, B.; Nair, K. G. M. and Satyam, P. V. *J. Phys.: Condens. Matter* 2008, 20, 485008.

[19] Ghatak, J.; Sundaravel, B.; Nair, K.G.M.; Satyam, P. V. *Journal of Physics D: Applied Physics* 2008, 41, 165302.

[20] Biersack, J. P. and Haggmark, L. *Nucl. Instr. and Meth B.* 1980, 174, 257 (also refer: www.srim.org)

[21] Saarilahti, J. and Rauhala, E. *Nucl. Instr. and Meth. B* 1992, 64, 734.

[22] Mayer, M. Nucl. Instr. Meth. B 194 (2002) 177; Available at http://www.rzg.mpg.de/~mam.

[23] Bullis, W. M. *Solid-State Elctron*. 1966, 9, 143.

[24] Frank, F.C. and Turnbull, D. *Phys. Rev.* 1956, 104, 617.

[25] Gösele, U.; Frank, W. and Seeger, A. *Appl. Phys.* 1980, 23, 36.

[26] Coffa, S.; Poate, J.M.; Jacobson, D.C.; Frank, W. and Gustin, W. *Phys. Rev. B* 1992, 45, 8355; Frank, W *Defect and Diffusion Forum* 1997, 143-147, 695; Frank, W.; Gustin, W. and Horz, M. J. *Non-Cryst. Solids* 1996, 205–207, 208.

[27] Ehrhardt, J.; Klimmer, A.; Eisenmenger, J.; Muller, T.; Boyen, H G.; Ziemann, P.; Biskupek, J. and Kaiser, U. *J. Appl. Phys.* 2006, 100, 063534.

[28] Poate, J.M., Priolo, F.; Jacobson, D.C.; Batstone, J.L. and Thompson, M.O. *Nucl. Instrum. Methods B* 1989, 37–38, 955.

[29] Jacobson, D C.;, Poate, J. M. and Olson, G. L. Appl. Phys. Lett. 1986, 43, 118.

[30] Lindner, J.K.N.; Heckling , N. and Kaat, E. te *Nucl. Instrum. Methods B* 1987, 26, 551.

[31] Poate, J.M.; Jacobson, D.C.; Williams, J.S.; Elliman, R.G. and Boerma, D.O. *Nucl. Instrum. Methods Phys. Res. B* 1987, 19–20, 480.

[32] Priolo, F.; Poate, J M.; Jacobson, D C.; Linnros, J.; Batstone, J L. and Campisano, S. U. *Appl. Phys. Lett.* 1988, 52, 1213.

[33] Alford, T.L. and Theodore, N.D. *J. Appl. Phys.* 1994, 76, 7265.

[34] Tsaur, B.Y. and Mayer, J.W. *Philos. Mag.* 1981, 43A, 345.

[35] Haynes, T E. and Holland, O W *Appl. Phys. Lett.* 1991, 59, 452.

[36] Goldberg, R D.; Elliman, R G. and Williams, J S. *Nucl. Instrum. Methods Phys. Res. B* 1995, 106, 242.

[37] Kamila, J.; Satpati, B.; Goswami, D K.; Rundhe, M.; Dev, B N. and Satyam, P V. *Nucl. Instrum. and Meths. Phys. Res. B* 2003, 207, 291.

[38] Sigmund, P. *Appl. Phys. Lett.* 1969, 14, 169.

[39] Nakata, J. *Phys. Rev. B* 1991, 43, 14643.

[40] Matteson, S. *Radiation effects* 1979, 42, 217.

[41] Cheng, Y. T.; Zhao, X. A.; Banwell, T.; Workman, T. W.; Nicolet, M. A. and Johnson, W. L. *J. Appl. Phys.* 1986, 60, 2615.

[42] Sigmund, P. and Marti A G. *Nucl. Instrum. and Meths. B* 1981, 182/183, 25.

[43] Haynes, T E. and Holland, O W. *Appl. Phys. Lett.* 1991, *59*, 452.

[44] Goldberg, R D.; Elliman, R G. and Williams, J S. *Nucl. Instrum. Methods Phys. Res. B* 1995, *106,* 242.

[45] Kamila, J.; Satpati, B.; Goswami, D K.; Rundhe, M.; Dev, B N. and Satyam, P V. *Nucl. Instrum. and Meths. Phys. Res. B* 2003, *207,* 291.

[46] Sigmund, P. *Appl. Phys. Lett.* 1969, *14,* 169.

[47] Nakata, J. *Phys. Rev. B* 1991, *43,* 14643.

[48] Matteson, S. *Radiation effects* 1979, *42,* 217.

[49] Cheng, Y T.; Zhao, X A.; Banwell, T.; Workman, T W.; Nicolet, M A. and Johnson, W L. J. *Appl. Phys.* 1986, *60,* 2615

[50] Sigmund, P. and Gras-Marti, A. *Nucl. Instrum. and Meths.* B 1981, *182/183*, 25.

In: Synthesis and Engineering of Nanostructures…
Editors: Devesh Kumar Avasthi & Jean Claude Pivin

ISBN 978-1-62100-261-1
© 2012 Nova Science Publishers, Inc

Chapter 12

Synthesis and Study of Nanoscale Magnetic Semiconductor and Magnetic Metal/Insulator Films: Role of Energetic Ions

S. Ghosh

Nanostech Laboratory, Indian Institute of Technology, Hauz Khas,
New Delhi-110 016, India

Abstract

Nanoscale magnetic semiconductors and magnetic metal/insulator nanogranular films are under significant focus in materials science research because of their promising applications in spin-mediated devices. The upcoming technology where these materials are going to be used are, spintronics, opto-spintronics, data storage and sensors. Better performance of the devices depends on proper synthesis of these materials and engineering their properties. Ions with different energy ranges (eV – keV- MeV) play an important role in synthesis of these materials as well as modification of their properties for better performance. This review is divided in three sections. In the first section, a comprehensive review on diluted magnetic semiconductors (DMSs), transparent magnetic semiconductors (TMSs), their importance, mechanism behind ferromagnetism, ZnO based DMSs and importance of different magnetic metal-insulator nanocomposite is given. Role of energetic ions in each case is highlighted. The second section deals with experimental studies on synthesis and characterization of Ni implanted/doped ZnO films in the perspective of DMS/TMS. The results are discussed on the basis of carrier mediated exchange interaction and bound polaron model. In the third section, results on Ni-SiO$_2$ nanocomposite films grown by atom beam sputtering technique are discussed. An attempt has been made to correlate microstructure, composition and magnetic properties of these nanocomposite films. Finally, the results obtained in these studies are summarized and future research scopes are highlighted.

1. Introduction

Transition metal (TM) doped nanoscale zinc oxide (ZnO) films as a diluted magnetic semiconductor (DMS) and TM-insulator nanocomposite films have been attracted great research attention because of their promising applications in future spintronics, optospintronics, data storage, high frequency etc. devices. Ions of different energy scales play a crucial role in synthesis as well as modification of these materials. Low energy ion beam sputtering and ion implantation have been routinely used for synthesis of DMS as well as nanocomposites. Ions with mega electron volt energy or swift heavy ions (SHI) have been used to engineer the properties of these materials down to nanoscale.

This section of this review article deals with a brief survey of DMS materials, mechanism of ferromagnetism (FM) in these materials, ZnO based DMSs followed by important aspects of metal-insulator nanocomposite films and their importance. Role of energetic ions is also highlighted in each subsection.

1.1. Zinc Oxide Based Diluted Magnetic Semiconductor

In this subsection, we initially discuss different DMS materials, mechanism behind ferromagnetism followed by different studies on ZnO based DMSs and role of energetic ions in this field.

1.1.1. Diluted Magnetic Semiconductor: Material Aspects and Importance

The present day semiconductor electronic and optoelectronic devices utilize the charge degree of freedom in their wide functionality in signal processing or light emission. The future semiconductor spintronic and optospintronic devices exploit the spin degree of freedom of charge carrier in new generation of transistors, lasers and integrated magnetic sensors. The ability to control spin injection, transfer and detection with high efficiency demand their utilities in ultra-low power high speed memory, logic and photonic devices. For practical purpose, spintronic devices need to use semiconductors those maintain their magnetic properties at room temperature or above. This is a challenge, because most magnetic semiconductors lose their magnetic properties at temperatures well below room temperature and would require expensive and impractical refrigeration in order to use in practical applications. The major criteria for selection of semiconductor spintronics materials are (i) existence of ferromagnetism above 300 K, (ii) capability to tune the ferromagnetic properties, like saturation magnetisation (M_s), coercivity (H_c), remnant magnetisation (M_r) by changing dopants, their concentration, physical properties of the materials, micro/nanostructures etc. and (iii) integration in future device with much ease. Scientific venture on transition metal (TM) doped wide band gap semiconductors (like GaAs, ZnO, GaN) have attracted significant research attention due to their promising characteristics, which satisfy the criteria mentioned above. Among various wide band gap semiconducting materials, transition metal doped ZnO became the most extensively studied materials, since the prediction by Dietl *at al.* [1] based on mean field theory, indicate them promising candidate to realize a diluted magnetic semiconducting (DMS) material, with Curie temperature above room temperature. Another importance of these materials is that they can be readily incorporated in the existing semiconducting heterostructure system where a number of optical and electronic devices could be realized. The magnetic behaviour of such materials depends upon the concentration of TM ions in the crystal, the carrier density and the crystal quality. Generally, when 3d transition metal ions are substituted for the cations of the host, the resultant electronic structure is influenced by strong hybridazation of the 3d orbitals of the magnetic ion and mainly the p orbitals of the neighbouring host anions.

There are two interacting subsystems of DMS materials, namely the delocalized conduction band electrons and valance band holes and the randomly localized magnetic moments associated with the magnetic atoms. For practical application in spintronic devices, a high Curie temperature (T_C) is one of the most important issues of research and for proper design of these materials the mechanism behind ferromagnetism must be clearly understood.

1.1.2. Mechanism behind Ferromagnetism

Besides all experimental studies, various theoretical approaches have been taken under consideration to understand the ferromagnetism in these materials. The theory dealing with ferromagnetism driven by the exchange interaction between charge carriers and localized magnetic moments was first proposed by Zener [2]. The features of DMS are induced by the exchange interaction between d-shell electrons of the magnetic ions and the delocalized band carrier states (s or p origin). In recent days a large number of models, based on mean field theory, first principle calculation and bound magneton polaron etc. [3] have been proposed to explain the exchange interaction and the experimental results, although each has its own limitation. Broadly, ferromagnetism in ZnO based DMSs can be explained by two models. In case of materials having lower electrical resistance, charge carrier mediated exchange interaction fits well, whereas materials having higher resistance, model based on bound magnetic polaron (BMP) gives a proper explanation. In case of first mechanism, delocalized electrons mediate a strong exchange interaction between localized moments associated with transition metals. However, when carriers are mostly localized (depending upon semiconductor host and doped metal), BMP forms by the alignment of the spins of many transition metal ions with that of much lower number of weakly bound carriers such as excitons within a polaron radius. Formation of BMP (here, Ni doped ZnO) is schematically illustrated in Figure 1.1, which clearly shows that neighbouring polarons overlap (at a particular condition, depending on the concentration of TM and or temperature), forming a correlated cluster of polarons, which eventually gives rise to ferromagnetism in these systems. If the overlapping is maximum at room temperature (RT) a DMS can be obtained at RT. Some metal ions may not interact and stay in the system as isolated ions.

Due to the complexity of the DMS systems, based on ZnO and especially, the possible presence of secondary phase precipitates, it is still difficult to find an universal theory. Recently, strong influence of microstructure on RT-FM of TM doped ZnO has been demonstrated [4], which adds another new aspect to this problem. The effect of crystallite size and overall morphology on RT-FM of Ni doped nanodimensional ZnO film is observed by our group recently [5]. This particular effect needs to be addressed in theory and therefore requires detailed investigations with more planned experiments. At this stage, it would be fair to state that the models on TM doped ZnO and GaN is still in the stage of its infancy and it is too early to give a definitive description of the exact mechanism, governing the experimental observations regarding the origin of reported magnetization behaviour.

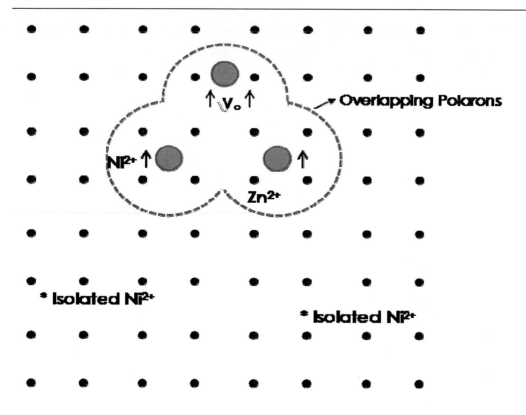

Figure 1.1 Schematic reperesantation of formation of bound magnetic polaron and their ovelappping to give rise FM ordering in TM doped ZnO. A typical case of Ni doped ZnO is taken here where lattice atoms of Zn are indicated by small circles (black) and nickel ions taking part in BMP by arrow. BMP formation is mediated by O-vacancy (Vo, bigger circles). The isolated Ni^{2+} ions (represented by '*'), which do not take part in BMP formation are also indicated.

1.1.3. Important experimental results of ZnO based DMS

The research impact of ferromagnetic properties of transition metal doped ZnO has gained significant status with various promising results [6].

Values of T_C above room temperature have been reported in Co doped ZnO films [7] Ando *et al.* [8] reported a large magneto optical effect in $Zn_{1-x}Co_xO$ thin films as measured by magnetic circular dichroism (MCD) spectra, suggesting the suitability of this material as DMS. Ferromagnetic phase was obtained in Co implanted ZnO at lower temperature (~5K) by Norton *et al.* [9]. Recently, above room temperature ferromagnetism (RT-FM) is also observed in Co implanted ZnO films grown on sapphire substrate. Fukumura and co workers first reported [10] the ZnMnO grown by PLD upto 35% Mn in ZnO matrix, without degradation of crystal quality, a distinct contrast with respect to III-V semiconductor based DMS. Kundaliya *et al.* [11] reported that the observed ferromagnetism is due to a metastable phase (oxygen vacancy stabilized $Mn_{2-x}Zn_xO_{3-\delta}$) rather than by carrier induced interactions between separated Mn atoms in ZnO. Similarly, Ni and Fe doped ZnO prepared by chemical methods, physical vapour deposition and ion implantation also show promising RT-FM behaviour [6,12]

1.1.4. Role of Energetic Ions

Ion implantation in ZnO has been established as an important synthesis route to achieve ferromagnetism [5,12]. FM in ion implanted ZnO arises either by charge carriers mediated interaction generated due to ion induced defects or by phase segregated metals. In case of intrinsic FM in ion implanted ZnO films, oxygen vacancy plays an important role as it acts as a source of charge carriers. In case of nanodimensional film, micro/nano structure has significant influence over exchange interaction and can be utilized to tune ferromagnetic properties [4,5,13]. Apart from the questions related to the origin of FM in this material, combination of RT-FM with high optical transmission in visible region has also been a subject of important investigation as these materials demand potential applications in magneto optical devices [14]. SHI due to its large energy deposition capability in materials, has been used to dissolve clustered transition metals in ZnO matrix, leading to room temperature ferromagnetic property [15].

1.2. Metal-Insulator Nanophase Composite Films

In this subsection we discuss important materials aspects of different metal-insulator nanocomposite films and role of energetic ions in this research area.

1.2.1. Material Aspects and Importance

Magnetic granular films [16,17], consisting of nanoscale magnetic particles such as Fe, Co, Ni and of their alloys embedded in an insulating matrix, for example Al_2O_3 and SiO_2 etc. have received much attention due to their unusual physical properties, and increasing possibilities for use in technological applications, such as reading heads, high frequency applications, sensors and high density magnetic recording [18]. These granular materials exhibit peculiar magnetic and magneto transport properties, like enhanced coercivity, superparamagnetism, giant tunnel magnetoresistance (GTMR) giant hall effect (GHE) and in many cases excellent soft magnetic properties [19]. All these properties lead to promising application of these materials as data-storage media and high frequency devices. GTMR originates from spin dependent tunnelling between magnetic metal granules through insulating intergranules. Besides, magnetic particles and clusters in nanometric size posses an increasing importance in quantum computing and as diagnostic and therapeutic in medical tools and other life sciences. The new phenomena in nanocomposites arise due to interplay between the intrinsic properties, size distribution of nanoparticles, finite size effects and the interparticle interactions. For an appreciable degree of coherence of inter particle interactions, long range domain structure is likely to form even much below the percolation threshold. All these properties can be controlled by varying the particle size and interoparticle distance. Overall, there are four major issues related in this area of research, which are (i) reduction of particle size for increasing their number density, (ii) uniform size distribution, (iii) better control over volume fraction of the magnetic particles and (iv) developing new techniques for synthesis and design.

1.2.2. Role of Energetic Ions

Energetic ions so far have played a significant role to engineer the properties of these nanocomposite films. C. D. Orleans *et al.* [20] have shown formation of spherical Co nanoparticle in SiO_2 film by 160 keV Co ion implantation, followed by an elongation of these particles under 200 MeV I ion irradiation. This induces an anisotropy in the magnetic properties of the nanoparticles as examined by SQUID magnetometry. In á work by J. C. Pivin *et al.* [21], It has been found that the shape of the precipitation kinetics of Fe particles in the silicon sub oxide as a function of the ion fluence, or of the average energy transferred per unit length, indicates that nucleation requires a threshold energy density per unit volume. The threshold value of specific energy loss indicated in this work is ~ 13 keV/nm and falls in the electronic energy loss regime [22]. Same authors have also reported 'hammering' effect by swift heavy ions on silica matrix causing a tilt of easy magnetization axes when fraction of metal particles is only a few percent. Recently, Shirai *et al.* [23] have studied irradiation 210 MeV Xe ions in FePt nanogranular films, $(FePt)_{47}(Al_2O_3)_{53}$ using advanced TEM including tomography. Ion irradiation induced coarsening of FePt nanoparticles with elongation along beam direction. At very high fluence (~ 5 x 10^{14} ions/cm^2) well coarsened FePt balls have been formed on the irradiated surface, whereas the particles in the film interior have been deformed into rods along the ion trajectory. Irradiation on similar system (FePt nanoparticles embedded in silica films) by 120 MeV Au ion leads to elongation of the particles and perpendicular magnetization [24]. The enhancement of coercivity of the particles perpendicular to the films surface is favourable to the perpendicular magnetic recording at high density.

2. SYNTHESIS AND STUDY OF NI DOPED/IMPLANTED ZNO FILMS

In this section, we discuss some of our results on room temperature ferromagnetism and transparent ferromagnetism in Ni doped/implanted ZnO films. The experimental tools used for these studies are following:

Crystalline phases of the films were identified by Glancing angle X-Ray Diffraction (GAXRD) technique, with CuKα x-ray radiation (λ = 1.54 Å). To identify the chemical states of the elements present in the surface of the films, X-ray photoelectron spectroscopy (XPS) measurements were carried out using Mg Kα radiation (hv=1253.6 eV) after etching with argon ions (Energy = 5 keV) for 1 min. The C1s peak at 284.6 eV was used, as a reference for correction of the shifts, due to charging effect. The microstructure of the films was investigated by transmission electron microscopy (TEM) associated with selected area diffraction (SAED), using a 200 kV TECNAI G^2 20 microscope. The magnetic characterization was performed using a MPMS SQUID magnetometer. Some implanted films (ZnO/Si by VPT) were also examined by alternating gradient magnetometry (AGM), at room temperature. The resistivity (ρ) and the carrier concentration of the films were measured by van der Pauw method. Optical transmittance across UV-Vis region has been studied by HITACHI UV-Vis spectrophotometer.

Results obtained from these studies are discussed in the following two subsections.

2.1. Room Temperature Transparent Ferromagnetism in Ni Doped Zno Films

This subsection deals with synthesis of pure ZnO and Ni doped ZnO films grown on quartz substrates by fast atom beam (FAB) sputtering technique, and study their magnetic and optical properties. Fast atom beam sputtering technique has been demonstrated as a potential synthesis route to grow metal-insulator composite and Ni doped ZnO films down to nanoscale [25,26]. Details of film deposition processes are described in our works [26, 27].

Figure 2.1 (a) and (b) shows M versus H and optical transmittance across UV-VIS range in sputtered Ni doped ZnO film. It is clear from the figures that the film is ferromagnetic at room temperature with high optical transmittance (~ 80%). M-H studies at various temperature shows that saturation magnetization (M_s) value [Table 2.1] decreases between 15 and 5 K. This is attributed to the thermal agitation effect at higher temperature. However, H_c is the highest at 15 K [Table 2.1] and is attributed to the thermally activated magnetization reversal, involving domain wall pinning [27].

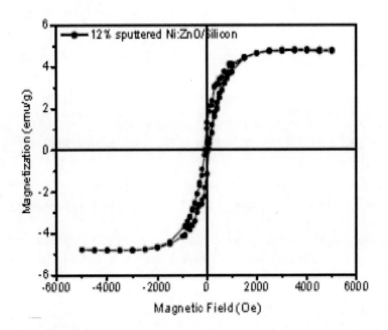

Figure 2.1. (a) M-H curves of Ni doped ZnO film grown by atom beam sputtering technique indicating RT-FM property [from Ref. 27 copyright (2008) by Elsevier].

Table 2.1. Saturation magnetization (M_s) and coercivity (H_c) values at 5, 15 and 300 K of Ni doped ZnO film grown by atom beam sputtering technique

Temperature	M_s (emu/gm)	H_c (Oe)
5 K	6.22	192
15 K	5.32	310
300 K	4.73	100

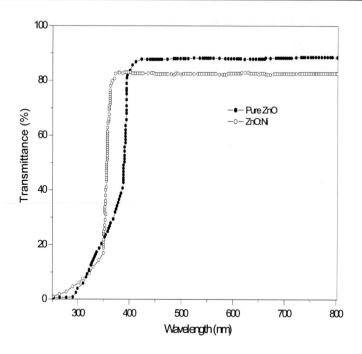

Figure 2.1. (b) Optical transmittance versus wavelength of the undoped ZnO and Ni doped ZnO films indicating ~ 80% transmission [from Ref. 26, Ghosh, S.; Srivastava, P.; Pandey, B.; Saurav, M.; Bharadwaj, P.; Avasthi, D.K.; Kabiraj, D.; Shivaprasad, S.M. *Appl. Phys. A* 2008, 90, 765–769, Copyright 2008, with kind permission of Springer Science and Business Media].

2.2. Studies on DMS Properties of 200 Kev Ni^{+2} Ion Implanted ZnO Films

Zinc oxide films deposited by vapor phase transport (VPT) and pulsed laser deposition (PLD) were used for implantation with 200 keV Ni^{2+} ions using LEIBF facility of IUAC, New Delhi. Incident ion fluence (incident ions/cm^2) were varied to obtain 2-7 at.% of Ni in ZnO.

In case of Ni implanted ZnO/Si films grown by vapor phase transport method clear ferromagnetic phase is obtained, at room temperature. A typical M-H plot of the sample irradiated with fluence 8 x 10^{15} ions/cm^2 is shown in Figure 2.2. It has also been observed that the FM strength (in terms of M$_s$) is maximum at this fluence (an intermediate fluence), which corresponds to 3 at. % of Ni in the film. The M$_s$ value decreases with the increase in fluence.

Similar result is also obtained in case of Ni implanted ZnO/sapphire films, grown by pulsed laser deposition. Maximum M$_s$ value with high optical transmission (~ 80%) is observed in the film having 3 at.% Ni films. The room temperature FM and transmittance versus wavelength corresponding to this film are shown in Figure 2.3 (a) and (b) respectively.

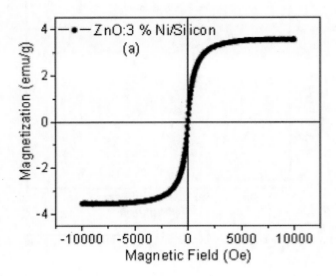

Figure 2.2. M-H plot of the ZnO/Si film irradiated with 200 keV Ni2+ ion with fluence 8 x 10^{15} ions/cm^2 (3% Ni ZnO film) [from ref. 5, REPRINTED WITH PERMISSION FROM Pandey, B. ; Ghosh, S. ; Srivastava, P.; Kumar P.; Kanjilal, D. *J. Appl. Phys.* 2009, 105, 033909-5. Copyright 2009 AMERICAN INSTITUTE OF PHYSICS]

According to Zener model, direct superexchange between the magnetic ions is not possible but is mediated by carriers mediation is. It is supposed that FM is induced by the exchange interaction between localized d shell electrons of the magnetic ions and the delocalized band carrier states (s or p origin).

In the Ni implanted ZnO films, we have seen that FM strength increases with decrease in conductivity and increase in charge carrier density, which is a clear indication that such exchange interaction plays an important role in RT-FM properties.

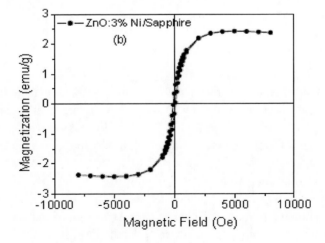

Figure 2.3. (a) M-H curve of 200 keV Ni (~3%) implanted ZnO film grown by PLD technique at room temperature, indicating RT-FM property.

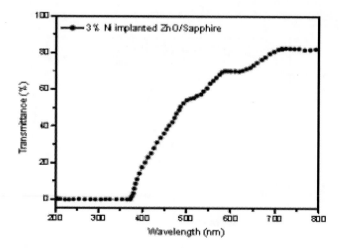

Figure2.3. (b) Optical transmittance versus wavelength of the same film indicating ~ 80% transmittance.

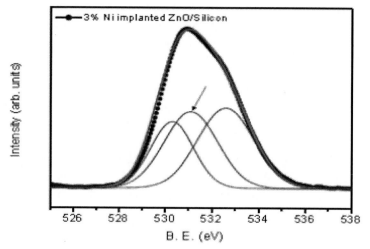

Figure 2.4. A typical O1s spectrum of Ni implanted ZnO film. The peak marked as O_b represents O-vacancy [from ref. 5, REPRINTED WITH PERMISSION FROM Pandey, B. ; Ghosh, S. ; Srivastava, P.; Kumar P.; Kanjilal, D. *J. Appl. Phys.* 2009, 105, 033909-5. Copyright 2009 AMERICAN INSTITUTE OF PHYSICS].

The enhancement of charge carrier density is correlated with generation of defects, like O-vacancies, which has been quantified by X-ray photoelectron spectroscopy. A typical O1s spectrum of Ni implanted is shown in Figure 2.4. It is fitted by three Gaussian. The region marked as O_b represents O-vacancy mediated peak [28] and the area under this peak gives the total O-vacancies.

An influence of film microstructure and overall morphology over exchange interaction has also been shown in case of VPT grown films. In case of a film, having smaller grains (for highest Ni concentration), trapping of charge carriers at grain boundaries can reduce the exchange interaction probability and hence overall FM strength [4,5]. The surface morphology of the films are shown in the following AFM micrographs (Figs. 2.5 (a), (b) and (c)):

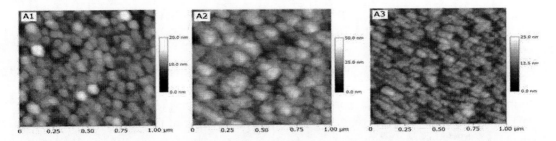

Figure 2. 5.A1, A2 and A3 AFM micrographs of the Ni (2%, 3% and 7%) implanted ZnO films, indicating enhancement of grain size from 2 to 3% followed by decrement of grain size in the film with highest fluence [from ref. 5, REPRINTED WITH PERMISSION FROM Pandey, B. ; Ghosh, S. ; Srivastava, P.; Kumar P.; Kanjilal, D. *J. Appl. Phys.* 2009, 105, 033909-5. Copyright 2009 AMERICAN INSTITUTE OF PHYSICS]

However, in case of ZnO:Ni/sapphire films, no systematic variation of FM with conductivity of the films are seen. The resistivity values as observed by four probe techniques are of the order of few tens of Ohm-cm and therefore, the charge carrier mediated exchange interaction may not be the probable cause of RT-FM properties of these films. Earlier, Kaminski and Sharma [29] theoretically studied the development of spontaneous magnetization in magnetic semiconductors, arising from percolation of bound magnetic polaron (BMP) and derived analytic agreement with the experimental results. Recently, BMP model based on the presence of defects, has been used to explain the intrinsic and extrinsic behavior of ZnO based diluted magnetic semiconductors [30]. It has been shown that ferromagnetic exchange is mediated through localized donor electrons in the impurity band derived from defect states. An electron, associated with a particular defect, is confined in a hydrogenic orbit. All the Ni ions within the polaronic radius interact ferromagnetically, shaping the BMPs, which try to spread out to overlap and interact with the adjacent BMPs to realize magnetic ordering, resulting in RT-FM.

Ion implantation is a tool to create defects in solids [31,32]. Oxygen vacancies and defect complexes are observed in different materials and its role in oxides and their role in the modification of the physical properties is well emphasized [33]. Defect production is chiefly caused by nuclear stopping, i.e. elastic collisions between a recoiling ion and the atoms in the medium. When an energetic ion collides with an atom in a crystal lattice and departs enough energy to it, the lattice atom will collide with other lattice atoms, resulting in a large number of successive collisions. All the atomic collisions, initiated by a single ion are called a collision cascade. A collision cascade can be divided into three phases. The initial stage, during which atoms collide strongly, is called the *collisional phase*, and typically lasts about 0.1 - 1 ps. As a result of the collisions, one can assume that all atoms near the initial ion path are in thermal motion at a high temperature. The high temperature will spread and be reduced in the crystal by heat conduction. This phase is called the *thermal spike*, and lasts roughly ~1 ns. When the thermal spike has cooled down, there will usually be left a large quantity of defects in the crystal. The defects can be of several different shapes, ranging from vacancies and interstitial atoms to complex interstitial-dislocation loops and volume defects.

Generation of O-vacancies due to Ni implanted ZnO films from XPS analysis have already shown [5]. O-vacancy acts as an electron donor in case of ZnO and hence plays a vital role in exchange interaction mediated RT-FM of Ni implanted ZnO films. The same defect under certain condition can play role to create and shape BMPs in ZnO:Ni films, causing FM ordering. Interaction between BMPs is higher in case of a film having higher defect density. For Ni implanted films, it has been observed that O-vacancies is the highest at an intermediate concentration (3%).

Overall, it has been established that Ni doped/implanted ZnO films show room temperature ferromagnetism and high optical transmission. Carrier mediated exchange and formation of BMP are the possible reasons for ferromagnetism. However, further investigations are required to completely rule out the possibility of formation of metal clusters and effects like superparamagnetism.

3. SYNTHESIS AND STUDY OF NI :SILICA NANOGRANULAR FILM

In this section we discuss some of the results on Ni:SiO$_2$ nanocomposite films grown by fast atom beam sputtering. The experimental tools used for these studies are following:

Ni:SiO$_2$ films were deposited for two different Ni concentration by varying the number of Ni foils on SiO$_2$ target by FAB technique. In another run, Ni:SiO$_2$ film having same Ni conc. was annealed for 30 minutes in a mixture of Ar-H$_2$ (5%) atmosphere at 400 °C. In this section firstly the (i) determination of composition of Ni-SiO$_2$ film by theoretical calculation and experimental studies and secondly (ii) the correlation between composition, microstrature and other properties of these films are discussed.

The characterization tools used for the above mentioned studies are Glancing angle X-Ray Diffraction (GAXRD) technique for structural phase identification, X-ray photoelectron spectroscopy (XPS) to identify the chemical states of the elements present in the surface of the films, transmission electron microscopy (TEM) associated with selected area diffraction (SAED) to examine microstructure and SQUID for magnetic characterization. The composition and the thickness of the films were determined by Rutherford backscattering spectrometry (RBS) using 2.4 MeV He^{2+} ions provided by ARAMIS accelerator of CSNSM, Orsay (France). Ni atomic fraction in the films was estimated by fitting backscattering spectrum using RUMP simulation code [34]. The microstructure of the films was investigated by a 200 kV TECNAI G^2 20 microscope.

Results obtained from these studies are discussed in the following two subsections.

3.1. Composition Analysis of Ni-SiO$_2$ Films

In nanophase metal insulator composite films, accurate estimation of metal fraction is an important job. The atomic fraction of an element of a nanocomposite film can be calculated by dividing the number of atoms of corresponding element by sum of metal silicon and O atom by the following equation [35]:

$$a_i = \frac{A_i Y_i}{A_M Y_M + A_{SiO_2}(Y_{Si} + Y_O)}$$

(i)

where i stands for metals, Si and O, M stands for metal only (here Ni) A, the area fraction and Y represents the sputtering yield. Sputtering yield can be estimated from Sigmund's theory

[36] or a modified form of the same [37] or from SRIM simulation code [22]. Another way of determining the same is based on RBS analysis. A typical RBS spectrum, associated with Rump plots of Ni:SiO$_2$ nanogranular film is shown in Figure 3.1. The Ni atomic fraction in this film can be determined by standard RBS formulation [34]. Now the theoretical estimate of at.% of Ni is compared with that of RBS analysis for a film having area ratio of Ni and SiO$_2$ ~ 1:1 (i.e. 50 % each) and given in table 3.1. It has clearly evident that the two results are in good agreement with each other.

3.2. Correlation Between Properties of Ni:SiO$_2$ Films with Composition and Microstructure

In this study four films are considered, 55% (A), 40% (B), 55% and annealed (C) and 90% (D) as per their at.% of Ni determined by RBS analysis.

Table 3.1. Area fraction of Ni and SiO$_2$, sputtering yield of Si, O and Ni, theoretical and experimental atomic composition of a typical Ni: SiO$_2$ film

AM (%)	ASiO2 (%)	YO, YSi	YM	Atomic Composition (theory)	Atomic Composition (experiment)
50	50	YO = 3.41 YSi = 0.902	YNi = 5.43	Ni55.7Si9.3O35	Ni58.4Si12O29.6

Table 3.2. Ni (at.%) and coercivity values of all Ni:SiO$_2$ granular films grown by atom beam sputtering. Film A to C shows the effect of annealing and B to D shows metal content effect

Sample	Ni at. %	H$_c$ (Oe)
A	55 %	90
C	55 %	170
B	40 %	30
D	90%	150

Transmission electron microscopy shows that the particle size enhances with the increase in Ni content (B to D) as well as with increase in annealing temperature (A to C). Typical TEM micrograph, and SAED pattern are shown in Figure 3.2 (a) and (b). Overall TEM analysis shows increase in Ni content (B to D), during deposition or annealing at higher temperature (A to C), after deposition leads to better crystallinity of the films and increase in crystallite size.

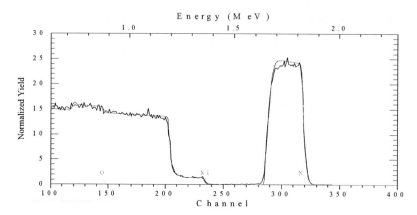

Figure 3.1. A typical RBS spectrum associated with Rump plots of Ni:SiO$_2$ nanogranular film [from Ref. 35, copyright (2008) by Elsevier].

The thickness of the film estimated from RBS analysis is ~ 238 nm. In case of other samples under present study, RBS analysis based atomic composition will be considered.

(a)

(b)

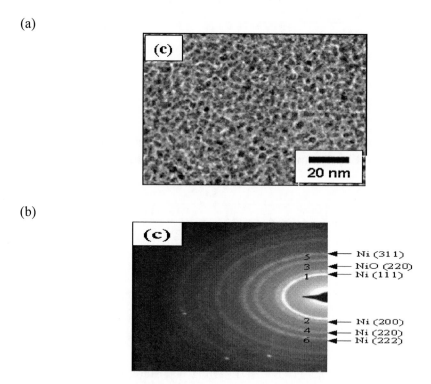

Figure 3.2. Typical (a) TEM micrograph, and (b) SAED pattern corresponding to film C. [from Ref. 39, copyright (2010) by Elsevier].

A typical hysterisis (M-H) curve corresponding to the film D, is shown in Figure 3.3. Magnetometry result shows enhancement of saturation magnetization (M$_s$) and coercivity (H$_c$) values with increase in Ni content as well as with annealing temperature. The H$_c$ values of all the films are given in Table 3.2. This can be easily understood on the basis of size dependent magnetic properties of such granular films [38]. However, dipolar interaction and magnetic percolation are also expected to play important role behind the properties of these films. This needs further investigations.

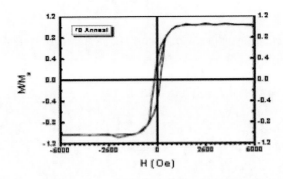

Figure 3.3. A typical M-H curve of Ni:SiO$_2$ film at room temperature. [from Ref. 39, copyright (2010) by Elsevier].

A detailed analysis microstructure and volume fraction dependent magnetic properties of Ni:SiO$_2$ granular films are in progress and will be reported elsewhere.

5. CONCLUSION

Room temperature ferromagnetism is observed Ni implanted ZnO films grown by VPT and PLD techniques. The strength of RT-FM is maximum at an intermediated Ni concentration (~ 3%). Theoretical models, based on Zener exchange and bound magnetic polaron have been used to explain RT-FM properties, in the two cases. Ni implanted ZnO/sapphire films grown by PLD technique also exhibit very high optical transmittance (~ 80%), and hence and is a candidate of transparent magnetic semiconductor. ZnO/quartz films grown atom beam sputtering, shows higher conductivity alongwith transparent magnetic properties.

A comparative analysis between theoretical and RBS based experimental estimation of Ni content in Ni:SiO$_2$ granular films, grown by atom beam sputtering technique is made. Improvement in crystallinity, enhancement in saturation magnetization and corecivity have been observed by increasing metal volume fraction and annealing temperature.

ACKNOWLEDGMENTS

Author gratefully acknowledges the scientific contribution and inspiration of Dr. D. K. Avasthi, Dr. D. Kanjilal, Dr. D. Kabiraj and Dr. Pravin Kumar from IUAC, New Delhi. This contribution would not have been materialized without constant effort and sincere suggestion of Mrs. Bhawana Pandey, Mr. Hardeep Kumar and Dr. P. Srivastava of IIT Delhi. Author is also grateful to Dr. J. C. Pivin, CSNSM, France, Dr. S. Zhou and Dr. H. Schmidt of FZD, Dreseden, Germany for many important suggestions and fruitful discussion.

The experimental facilities like TEM, AFM provided by IIT Delhi, ion implantation and FAB by IUAC, New Delhi, RBS by CSNSM, France and SQUID by FZD, Germany are thankfully acknowledged.

REFERENCES

[1]   Dietl, T.; Ohno, H.; Matsukura, M.; Cibert, J.; Ferrand, D. *Science* 2000, 287, 1019-1022.

[2]   Zener, C. *Phys. Rev.* 1951, 81, 440-4.

[3]   Coey, J. M. D.; Venkatesan, M.; Fitzgerald, C. B. *Nat. Mater.* 2005, 4, 173-179.

[4]   Yu, W.; Yang, L. H. ; Teng, X. Y.; Zhang, J. C.; Zhang, L.; Fu, G. S. *J. Appl. Phys.* 2008, 103, 093901-4.

[5]   Pandey, B. ; Ghosh, S. ; Srivastava, P.; Kumar P.; Kanjilal, D. *J. Appl. Phys.* 2009, 105, 033909-5.

[6]   Pearton, S. J. ; Norton, D. P.;. Ivill, M. P.; Hebard, A. F.; Zavada, J. M.; Chen, W. M.; Buyanova, I.A. *IEEE Trans. Electron. Dev.* 2007, 54, 1040-1048, and references therein.

[7]   Lee, H. J.; Jeong, S. Y.; Cho C. R.; Park, C. H.; *Appl. Phys. Lett.* 2002, 81, 4020-4022.

[8]   Ando, K.; Saito, H.; Zin, J.; Fukumura, T.; Kawasaki, M.; Matsumoto, Y.; Koinuma, H. *Appl. Phys. Lett.* 2001, 78, 2700-2702.

[9]   Norton, D. P.; Pearton, S. J.; Hebard, A. F.; Theodoropoulo, N.; Boatnar, L. A.; Wilson, R. G.; *Appl. Phys. Lett.* 2003, 82, 239-241.

[10]   Fukumura, T.;.Toyosaki, H.; Yamada, Y. Semicond. Sci. Technol. 2005, 20, S103-S111.

[11]   Kundaliya, D. C.; Ogale, S. B.; Lofland, S. E.; Dhar, S.; Metting, C. J.; Shinde, S. R.; Ma, Z.; Varughese, B.; Ramanujachary, K. V.; Salamanca-Riba L.; and Venkatesan, T. *Nat. Mater.* 2004, 3,709-714.

[12]   Zhou, S.; Potzger, K.; Talut, G.; Grenzer, von Borany, J.; Skorupa, W; Helm, M.; Fassbender, *J. Appl. Phys.* 2008, 103, 07D530-3.

[13]   Ronning, C.; Gao, P. X.; Ding, Y.; Wang, Z. L.; Schwen, D. *Appl. Phys. Lett.* 2004, 84, 783-785.

[14]   Ando, K; Solid State Sciences: Magneto-Optics, vol. 128, Springer, New York, 2000, p. 211.

[15]   Angadi, B.; Jung, Y. S.; Choi, W. K.; Kumar, R.; Jeong, K.; Shin, S. W.; Lee, J. H. ; Song, J. H. ; Khan M. W.; Srivastava, J. P. *Appl. Phys. Lett.* 2006, 88, 142502-3.

[16]   Asakura, S. ; Ishio, S.; Okada, A.; Saito: H. *J. Magn. Magn. Mater.* 2002, 240 485-489.

[17]   Denardin, J.C.; Pakhomov, A.B.; Knobel, M.; Liu, H.; Zhang, X.X. *J. Magn. Magn. Mater.* 2001, 226, 680-682.

[18]   Wang, C.; Xiao, X.; Rong, Y.; Hsu, T. Y. *J. Mater. Sci.* 2006, 41, 3873-.3879.

[19]   Franco, V.; Batlle, X; Labarta, A.; *J. Magn. Magn. Mater.* 2001, 210, 295-301.

[20]   D'Orle'ans, C.; Stoquert, J. P.; Estourne`s, C.; Cerruti, C.; Grob, J. J.; Guille, J. L.; Haas, F.; Muller, D. *Phys. Rev. B* 2003, 220101-4.

[21]   Pivin, J. C.; Esnouf, S.; Singh, F.; Avasthi, D. K. *J. Appl. Phys.* 2005, 98, 023908-1 to 023908-6

[22]   Ziegler, J. F.; Biersack, J. P.; Littmark, U. *The Stopping Power of Ions in Solids* (Pergamon), Oxford, (1980).

[23]   Shirai, M.; Tsumori, K.; Kutsuwada, M.; Yasuda, K.; Matsumura, S. *Nucl. Instr. and Meth. Phys. Res. B* 2009, 267, 1787- 1791.

[24] Pivin, J. C. ; Singh, F.; Angelov , O; Vincent, L.; *J. Phys. D, Appl. Phys.* 2009, 42, 025005-6.

[25] Avasthi, D.K., Mishra, Y.K. ; Kabiraj, D.; Lalla, N.P.;. Pivin, J.C; Nanotechnology, 2007, 18, 125604 -125604 - 4.

[26] Ghosh, S.; Srivastava, P.; Pandey, B.; Saurav, M.; Bharadwaj, P.; Avasthi, D.K.; Kabiraj, D.; Shivaprasad, S.M. *Appl. Phys. A* 2008, 90, 765–769.

[27] Pandey, B.; Ghosh, S.; Sriastava, P.; Avasthi, D. K.; Kabiraj, D.; Pivin, J. C. *J. Mag. Mag. Mater* 2008, 320, 3347-51.

[28] Chen, M.; Wang, X; Yu, Y. H.; Pei, Z. L. ; Bai, X. D.; Sun, C.; Huang, R. F.; Wen, L. S. *Appl. Surf. Sci.* 2000, 158, 134-140.

[29] Kaminski, A; Sharma, D. S. *Phys. Rev. Lett.* 2002, 88, 247202-4.

[30] Liu, X. J. ; Zhu, X. Y.; Song, C.; Zeng, F.; Pan, F.; *J. Phys. D: Appl. Phys.* 2009, 42, 035004-7.

[31] Saarinen; Hautojärvi, P.; Keinonen, J.; Rauhala, E.; Räisänen, J.; *Phys. Rev. B*, 1991, 43, 4249-4262.

[32] de la Rubia, T.D.; Guinan, M. W.; *Phys. Rev. Lett.* 1991, 66, 2766-.2769.

[33] Kucheyev, S. O. ; Williams, J. S.; Jagadish, C.;. Zou, J ; Evans, C.; Nelson, A. J. Hamza, A. V. *Phys. Rev. B* 2003, 67, 094115-11.

[34] Doolittle, L.R.; *Nucl. Instr. and Meth. B* 1985, 9, 344-351.

[35] Kumar, H.; Mishra, Y.K; Mohapatra, S.; Kabiraj, D.; Pivin, J.C.; Ghosh, S.; Avasthi, D.K. *Nucl. Instr. and Meth. B* 2008, 266, 1511-1516.

[36] Sigmund, P. *Phys. Rev. B* 1969, 184, 383-416.

[37] Anderson, H.H.; Bay, H.L. *J. Appl. Phys.* 1975, 46, 2416-2422.

[38] Löffler, J. F.; Meier, J. P.; Doudin, B.; Ansermet, J.; Wagner, W. *Phys. Rev. B* 1998, 57, 2915-2924.

[39] Kumar, H.; Ghosh., S.; Avasthi, D. K. ; Kabiraj, D. ; Lalla, N. P.; Shripati, T.; Pivin, J. C.; *Vacuum* 2010, 85, 139

C. Swift Heavy Ions in Synthesis and Modification of Nanodimensional Systems

In: Synthesis and Engineering of Nanostructures…   ISBN 978-1-62100-261-1
Editors: Devesh Kumar Avasthi & Jean Claude Pivin   © 2012 Nova Science Publishers, Inc

Chapter 13

ION TRACKS IN POLYMERS

Jean-Claude Pivin[1] and Marie-Claude Clochard[2]

[1]CSNSM-IN2P3, Bat. 108, 91405 Orsay Campus, France
[2]LSI, Ecole Polytechnique, 91128 Palaiseau, France

ABSTRACT

Electronic excitations produced by ions in polymers results in the formation of free radicals making them highly sensitive to chemical agents. Besides the widely developed application to the etching of membranes with controlled pore sizes and densities, the grafting of molecules selected for their chemical properties inside the tracks of swift ions offers interesting potentialities such as the fabrication of intelligent membranes, detectors and captors. Carbon, silicon or metal clusters which are formed in the heavily damaged core of tracks, especially within partially inorganic polymers, are also of high interest for their optical or magnetic properties.

1. INTRODUCTION

The high sensitivity of polymers and other molecular solids (fullerenes, nanotubes) to radiation effects makes of these materials the most interesting targets for industrial applications of ion beam irradiation and at same time limit their potential use in some specific environments (space, reactors). Since the discovery of ion tracks in minerals and thereafter in different kind of solids such as polymers [1-3], a substantial research effort has been devoted to the analysis of the damaging mechanisms and their applications as radiation detectors [4-5], etched membranes [6-15], templates for the growth of nanometric cylinders or tubes of other materials [[16-28], with real industrial developments [29]. Irradiation with low energy ions producing a superficial carbonization finds also some practical use in the hardening and conductivity improvement of the surface of plastics which will not be considered in this paper.

The modifications of structure at molecular scale provoked by electronic excitations and ionizations occurring in the electronic regime of ion slowing down are well documented and can be summarized as follows. First, atomic displacements induced by ions of medium energies (10 to 100 keV/ amu where nuclear and electronic stopping are competing) contribute only to the fragmentation of molecular chains without influencing too much the properties of the irradiation product because of the most important effect of electronic stopping (see for example [30]). The formation of free radicals under the effect of the later leads mainly to three molecular transformations: (i) their combination under the form of volatile species of which the main is H_2, (ii) the crosslinking of chains, (iii) the formation of double and triple bonds. The probability of all these events increases of course with the local concentration of radicals and consequently decreases with ion fluence on a same spot and the degree of substitution of C-H bonds by side groups [31, 32]. The most resistant molecular structures are aromatic rings, except under very high densities of electronic energy deposition where the radiation sensitivity becomes almost independent on the initial molecular structure [33]. New moieties involving conjugated double and triple bonds are obtained in these ultimate conditions [33-35]. However the importance for material scientists is somewhat limited because the major effect concerning the macroscopic properties is the carbonization of the core of tracks, i.e. conversion into amorphous semiconducting carbon clusters (diamond like) and possibly nanocylinders beyond a threshold linear density of deposited energy [36-39]. This product of the ion-polymer interaction is of considerable interest for electronic properties as the confinement of excitons in semiconducting nanoclusters is a source of luminescence [40, 41] and the local increase of conductivity can be used for patterning the surface with nanocontacts or field emission tips. Some example will be presented, selecting the less documented case of semi-organic polymers. However, the main interest of swift ion tracks lies in the presence of radicals, because of their reactivity, at the origin of the track etchability by chemical agent (from which comes the qualifying term latent track) and of the possibility of grafting non-indigenous groups for combining the properties of two types of macromolecules in a polymeric membrane. This application of ion irradiation in materials chemistry will constitute the main part of the present report.

2. TRACK ETCHED POROUS MEMBRANES AND TEMPLATES

One important characteristic of porous membranes issued from the chemical etching of ion tracks (mainly in polymers) with respect to other types such as porous anodic alumina. is the inherent possibility to etch a perfectly controlled areal density of pores, from a single one to a few 10^{11} /cm^2, with a size and shape modifiable through the following parameters: (i) the local density of defects produced by the ions (i.e. electronic stopping power and ion mass), (ii) the irradiated matrix chemical composition on which depends the track versus bulk etching rates ratio, (iii) the chemical agent and additional surfactant limiting the surface sensitivity to etching, [17, 42]. The control of the track size and shape is in itself a domain of research and requires a combination of techniques including GISAXS, SANS, permeation tests, FESEM, AFM [43]. Sophisticated techniques are also sometimes used such as a passivation of the surface by an annealing treatment followed by a localized sensitization through a mask by UV for drawing patterns [17]. The pore size is of prime importance for the selective filtering of molecules or biological cells [11], the kinetics of permeation through membranes and the physical properties of nanocylinders grown in such templates.

Some investigations performed at LSI show the possibility to copolymerize conducting polypyrrole and pyrrole functionalized by carboxylic acid to design interesting polymer conductive poly(Py-*co*-PyCOOH) membranes for applications as biosensors [44, 45]. The figure 1 displays an example of such poly (Py-co-PyCOOH) membrane made of conductive copolymer nanotubes. The experiment was performed at GANIL where the sample holder allows the irradiation to occur at various angles leading to some interesting structures. Such architecture of crossing nanotubes may help to increase the mechanical properties of thin wall nanotubes. Due to the presence of carboxylic functions linked to the conductive copolymer backbone, some interactions with biomolecules may lead to change the electrical conductivity through the nanotube. A nanosensoring would be then possible.

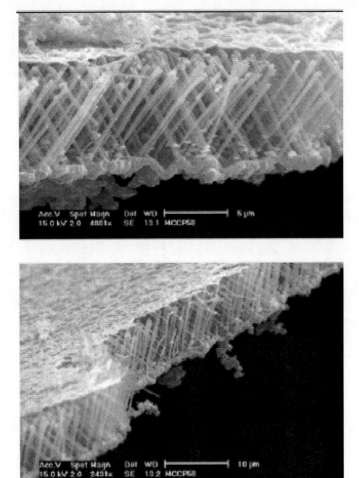

Figure 1. SEM pictures of poly(Py-co-PyCOOH) copolymers membranes made of nanotubes grown inside track-etch polycarbonate, initially irradiated with swift heavy ions at two angles 30° and -30° at GANIL (France). The track-etched polycarbonate has just served as template and was removed by hydrolysis in 2M NaOH solution (from Ref. 45).

3. Grafting in Polymeric Membranes

The purpose is to combine the properties of the most widely used polymeric membranes, selected for their mechanical strength, resistance to solvents, temperature, easy etchability. with some specific chemical or electronic properties of other monomers. For instance polyvinylidene difluoride (PVDF) is interesting due to its biocompatibility and chemical stability but its hydrophobicity restricts applications in aqueous media and therefore polymerization of hydrophilic monomers in the pores is researched for biological applications or the titration of metals in waters. Acrylic acid or isopropyl acryl amide monomers are grafted in tracks for this purpose.

Some applications studied by the LSI group are the titration of metals in waste waters after filtering, pH responsive membranes, the translocation of proteins. The LSI irradiated polymer group is involved in several IAEA (International Agency of Energy Atomic) workshop meetings for its expertise on polymer radiografting. In this framework, one recent objective was the synthesis of a nanosensor for diagnosis of heavy metal ions residue. Indeed, wastewater treatment processes are generally effective in limiting the discharge of potentially toxic elements to the aquatic environment because a high proportion of the contaminant load is extracted and concentrated in the sewage sludge. Wastewater sludge quality must be protected and improved in order to secure the agricultural outlet as the most cost effective and sustainable solution. In the face of increasing levels of sludge production, there is a need for a low cost, time effective, easy to handle and very sensitive analysis system to determine the concentration of heavy metals in wastewater. To respond to this requirement, the LSI irradiated polymer group and LSI nanotechnology group have succeeded to develop a small device combining Polymer Ion Tracks technology and Anodic Stripping Voltammetry (ASV) [46]. The resulting nanosensor is able to diagnose traces of heavy metal residue at a sub-ppb level. To achieve this goal, several track-etched PVDF membranes of 9μm thick and of pore diameters from 20 nm to 100 nm have been prepared. The remanence of radical within the nanopore walls after etching allowed to radiograft specifically a carboxylic hydrogel inside the nanopore and not on the membrane surface (Figure 2) [10]. Under wasted water stream, the functionalized radiografted track-etched membrane (FRTEM) traps cations and concentrate them. Gold sputtering on one side of the FRTEM and a connection to an open circuit transform it to an electrode ready to re-use after anodic stripping analysis (Figure 3).

Introducing inside ion track a polyelectrolyte such as PAA, which is already known for its swelling properties depending on the pH, allows consequently to enlarge the applications field to pH responsive membranes. Some other teams are also working on such development [9]. Creating a nanoporous biocompatible polymer membrane with controllable pore opening by a simple external stimulus is mainly of medical interest (for instance, drug release bags fabrication).

4. Clusters synthesis in semi-organic polymers:

Inorganic polymers is this class of macromolecules in which main chains contain Si or metal atoms, such as polysilanes, polysiloxanes, polycarbosilanes, including gels with more disordered structures.

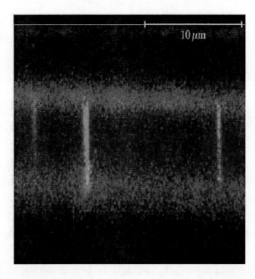

Figure 2. Confocal Scanning Laser Microscopy images of labeled PVDF-g-PAA films modified with ethylenediamine prior to grafting. Images are xz-plan (cross-section) reconstructions of series of xy slices. z axis has been rescaled to account for refractive index of PVDF. Red: fluorescein isothiocyanate labeling reveals amine groups, i.e. surface oxidation. Green: Alexa Fluor R hydrazide labeling reveals carboxyl group, i.e. poly(acrylic acid) (from Ref 10).

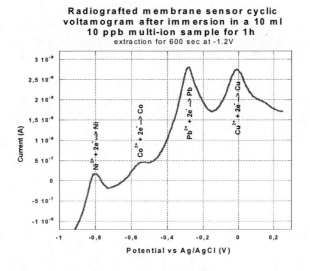

Figure 3. Typical ASV response of PVDF-g-PAA track-etched membrane sensors after immersion in a 10ml 10ppb multi-ions aqueous solution for 1 hour (initially PVDF films of 9 μm thick were irradiated using swift Kr ions with a total fluence of 10^{10} cm^{-2} at GANIL, France; the etching time was 30 min at 65°C in 10N KOH and 0.25N KMnO$_4$ aqueous solution, the grafting occurred consecutively in pure AA solution containing 0.6 wt% of Mohr salt at 60°C for 1 hour; the sputtered gold layer on both surfaces of the resulting membrane was of 45 nm thick), from Ref. 10.

Their conversion into ceramics by thermal processing at low temperatures has become a commonly used route for fabricating fibers, cast pieces and coatings. Ion beam irradiation is an interesting alternative to thermal treatments in later case, permitting to avoid the loss of some of the elements by gas evolution, the formation of voids and cracking under the conjugated effects of film compaction and difference in thermal dilatation coefficient with respect to the substrate [37, 38]. Another advantage of irradiation processing is the limitation in the size of carbon clusters which are quite always formed because of the larger C content than in ceramics at thermodynamic equilibrium: for instance, in SiO_xC_y glasses, the C concentration y is limited to 1-x/2 and the maximum value of x is 2. In ceramics derived from polysiloxanes, y can reach 6 so that clusters of amorphous C are formed during irradiation or thermal treatment as well, with the noticeable difference that those produced by irradiation are intrinsically more diamond like because of their smaller size. Therefore they show a yellow orange luminescence originating from the radiative recombination of excitons (as long as they don't percolate or grow by irradiation at an excessive fluence) and they provide to the films hardness values close that of SiC (30 GPa). An interesting characteristic when they are formed under swift heavy ion irradiation is their alignment along the tracks [39] and may possibly percolate under the form of isolated nanocylinders at low fluences in precursors with high C/Si contents [47].

Other types of precipitations are obtained by irradiation in gels derived from triethoxysilane $SiH(OC_2H_5)_3$ which is converted into a suboxide with stoichiometry $SiO_{1.7}$ either by irradiation or thermal treatment in vacuum. The breaking of Si-H bonds in the [SiH-OH]n network of the gel followed by bonds rearrangements in the glass network give rise to the precipitation of Si nanoparticles with a size of 1-3 nm showing an excitonic luminescence like the C particles in other polymers [38]. However metal particles are formed instead, by an oxidation reduction process, when less oxidable metal species are added to the sol under the form of salts, as for instance nitrates of Cu, Ni, Fe, Co [48-50]. The reduction of metal ions by irradiation is more efficient than by thermal treatment and the particle size is limited by that of ion tracks, providing them more interesting optical or magnetic properties [48] (Figure 4).

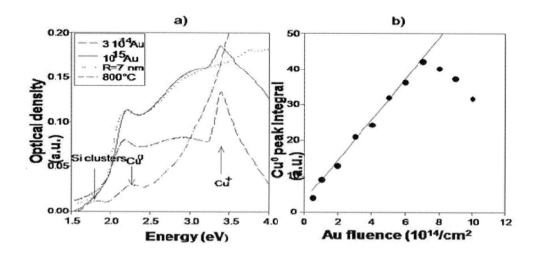

Figure 4. a) Optical absorption in TH:Cu films containing 3 at.% Cu after irradiation with two fluences of 3 MeV Au ions or annealing in vacuum for 1h at 800°C and Mie simulation for clusters of radius 7 nm fitting approximately the spectrum for the highest fluence (dotted line); b) increase of the optical density in the energy range 1.5 to 3.3 eV with the ion fluence. The absorption of the glass substrate was subtracted from spectra of irradiated films. The spectrum of the annealed film (on a silica substrate) includes an absorption peak of Si clusters, emitting a luminescence at 1.5eV (from Ref. 38).

5. CONCLUSIONS

The high density of electronic excitations produced by more or less swift ions induces the formation of amorphous carbon clusters in the core of cascades or of tracks. These clusters have semimetal properties and harden the polymer surface. Radicals keeping an organic structure are also formed at the periphery of swift ions tracks. These radicals help in the cross-linking of the structure, especially in aliphatic polymers with secondary and ternary carbon in chains. They constitute also sites for the grafting of other monomers in partially etched tracks and their functionalization. For instance, organic groups sensitive to the pH or temperature or reacting easily with biological products of cells can be introduced as sensors or for the culture of cells. Etched ion tracks constitute excellent templates with a controlled areal density, size and shape for the growth of a huge variety of nanowires and nanotubes.

Nanocomposite films can also be synthesized from inorganic gels and polymers by irradiation. The formed nanoparticles can either be made of amorphous carbon and exhibit semiconducting properties due to their small size, or metal particles with potentially useful optical or magnetic properties.

REFERENCES

[1]   Young D.A. "Etching of Radiation Damage in Lithium Fluoride", *Nature,* 1958, *182*, 375-377

[2]   Fleischer R.L., Price P.B., Walker R.M. *"Nuclear Tracks in Solids: Principles and Applications"* University of California, Berkeley, 1975 , vol.1, 605.

[3]   Fischer B.E., R. Spohr "Production and Use of Nuclear Tracks: Imprinting Structure on Solids" *Rev. Mod. Phys.* , 1983, *55*, 4, 907-948

[4]   Gautier D C, Kline J L, Flippo K A, Gaillard S A, Letzring S A, Hegelich B M "A simple apparatus for quick qualitative analysis of CR39 nuclear track detectors" *Rev. Sci. Instrum.* , 2008, *79*, 10, 10E536

[5]   Balcazar M, Tavera L "Ion-track simulation in plastics", *Nuclear Instruments and Methods in Physics Research Section B* ,2003, *209*, 118-121

[6]   Hanks PL, Forschner CA, Lloyd DR "Sieve mechanism estimations for microfiltration membranes with elliptical pores" *Journal of Membrane Science* ,2008, *322*, 1, 91-97

[7]   Apel PY, Blonskaya IV, Dmitriev SN, Mamonova TI, Orelovitch OL, Sartowska B, Yamauchi Y "Surfactant-controlled etching of ion track nanopores and its practical applications in membrane technology" *Radiation Measurements* ,2008, *43*, S552-S559

[8]   Wang J, Martin CR "A new drug-sensing paradigm based on ion-current rectification in a conically shaped nanopore, *Nanomedecine,*2008, *3*, 1, 13-20

[9]   Mazzei R; Bermudez GG; Fernandez A, Torres A, Betz N., Tadey D. "Grafting of PNIPAAm on PVDF submicroscopic tracks induced by the active sites remainders of the etching process" *Nuclear Instruments and Methods in Physics Research B* , 2008, *266*, 6 ,937-943

[10]   Cuscito O; Clochard MC; Esnouf S, Betz N., Lairez D "Nanoporous beta-PVDF membranes with selectively functionalized pores", *Nuclear Instruments and Methods in Physics Research B* , 2007, *265*, 1, 309-313

[11]   Martin, CR; Siwy, ZS "Learning nature's way: Biosensing with synthetic nanopores"
        Science , 2007, *317*, 5836, 331-332
[12]   12. Vlassiouk I, Siwy ZS "Nanofluidic diode" *Nano Letters,* 2007,   7, 3,   552-556
[13]   Harrell CC, Choi Y, Horne LP, Baker LA, Siwy ZS, Martin CR "Resistive-pulse DNA
        detection with a conical nanopore sensor" *Langmuir* ,2006, *22*, 25, 10837-10843
[14]   Siwy Z, Apel P, Baur D, Dobrev DD, Korchev YE, Neumann R, Spohr R, Trautmann
        C, Voss KO "Preparation of synthetic nanopores with transport properties analogous to
        biological channels", *Surface Science* ,2003, *532*, 1061-1066
[15]   Yoshida M, Tamada M, Asano O, Michi H, Kubota H, Katakai R, Spohr R, Vetter JM
        "Stimulus-Responsive Track Pores", *Radiation Effects and Defects in Solids,* 1993,
        126, 1-4, 409-412
[16]   Wade TL, Wegrowe JE "Template synthesis of nanomaterials" *European Physical
        Journal – Applied Physics* ,2005, *29*, 3-22
[17]   Ferain E, Legras R "Track-etch templates designed for micro- and nanofabrication",
        Nuclear Instruments and Methods in Physics Research Section B ,2003, *208*, 115-122
[18]   Chakarvarti SK, Vetter J "Template synthesis - A membrane based technology for
        generation of nano-/micro materials: A review", *Radiation Measurements,* 1998, *29*, 2,
        149-159
[19]   Brumlik CJ, Menon VP, Martin CR "Template Synthesis of Metal Microtubule
        Ensembles Utilizing Chemical, Electrochemical and Vacuum Deposition Techniques"
        Journal of Materials Research ,1994, *9*, 5, 1174-1183
[20]   Piraux L; George JM; Despres JF, Leroy C, Ferain E, Legras R, Ounadjela K, Fert A
        "Giant Magnetoresistance in Magnetic Multilayered Nanowires" *Applied Physics
        Letters,* 1994, *65*, 2484-2486
[21]   Molares, M. E. T.; Hohberger, E. M.; Schaeflein, C.; Blick, R. H.; Neumann, R.;
        Trautmann, C. *Appl. Phys. Lett,* 2003, *82,* 2139.
[22]   Chakarvati, S.K.; and Vetter, J. *J. Rad. Measur,* 1998, *29,* 149.
[23]   Fink, D. *J. Phys.* 1995,*25*,54.
[24]   Fink, D. *Rad. Eff. and Def. in Solids* 1997, *140,* 263.
[25]   Biswas, A.; Avasthi, D.K.; Singh, B. K.; Lotha, S.; Singh, J.P.; Fink, D.; Yadav, B.K.;
        Bhattacharya, B.; Bose, S.K. *Nucl. Instr. and Meth. in Phys. Res. B* 1999, *151,* 84.
[26]   Vetter, J.; Dobrev, D. *Nucl. Instr and Meth. in Phys. Res. B* 1999, *62,* 109.
[27]   Gudiksen, M.S.; Wang, J.; Lieber, C.M. *J. Phys. Chem.* 2002, *B106,* 4036.
[28]   Klein, J.D.; Herrick, R.D.; Palmer, D.; Sailor, M. J.; Brumlik, C. J.; Martin, C. R.
        Chem. of Mat. 1993, *5,* 902.
[29]   Fert, A. "Nobel Lecture: Origin, development, and future of spintronics" *Reviews of
        Modern Physics* 2008, *80*, 1517-1530.
[30]   Pivin, J. C.; Viel, P.; Zalczer, G.; Marletta, G. "Effects of ionizations and displacements
        on the hardness and optical absorption of some ion irradiated polymers." *Nucl. Instrum.
        and Methods in Phys. Research B,* 1995, *105,* 192.
[31]   Adel, M.E.; Amir, O.; Kalish, R.; Feldman, L.C. *J. Appl. Phy.,*1989, *66,* 3248.
[32]   Srivastava, S.K.; Avasthi, D. K.; Pivin, J.C. "Mechanism of H release from Si-based
        polymers under ion irradiation" *Nucl. Instr. and Meth. in Phys. Research B* 2002, *191,*
        718.
[33]   Balanzat. E.; Bouffard, S.; Bouquerel, A.; Devy, J.; Gaté, C. *Nucl. Instr. and Meth in
        Phys. Research. B,* 1996, *116,* 159.

[34]   Ravache, Y. N. ; Corbin, D.; Gate, C.; Mélot, M.; Balanzat, E. *J. Phys. Chem.,* 2007, *111,* 2813.

[35]   Fink, D.; Klett, R. *Brazilian J. Phys.* 1995, *25,* 54.

[36]   Pivin, J. C.; Viel, P.; Zalczer, G.; Marletta, G. *Nucl. Instrum. and Methods in Phys. Research B* 1995, *105,* 192.

[37]   Pivin, J. C.; Colombo, P. *J. Mat. Sci.* 1997, *32,* 6163.

[38]   Pivin, J. C.; Colombo, P.; Martucci, A.; Soraru, G.D.; Pippel, E.; Vassileva, M. S. *J. Sol-gel Sci. and Techno.,* 2003, *26,* 251.

[39]   Pivin, J. C.; Pippel, E.; Woltersdorf, J.; Avasthi, D. K.; Srivastava, S. K.; *Z. Metallkd.* , 2001, *92,* 7.

[40]   Pivin, J. C.; Vassileva, M. S. *Solid State Commun.* 1998, *106,* 133.

[41]   Pivin, J. C.; Vassileva, M. S.; Colombo, P.; Martucci, A. *Mat. Sci. and Engineer.* 2000, *B69,* 574.

[42]   Apel, P. *Rad. Measur.* 2001, *34,* 559.

[43]   Clochard, M. C.; Wade, T. L.; Wegrowe, J. E.; Balanzat, E. "Influence of asymmetric etching on ion track shapes in polycarbonate" *Nucl. Instr. and Meth. in Phys. Res. B,* 2007, *265,* 325-329

[44]   Clochard, M. C.; Baudin, C.; Betz, N.; Le, M. A.; Bittencourt, C.; Houssiau, L.; Pireaux, J. J.; Caldemaison, D.; "New sulfonated pyrrole and pyrrole 3-carboxylic acid copolymer membranes via track-etched templates" *Reactive and Functional Polymers* 2006, *66* ,11, 1296-1305.

[45]   Berthelot, T.; Baudin, C.; Balanzat, E.; Clochard, M. C. *Nucl. Instr. and Meth. in Phys. Research B* 2007, *265,* 320.

[46]   European Patent Office, under reference 08305237 « Method and device using nanoporous membrane for detecting and quantifying heavy metal ions in a fluid », inventors : Travis WADE, Marie-Claude CLOCHARD.

[47]   Kumar, A. ; Singh, F. ; Tripathi, A. ; Pernot, J. ; Pivin, J. C. ; D. K. Avasthi "Conducting carbon nanopatterns (nanowire) by energetic ion irradiation" *J. Phys. D: Appl. Phys.* ,2008, *41,* 095304.

[48]   Pivin, J.C. *Nucl Instr and Methods in Phys. Research B,* 2004, *216,* 239.

[49]   Pivin, J.C. ; Vincent, E. ; Esnouf, S.; Dubus, M. *Euro. Phys. J. B.* 2004, *37,* 329.

[50]   Pivin, J.C. ; Esnouf, S. ; Singh, F. ; Avasthi, D.K. *J. Appl. Phys.* 2005, *98,*1.

In: Synthesis and Engineering of Nanostructures…   ISBN 978-1-62100-261-1
Editors: Devesh Kumar Avasthi & Jean Claude Pivin   © 2012 Nova Science Publishers, Inc

Chapter 14

SWIFT HEAVY-IONS FOR CONTROLLED MODIFICATIONS OF MAGNETIC THIN FILMS AND MULTILAYERS

Ajay Gupta

UGC-DAE Consortium for Scientific Research, Khandwa Road, Indore 452017

ABSTRACT

Passage of swift heavy ions can result in considerable atomic motion in the target material, as part of the energy dissipated by the bombarding ion in the electronic system gets transferred to the lattice. The resultant atomic motion can create substantial material modifications. Various possible effects of swift heavy ion irradiation in thin films and multilayers include, i) stress relaxation, ii) modifications in the structure of the interfaces in terms of rms roughness or in-plane correlation of the interface height variation, iii) intermixing at the interfaces which may lead to formation of new phases. All these effects can be exploited to modify the magnetic properties of thin films and multilayers in a desired manner. In the present chapter we briefly discuss various aspects of the modification of magnetic properties of thin films and multilayers using swift heavy ion irradiation. Some novel x-ray based experiments are also described which aim at elucidating the mechanism of the observed effects.

1. INTRODUCTION

Thin films and multilayers form an important class of nanostructured materials. A large variety of new materials have been developed using such structures. Multilayers consisting of alternate layers of a high-Z and a low-Z elements like W/Si, Pt/C are used as x-ray mirror and monochromators. Magnetic multilayers like Fe/Cr exhibit giant magnetoresistance and are used as magnetic sensors in read/write heads and in memory devices. Soft magnetic thin films are also extensively used in tunnel magneto-resistance devices, exchange spring magnets or high frequency passive circuit elements. Interfaces in multilayers play an important role in controlling their magnetic properties. Quite often post-deposition treatments are required in order to modify the interfaces so as to optimize the desired properties.

High-energy heavy-ion beams have been well established as a powerful tool for modifying the surfaces and interfaces at a nanometer scale. Low energy ion-beams (having energies ~keV/nucleon) are in use for several decades for surface modifications via ion implantation or ion-beam mixing. More recently, material modifications produced by swift heavy ions (having energies ~MeV/nucleon), have been a subject of great interest. Swift heavy ions differ from the low energy (~keV/nucleon) ions in their interaction with the atoms of the target: At low energies the interaction with the target atoms is via elastic collisions in which energy is directly transferred from the bombarding ions to the motion of the target atoms (termed as nuclear energy loss). On the other hand, at higher energies the inelastic collisions involving excitation and ionization of the target atoms become dominant [1], and thus energy is transferred mainly to the electrons in the target (termed as electronic energy loss). A part of this energy subsequently gets transferred to the atomic motions, and may create substantial modifications in the target material. Damage creation in insulators via electronic energy loss is quite strong and was demonstrated more than three decades back [2]. On the contrary, in metallic systems effects of electronic energy loss are relatively week, since i) due to high mobility of conduction electrons, any energy deposited in the electronic system gets distributed quickly over a large volume , and ii) the conduction electrons screen very efficiently the ionic charges created in the wake of the projectile. A peculiarity of the metallic systems is the existence of a threshold value for the electronic energy loss $(dE/dx)_e$ below which no significant atomic rearrangement can take place [3]. This threshold $(dE/dx)_e$ value varies substantially from metal to metal, being <15 keV/nm for Ti and > 40 keV/nm for Fe [3].

Various possible effects of swift heavy ion irradiation in thin films and multilayers include, i) stress relaxation, ii) modifications in the structure of the interfaces in terms of rms roughness or in-plane correlation of the interface height variation, iii) intermixing at the interfaces which may lead to formation of new phases. All these effects can be exploited to modify the magnetic properties of thin films and multilayers in a desired manner. However, a detailed understanding of the atomic level mechanisms involved in the above effects is necessary in order to achieve controlled modification of the properties. In the present chapter we briefly discuss various aspects of the modification of magnetic properties of thin films and multilayers using swift heavy ion irradiation. Emphasis is on the use of some novel x-ray based techniques for elucidating the mechanism of the observed effects.

2. STRESS RELAXATION IN SOFT MAGNETIC FILMS USING SWIFT HEAVY IONS

Soft magnetic films are important for several applications including tunnel magneto-resistance devices, exchange spring magnets, soft magnetic cores in high frequency passive elements etc. For such applications both amorphous as well as nanocrystalline films have been used. As-deposited films in general contain a high density of structural defects and quenched-in long range stresses. These structural imperfections may result in severe deterioration of soft magnetic properties. Therefore, quite often post-deposition thermal annealing is required in order to relive the stresses and structural defects so as to achieve the optimal magnetic properties. For example, in tunnel magnetoresistance multilayers thermal annealing around 375°C results in an increase in tunnel magnetoresistance from a few percent to about 200% [4]. This enormous increase in magnetoresistance can partly be attributed to the improvement in the soft magnetic layer. However, with thermal annealing interdiffusion between different layers can also take place which is not desirable [5]. Thus, though thermal annealing can significantly improve the soft magnetic properties of films, it also gives rise to interdiffusion in multilayers which is not desirable. Therefore, alternative ways of relieving the structural imperfections in thin films in order to improve their soft magnetic properties without significant interdiffusion are highly desirable. Swift heavy ion irradiation of soft magnetic films can be an effective technique to improve their soft magnetic properties via stress relaxation. In general, metallic systems are known to be relatively insensitive to swift heavy ion irradiation, and intermixing at the interfaces in multilayers is known to occur only above a threshold value of electronic energy loss in the material. Therefore, by appropriately choosing the energy and the species of the bombarding ions, it may be possible to improve soft magnetic properties of the films without significant interdiffusion at the interfaces.

Iron nitride films of composition $Fe_{0.85}N_{0.15}$ prepared by ion beam sputtering develop a strong perpendicular magnetic anisotropy with increasing film thickness. The existence of a compressive stress in such films has been demonstrated by doing simultaneous in-plane and out-of-plane x-ray diffraction measurements [6]. This compressive stress results in the development of perpendicular magnetic anisotropy via magnetoelastic coupling. With thermal annealing compressive stresses are relieved gradually and annealing at 250°C results in almost complete removal of the long range stresses, with concurrent improvement in soft magnetic properties. However, thermal annealing also results in development of another phase which has been identified as either γ-Fe_4N or ε-Fe_3N. Development of this second phase results in an increase in the coercivity.

Swift heavy ion irradiation is also known to induce substantial atomic motion in the target, as a part of the energy deposited in the electronic system gets transferred to the lattice. This may relieve the stresses resulting in a possible improvement in the magnetic properties. Therefore films of composition $Fe_{0.85}N_{0.15}$ have been irradiated with 120 MeV Ag ions to various fluences varying from 2×10^{11} ions/cm^2 to 5×10^{13} ions/cm^2. The evolution of structural and magnetic properties of the film with ion fluence has been studied using XRD, Mössbauer and MOKE measurements. The as-deposited film exhibits a broad hump in XRD pattern, suggesting that the film is x-ray amorphous (Figure 1). With heavy ion irradiation a second broad peak starts developing. The position of this second peak matches with that of the peak in the thermally annealed sample after complete structural relaxation. Thus, as a result of irradiation a certain volume fraction of the film is transformed into fully relax state. As expected, this volume fraction of the relaxed structure increases with fluence (Figure 2). At the highest fluence of 5×10^{13} ions/cm^2, 70% volume of the film is in relaxed state, however, no sign of any additional phase is observed. Thus, irradiation results in stress relaxation in the film without appearance of any additional crystalline phase. The fluence dependence of the volume fraction of the relaxed film can be fitted with the relation [7]

$$V = V_0 + \Delta V (1 - e^{-\sigma\Phi}) \tag{1}$$

Where σ is the average area over which stresses are relived on the passage of a single ion, and Φ is the irradiation fluence.

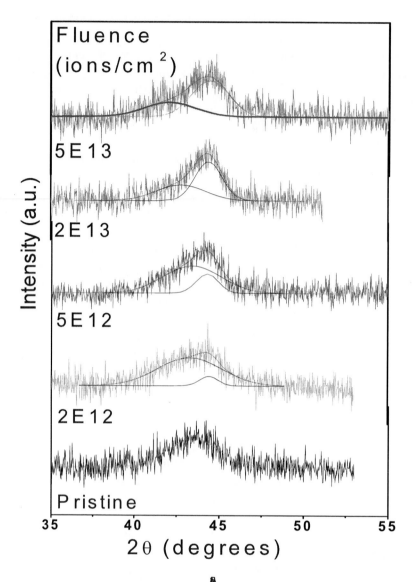

Figure 1. X ray diffraction of $Fe_{0.85}N_{0.15}$ film as a function of fluence of 120 MeV Ag ions.

The fit to the data shown by continuous curve gives the value of σ = 17.8 nm^2 giving an effective track diameter d_s = 4.8 nm, where d_s is an effective cross-esection over which stresses get affected by a single ion. The spin texture in the films can be obtained from Mössbauer measurements. The relative intensity of the 2nd and 5th lines of the magnetic sextet gives the average angle β between magnetic spin and the film normal. The variation of β with irradiation fluence is shown in Figure 3. Fitting of fluence dependence of β with relation similar to Eq. (1) gives an effective trace diameter d_β=5.6 nm, where d_β is the average diameter over which magnetic anisotropy is influence by a single ion. The fluence dependence of the coercivity of the film as obtained from MOKE measurements is shown in Fig 4. One may note that even at the lowest fluences 2×10^{11} ions/cm^2 the coercivity exhibit a sudden decrease to 38 Oe. For higher fluences coercivity remain almost constant.

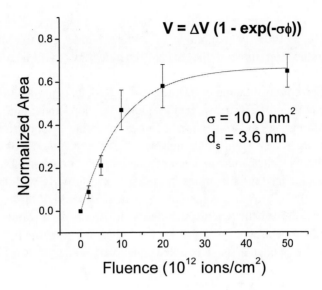

Figure 2. Irradiation fluence dependence of the relaxed volume fraction in $Fe_{0.85}N_{0.15}$ film. Continuous curve represents fit to the data with equation (1).

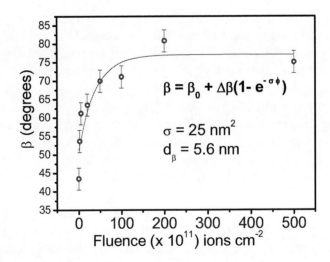

Figure 3. Irradiation fluence dependence of the angle β in $Fe_{0.85}N_{0.15}$ film. Continuous curve represents fit to the data with equation (1).

It is not possible to fit the data with Eq. (2) to obtain the effective area over which coercivity is influence by a single ion. However one can see that the coercivity reaches its saturation value at a fluence of 2×10^{11} ions/cm^2, which is about two orders of magnitude less than that needed for saturating D or β. Thus the effective diameter over which the coercivity gets affected by a single ion $d_c \sim 50$nm.

From the above results we see that relaxation of magnetic anisotropy is very well correlated with that of the long range stresses, and d_s is comparable in magnitude to d_β. On the other hand, d_c is an order of magnitude larger than both d_s and d_β. Moreover, there are several studies in the literature on the tracks generated by swift heavy ions in various materials. These tracks which are amorphous region formed along the trajectory of the bombarding ions, have typical diameter of a few nm in various materials [8]. These tracks are formed due to melting of a narrow region along the ion track and subsequent rapid solidification resulting in amorphization .Thus, depending upon the property being investigated (structure, stresses, magnetic anisotropy or coercivity) the obtained diameter of the track varies. These results can be understood qualitatively in terms of thermal spike model for swift heavy ions induced modifications in materials as follows. Swift heavy ion primarily deposit energy in the electronic system of the target material through excitation and ionizations of atoms. Part of this energy transferred to lattice via electron phonon coupling. The temperature of the electronic system as well as lattice as a function of time t and distance r from the track can be calculated using coupled equations for energy flow [9]:

$$Ce(Te)\partial Te/\partial t = \nabla(Ke(Te)\nabla Te) - g(Te\text{-}T) + A(r,t) \tag{2}$$

$$C(T)\partial T/\partial t = \nabla(K(T)\nabla T) + g(Te\text{-}T) \tag{3}$$

where various symbols have been defined in ref. 9. Equations. 2 and 3 can be solved numerically to get the electronic and lattice temperatures at a distance r from the core as a function of time. Time dependence of the lattice temperature exhibits a peak. Larger the distance from the core of the ion track, lower will be value of peak lattice temperature. Now, if T is the temperature needed to modify a given physical property (e.g., relaxation of long range stresses), the modification will take place in a cylindrical zone of radius r within which the peak temperature is greater than or equal to T. Lower the value of T larger will be the radius of the cylindrical zone in which the corresponding property gets modify. It may be noted that the coercivity is related with random stresses or defects, which act as pinning centers for the domain walls, while magnetic anisotropy is related with long range stresses. Relaxation of random stresses and/or defects would occur at a lower temperature as compared to that needed for relaxation of long range stresses. Therefore, random stresses and hence the coercivity will get affected over a larger radius as compare to the long range stresses, which are responsible for magnetic anisotropy. This can qualitatively explain different track diameters obtained for magnetic anisotropy and coercivity. Therefore, d_s and d_β are smaller than d_c.

2.1. Diffusion Measurements

Swift heavy ion irradiation results in substantial atomic motion accompanied by relaxation of long range and short range stresses and defects. However for practical applications of soft magnetic layer in a multilayer structure e.g., tunneling magnetoresistance devices, such atomic motions would results in blurring of the interfaces and possible diffusion of atoms from one layer to the other. Such interdiffusion is highly undesirable as it may deteriorate the magnetic properties [5]. Therefore it is meaningful to estimate the range of atomic motions associated with various irradiation fluence needed for improving the soft magnetic property. For this purpose nuclear resonance reflectivity from isotropic multilayers has been used. Multilayer having structure $[^{nat}Fe_{0.85}N_{0.15} (4nm)/ {}^{57}Fe_{0.85}N_{0.15} (3nm)]_{30}$ was prepared for this purpose. Nuclear resonance reflectivity was measured at ID18 beamline of ESRF. When the energy of the incident x-ray beam is tuned to the 14.4 keV Mössbauer transition of ^{57}Fe, a strong scattering contrast develops between $^{nat}Fe_{0.85}N_{0.15}$ and $^{57}Fe_{0.85}N_{0.15}$ layers resulting in a Bragg peak in the x-ray reflectivity of the multilayer [10]. As the Fe atoms diffuse the boundary between $^{nat}Fe_{0.85}N_{0.15}$ and $^{57}Fe_{0.85}N_{0.15}$ layers become blurred and the height of the Bragg peak comes down. The average diffusion length (L_d) for self diffusion of Fe can be obtained using the relation [10]

$$\ln(I(\Phi))/I(0)) = -4\pi^2 n^2 L_d^2/\lambda^2 \qquad (4)$$

where I(0) is the intensity of the nth order Bragg peak at $\Phi = 0$, $I(\Phi)$ is the intensity of the nth order Bragg peak after a fluence Φ, L_d is the average diffusion length and λ is the periodicity of the multilayer. The fluence dependence of L_d^2 is given in Figure 5. One finds that L_d^2 varies linearly with irradiation fluence. This is in accordance with several indirect measurements of interdiffusion [1, 11]. From the curve one finds that fluence of 2×10^{11} ions/cm^2, at which the coercivity reaches its minimum value, is only above 0.1 nm while after a fluence of 1×10^{13} ions/cm^2 at which most of perpendicular magnetic anisotropy disappears the diffusion length is about 0.9 nm. These diffusion lengths are of the order of interface roughness in typical multilayer structure and therefore diffusion length of this order would not significantly affect the quality of the interface. Thus, swift heavy ion irradiation can be used to improve the soft magnetic properties of the thin films without significantly affecting the quality of multilayer.

3. CONTROLLED VARIATION IN INTERFACE ROUGHNESS USING SWIFT HEAVY ION IRRADIATION

Multilayers exhibiting giant magnetoresistance (GMR) have been studied in literature because of their practical application in memory devices and read write heads. While the basic understanding of the origin of the GMR in these systems has long been developed [12], effects of deviation from an ideal multilayer structure on interlayer coupling and GMR are still a subject of considerable interest. Particularly a large number of the studies have been devoted in the literature on the effect of interface roughness on GMR. The theoretical studies [13] predict that as compared to ideal multilayers with perfectly smooth interfaces, a small amount of interface roughness should result in an increase in the GMR effect due to increased spin dependent scattering at the interfaces.

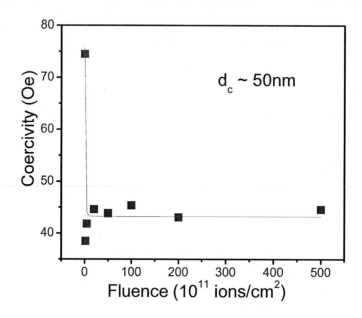

Figure 4. Irradiation fluence dependence of coercivity in $Fe_{0.85}N_{0.15}$ film. Continous curve is a guide to the eye.

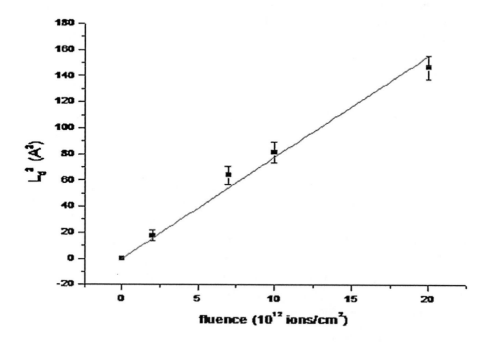

Figure 5. Square of the diffusion length L_d^2 of Fe in $Fe_{0.85}N_{0.15}$ film as a function of the irradiation fluence.

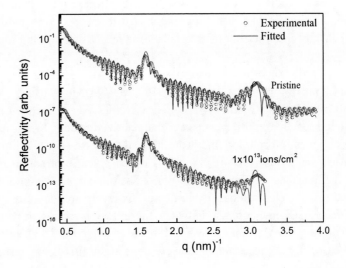

Figure 6. X-ray reflectivity of the pristine and irradiated (1×10^{13} ions/cm^2) samples taken at the K- edge of Fe (from Ref. 14, copyright(2006) by Elsevier).

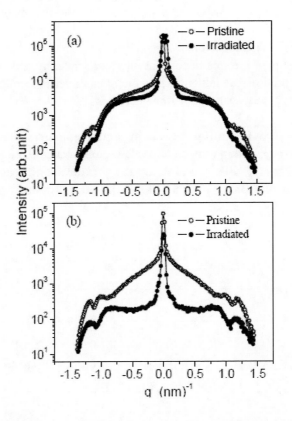

Figure 7. Diffuse scattering curves at first Bragg peak (a) and at the adjacent minimum (b) (from Ref. 14, copyright(2006) by Elsevier).

Swift heavy ion irradiation can be used for a controlled modification of the interface roughness without significantly affecting the microstructure of the multilayers, and thus would provide insight into the role of interface structure in determining the GMR properties of multilayers.

Epitaxial Fe/Cr multilayer having the structure: MgO (001) substrate / Cr (10.0 nm) / [Fe (3.0 nm) / Cr (1.2 nm)] $_{20}$ was irradiated with 100 MeV Au ions using 15 UD pelletron of Inter University Accelerator Centre (IUAC), New Delhi, with a fluence of $1x10^{13}$ ions/cm^2. Interface structure of the multilayers was characterized using X-ray reflectivity (XRR) (Figure6), which gives information about the layer thicknesses and rms interface roughness, and X-ray diffuse scattering (XDS) (Figure 7), which gives information about the in-plane correlation of the interface roughness, using ID32 beamline of ESRF, Grenoble, France [14]. It may be noted that the electron density in Fe and Cr layers are very close to each other and therefore, in general, X-ray contrast between these two layers is very poor. In order to increase the contrast, measurements were done at energy of 7.111 keV, just below the absorption edge of Fe. XDS measurements were done at the first Bragg peak of reflectivity as well as at the adjacent minimum, in order to get information about the correlated and uncorrelated parts of the roughness, respectively. Results of analysis of the XRR and XDS data are summarized in table 1. Irradiation results in a small increase of 0.15nm in the average interface roughness. XDS measurements suggest that changes occur mainly in the uncorrelated part of the roughness. Corresponding decrease in the magnetoresistance is only by 0.6%. However, decrease in the interlayer coupling, as obtained from the remanence M_R is significant. Interestingly the magnetoresistance normalized to the interlayer coupling MR/(1-M_R), which is a measure of the spin-dependent interface scattering, exhibits an increase. This corroborates the theoretical prediction that an optimal interface roughness is needed to maximize the spin-dependent scattering at the interfaces [13].

Table 1. Results of the XRR, diffuse scattering and magnetoresistance measurements on Fe/Cr multilayer. σ_{Fe} and σ_{Cr} are the interface roughness of Cr-on-Fe and Fe-on-Cr interface, respectively, while v_c and v_u are the variance of diffuse scattering data taken at the first Bragg peak and the adjacent minimum, respectively

Fluence (ions /cm2)	σFe (nm)	σCr (nm)	vc (10-2) (nm)-2	vu (10-2) (nm)-2	MR %	1-MR	$\dfrac{MR}{1-M_R}$
0	1.2 ± 0.05	0.6 ± 0.05	15.6	10.1	11.62 ± 0.01	0.97	11.97
1x1013	1.3 ± 0.05	0.8 ± 0.05	17.8	25.7	11.02 ± 0.01	0.82	13.43

4. SWIFT HEAVY ION INDUCED MIXING AT THE INTERFACES IN MULTILAYERS

Since the first observation of swift heavy ion beam induced mixing in metallic systems [15], the process has been extensively studied in the literature. However, the atomic level mechanism of mixing and the formation of phases at the interfaces is not yet fully understood.

In multilayers, phase formation at the interfaces can modify their magnetic properties. For example, in Fe/Si multilayers the interlayer magnetic coupling between Fe layers sensitively depends upon the phase formed at the interfaces [16]. Swift heavy ion irradiation can be advantageous in such interface modifications as compared to the conventional technique of thermal annealing. Therefore, there is a great deal of interest in understanding the process of SHI induced mixing.

The x-ray standing wave technique combined with x-ray reflectivity can provide concentration profile of a marker layer with sub-nanometer accuracy [17,18]. This accuracy is about an order of magnitude larger than that achievable using conventional techniques like, RBS, SIMS etc. Therefore, use of such x-ray based techniques can provide a better insight into the atomic level mechanism for swift heavy ion induced mixing.

4.1. Comparison of the Mixing Efficiencies of Different Metals with Si

Concentration profiles of a number of marker layers in a multilayer can be determined simultaneously using x-ray standing wave technique. Therefore, this technique has been used to compare mixing efficiencies of three different metals, namely, Ti, Fe and W with Si, by embedding thin marker layers of the three metals in a single Si layer, which is then irradiated with 100 MeV Au ions to a fluence of 1×10^{13} ions/cm^2. Embedding three different marker layers in a single film ensures that all the three systems namely, Ti/Si, Fe/Si and W/Si are prepared under identical conditions and also, their irradiation fluences are identical. This allows one to make a precise comparison of the mixing efficiencies of the three metals with Si. Figure 8 gives the x-ray reflectivity and Fe fluorescence as a function of the scattering vector $q = 4\pi \sin\theta/\lambda$, 2θ being the scattering angle and λ being the wavelength of the x-rays. Combined fitting of reflectivity and fluorescence data of all the three metallic marker layers yields the electron density profile, which essentially reflects the concentration profiles of the three metallic marker layers (Figure 9)[19,20]. Perusal of figure 9 shows that irradiation results in significant intermixing of the metal layers with Si. However, there is large variation in the efficiency of mixing of different metals. While Ti exhibits a strong mixing with Si, Fe exhibits relatively less mixing. Intermixing of W layer with Si is rather small. This is in accordance with the mixing efficiencies predicted by the thermal spike model; Ti and Fe are sensitive to electronic energy loss with Fe having a higher S_e threshold, whereas W is known to be S_e insensitive [9]. Fe layer exhibits intermixing even though the electronic energy loss S_e in Fe layer is below the threshold value of 30 keV/nm for bulk Fe. However, the observed intermixing can be understood in terms of a reduction in the threshold S_e value in thin film as compared to that in bulk metal. A decrease in the electron mobility due to scattering from the grain boundaries and surface/interfaces and a possible modification in the electron-phonon interaction can result in a decrease in threshold S_e value in Fe film as compared to the bulk [21].

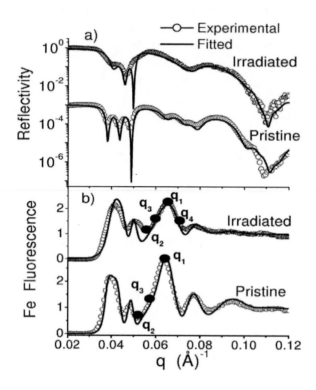

Figure 8. a) X-ray reflectivity and, b) Fe- fluorescence of Pr and Ir samples as a function of q. Filled dots on the fluorescence curves denote the q-values at which XAFS measurements have been taken (from Ref. 20, copyright(2007) by American Physical Society).

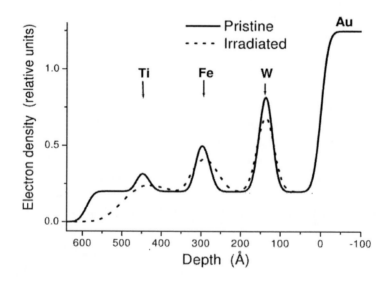

Figure 9. Electron density profiles in Pr and Ir samples as obtained from simultaneous fitting of x-ray reflectivity and x-ray fluorescence data (from Ref. 20, copyright(2007) by American Physical Society).

4.2. Depth-Resolved XAFS Study of SHI Induced Phase Formation

X-ray standing waves also provide the possibility of doing x-ray based structural studies, e.g. XAFS, as a function of depth. By appropriately choosing the value of q, the antinodes of x-ray standing waves can be moved to different depths in the multilayer. XAFS measurements done at a fixed q-value would then provide preferential information about the region of antinode [20,22,23]. Thus, by making an antinode to coincide with either the center of a layer or with the interfacial region, preferential structural information about the center of a layer or its interfaces can be achieved. Fe-XAFS measurements were done at q-values denoted by filled circles in Figure 8 (b). [20]. In this way it was found that, after an irradiation fluence of $1x10^{13}$ ions/cm^2 in the above system, in the center of the Fe layer an equiatomic FeSi phase is formed, while away from the center FeSi$_2$ phase is observed. Deep inside the Si layer, isolated Fe atoms in Si are observed. On the other hand, a depth integrated XAFS study would have suggested the formation of FeSi$_2$ phase only. Similar studies done in W/Si system irradiated with 350 MeV Au ions also show formation of different phases as a function of distance from the W layer [23]. These studies suggest the importance of doing depth resolved measurements in understanding the irradiation induced mixing process.

4.3. Asymmetry of Intermixing Induced by Swift Heavy Ions at the Interfaces

High depth resolution of x-ray standing waves can be used to study some subtle effects associated with swift heavy ion irradiation, which otherwise would have been difficult to distinguish. The ability of the technique to resolve the two types of interfaces in a multilayer A/B, namely A-on-B and B-on-A, makes it possible to explore the possible asymmetry of mixing at the interfaces. The multilayer structure used for the experiment consisted of: substrate (float glass)/ Pt (70 nm)/Ti (15 nm)/Fe (2 nm)/Ti (10 nm)/Pt (2 nm). Ti/Fe/Ti is the trilayer in which irradiation effects are to be studied. This trilayer is sandwiched between two layers of Pt which form a planar waveguide. It has been shown that the sensitivity of x-ray standing waves can be further improved by using a waveguide structure [18]. Intermixing between Fe and Ti layers was induced by irradiation with 120MeV Au ions to a fluence of $2x10^{13}$ ions/cm^2. Figures 10 and 11 give the reflectivity and Fe fluorescence from the multilayer before and after irradiation [24]. Fe fluorescence exhibits a number of peaks corresponding to the excitation of TE$_0$, TE$_1$, TE$_2$ and TE$_3$ modes of the waveguide. Reflectivity exhibits dips corresponding to the waveguide modes, due to increased absorption in the film [18]. Concentration profile of Fe as obtained from simultaneous fitting of the reflectivity and fluorescence data is shown in Figure 12. One may note that after irradiation the concentration profile of Fe layer becomes skewed towards the surface side. This suggests that the intermixing at the two interfaces is not symmetric. Mixing is more on the Ti-on-Fe interface as compared to Fe-on-Ti interface. Conversion electron Mössbauer measurements have been done on Fe/Ti multilayers with a thin layer of ^{57}Fe put either on Fe-on-Ti or Ti-on-Fe interface. It is found that in the as-deposited film itself the Ti-on-Fe interface is more diffused as compared to Fe-on-Ti interface. This difference in the structure of the two interfaces in the as-deposited film may be the cause of the observed asymmetry in intermixing.

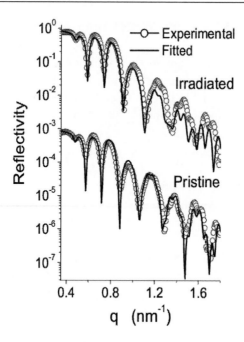

Figure 10. X-ray reflectivity of pristine and irradiated samples with 120 MeV Au ions (2×10^{13} ions cm^{-2}) as a function of scattering vector q. The continuous curves represent the best fit to the data (from Ref. 24, copyright(2008) by Elsevier).

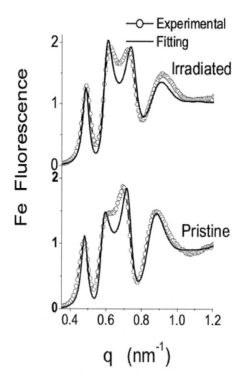

Figure 11. Fe fluorescence of pristine and irradiated samples with 120 MeV Au ions (2×10^{13} ions cm^{-2}) as a function of scattering vector q (from Ref. 24, copyright(2008) by Elsevier).

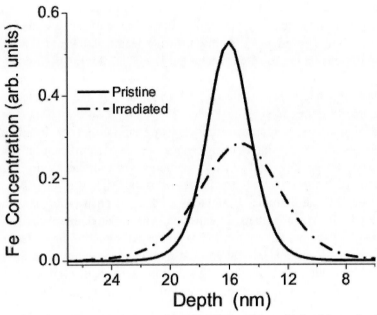

Figure 12. Concentration profiles in pristine and irradiated samples as obtained from simultaneous fitting of x-ray reflectivity and x-ray fluorescence data. On the depth scale the top of the Pt buffer layer has been taken as the origin (from Ref. 24, copyright(2008) by Elsevier).

CONCLUSIONS

In conclusion, it is shown that swift heavy ions are an effective tool to tailor the magnetic properties of thin films and multilayers. Various effects which can be induced include relaxation of internal stresses, variation in the interface structure in terms of interface roughness and in-plane correlation length, or intermixing at the interfaces resulting in formation of new phases.

Irradiation of $Fe_{0.85}N_{0.15}$ thin film with 120 MeV Ag ions results in a decrease in its coercivity as well as magnetic anisotropy. Coercivity exhibits a dramatic decrease from 130 Oe to 38 Oe at a low fluence of 2×10^{11} ions/cm^2, while magnetic anisotropy exhibits a more gradual decrease with fluence. Decrease in the anisotropy is correlated with relaxation of long range compressive stresses in the film. Decrease in coercivity is expected to be associated with relaxation in the random stresses in the film which act as pinning centers for the domain walls. The fluence dependence of coercivity and magnetic anisotropy suggests that the relaxation of random stresses takes place in a diameter about 50 nm around the ion track, while for the relaxation of long range stresses the effective track diameter is ~ 5 nm. This difference in the relaxation behavior of coercivity and magnetic anisotropy can be understood in terms of thermal spike model, if one conjectures that the effective lattice temperature needed for relaxing the random stresses is significantly lower than that needed for long range stresses. For high frequency soft magnetic applications certain amount of uniaxial anisotropy is needed in order to achieve a flat frequency response. By appropriately choosing the ion fluence, films with minimum coercivity and desired magnetic anisotropy can be achieved. Diffusion measurements done using nuclear resonance reflectivity show that after a fluence of

2×10^{11} ions/cm^2, which is needed to achieve the minimum coercivity, the average diffusion length of Fe atoms is only about 0.1 nm, while after a fluence of 1×10^{13} ions/cm^2 when most of the PMA is relieved, average Fe atoms diffusion length is 0.9 nm. These results have important implications on the use swift heavy ion irradiation for modifying the properties of soft magnetic behavior in a multilayer structure; since the Fe diffusion length is comparable to the interface roughness in multilayer, the irradiation is not expected to significant modifying the interface structure.

In case of multilayers, by appropriately choosing the ion energy, irradiation can either result in modification of the interface roughness or in a significant intermixing at the interfaces. X-ray reflectivity and diffuse scattering measurements in epitaxial Fe/Cr multilayers show that the effect of irradiation with 100 MeV Au ions is to increase the uncorrelated part of the interface roughness and to decrease the associated in-plane correlation length. It is found that, as expected, uncorrelated interface roughness has a stronger influence on the interlayer coupling as compared to that of the correlated roughness. On the other hand, spin-dependent scattering at the interfaces exhibits an increase due to a small increase in the interface roughness. This corroborates the theoretical prediction that an optimal interface roughness is needed to maximize the spin-dependent scattering at the interfaces.

Swift heavy ion irradiation results in a substantial intermixing in the systems like Fe/Si, Ti/Si. A precise comparison of mixing of Ti, Fe and W with Si, using x-ray standing wave technique, shows that the mixing efficiency varies in the order: Ti > Fe > W. This is in accordance with the predictions of the thermal spike model. Depth-resolved XAFS measurements show that in Fe/Si system, even after complete mixing, a number of phases exist at different depths. In the center of Fe layer a highly disordered FeSi phase is formed, while away from the center FeSi$_2$ phase is observed. It is found that in a number of systems like Fe/Ti, Fe/Si, intermixing is not symmetric at the interfaces. One interface gets mixed more than the other. A difference in the structure of the two interfaces in the as-deposited film itself may be the cause of this asymmetry.

REFERENCES

[1]   Gupta, A. Vacuum, 2000, 58, 16; Bolse, W. *Surface and Coatings Technology,* 2002, 158-159, 1.

[2]   Fleischer, R.L.; Brice, P.B.; Walker, R.M. *J. Appl. Phys.* 1965, 36, 3645

[3]   Dunlop, A.; Lesueur, D.; Legrand, P.; Dammak, H. J. Dural, *Nucl. Instr. and Meth. in Phys. Research* B, 1994, 90, 330; Dunlop, A.; Lesueur, D. *Radiation Effects and Defects in Solids*, 1993, 126, 123.

[4]   Scola, J.; Polovy, H.; Fermon, C.; Pannetier-Lecoeur, M.; Feng, G.; Fahy, K.; Coey, J.M.D. *Appl. Phys. Lett.* 2007, 90, 252501.

[5]   Wang, Y.; Zeng, Z.M.; Han, X.F.; Zhang, X.G.; Sun, X.C.; Zhang, Z. *Phys. Rev. B*, 2007, 75, 214424.

[6]   Gupta, A.; Dubey R.; Litenberger, W.; Pietsch, U. *Appl. Phys. Lett.* 2008, 92, 052504.

[7]   Bauer, Ph.; Dufour, C.; Jaouen, C.; Marchal, G.; Pacaud, J.; Grilhe´, J.; Jousset, J.C. *J. Appl. Phys.* 1997, 81, 1.

[8]   Dunlop, A.; Dammak, H.; Lesueur, D. *Nucl. Instr. Meth. in Phys. Research.* B, 1996, 112, 23.

[9]   Wang, Z.G.; Dufour, Ch.; Paumier, E.; Toulemonde, M. *J. Phys.: Condens. Matter,* 1994, 6, 6733.

[10] Gupta, A.; Gupta, M.; Chakravarty, S.; Rüffer, R.; Hans-Christian Wille, Olaf Leupold, *Phys. Rev.* B, 2005, 72, 014207.

[11] Nastasi, M.; Mayer, J.W. *Mater. Sci. Eng. R,* 1994, 12, 1.

[12] Schreyer, A.; Ankner, J.F.; Zeidler, Th.; Zabel, H.; Schäfer, M.; Wolf, J.A.; Grünberg, P.; Majkrzak, C.F. *Phys. Rev.* B, 1995, 52, 16066 ; Schad, R.; Belien, P.; Verbanck, G.; Potter, C.D.; Fischer, H.; Lefebvre, S.; Bessiere, M.; Moshchallkov, V.V.; Bruynseraede, Y. Phys. Rev. B, 1998, 57,13692; Gupta, A.; Paul, A.; Chaudhari, S.M.; Phase, D.M. *J. Phys. Soc. Japan,* 2000, 69, 2182.

[13] Barnas´, J.; Bruyenseraede, Y. *Europhys. Lett.* 1995, 32, 167; Hood, R.Q.; Falicov, L.M.; Penn, D.R. *Phys. Rev.* B, 1994, 49, 368; Barnas, J.; Bruynseraede, Y. *Phys. Rev.* B, 1996, 53, 5449.

[14] Gupta A.; Kumar D. *Nucl. Instr. Meth. in Phys. Research* B 2006, 244, 202.

[15] Leguay, R.; Dunlop, A.; Dunstetten, F.; et al., *Nucl. Instrum. Meth. in Phys. Research* B, 1995, 106, 28; Bauer, Ph.; Dufour, C.; Jaouen, C.; et al., *J. Appl. Phys.* 1997, 81, 116.

[16] Strijkers, G.J.; Kohlhepp, J.T.; Swagten, H.J.; de Jonge, W.J. *Phys. Rev. Lett.* 2000, 84, 1812; Tugushev, V.V.; Men'shov, V.N.; Nechaev, I.A.; Chulkov, E.V. *Phys. Rev.* B, 2006, 74, 184423; Planckaert, N.; L'abbé, C.; Croonenborghs, B.; Callens, R.; Laenens, B.; Vantomme, A.; Meersschaut, J. *Phys. Rev.* B, 2008, 78, 144424.

[17] Ghose, S.K.; Dev, B.N.; Gupta, A. *Phys. Rev.* B, 2001, 64, 233403.

[18] Gupta, A.; Rajput, P.; Saraiya, A.; Reddy, V.R.; Bernstorff, S.; Amenitsch, H. *Phys. Rev.* B, 2005, 72, 075436

[19] Gupta, A.; Meneghini, C.; Saraiya, A.; Principi, G.; Avasthi, D.K. *Nucl. Instr. Meth. in Phys. Research* B, 2003, 212, 458.

[20] Gupta, A.; Rajput, P.; Meneghini, C. *Phys. Rev.* B, 2007, 76, 195401.

[21] Gupta, A.; Awasthi, D.K. *Phys. Rev.* B, 2001, 64, 155407.

[22] Rajput, P.; Gupta, A.; Meneghini, C.; Avasthi, D.K.; Darowski, N.; Zizak, I.; Erko, A. *Hyperfine Interactions,* 2008, 185, 9.

[23] Gupta, A.; Darowski, N.; Zizak, I.; Meneghini, C.; Schumacher, G.; Erko, A. *Spectrochimica Acta* B, 2007, 62, 622.

[24] Rajput, P.; Gupta, A.; Avasthi, D.K. *Nucl. Instr. Meth. in Phys. Research* B, 2008, 266, 1680.

In: Synthesis and Engineering of Nanostructures...   ISBN 978-1-62100-261-1
Editors: Devesh Kumar Avasthi & Jean Claude Pivin   © 2012 Nova Science Publishers, Inc

Chapter 15

ION BEAM INDUCED FORMATION OF CONDUCTING TRACKS IN FULLERENE FILMS

Ambuj Tripathi

Inter University Accelerator Centre, Aruna Asaf Ali Marg, New Delhi 110067

ABSTRACT

A brief introduction of the scanning probe microscopy (SPM) techniques (such as STM, AFM, MFM, C-AFM, and associated IV and FV studies), which are widely used in characterization of ion beam induced nanostructures, is given with some representative studies. The following case is discussed in detail: We have demonstrated the fabrication of conducting carbon nanowires in fullerene matrix by heavy ion irradiation. The conductive AFM measurements show that the nanowires (CNWs) are parallel to each other and perpendicular to the substrate. The electrical and field emission properties of these carbon nanostructures are studied. These CNWs may be useful as field emitters and large scale applications.

1. INTRODUCTION

Surface Probe Microscopy

The field of microscopy has been revolutionized with the advent of surface probe microscopy techniques. The scanning probe microscopy techniques do not use any type of lenses in imaging and hence their ultimate resolution is not affected by the diffraction limit, which plays an important role in the case of optical and electron microscopes. The first microscope in this category, of the Scanning Tunneling Microscope (STM) was developed in early 1980s by G. Binnig, H. Rohrer, and coworkers from the IBM Zürich Research Laboratories. The instrument showed the possibility of imaging conducting solid surfaces with ultrahigh atomic resolution. The discovery led to a revolution in surface microscopic and spectroscopic studies as it led to the development of a whole new family of similar instruments over the next couple of decades. The most popular among the SPMs are Atomic

Force Microscope (AFM) for topographic studies of insulating surfaces and Scanning Near-Field Optical Microscopy (SNOM) for optical studies with nanometer scale spatial resolution. The techniques were further extended to study the magnetic and conducting properties with the development of magnetic force microscopy (MFM) and conducting atomic force microscopy (C-AFM).

2. SCANNING TUNNELING MICROSCOPE (STM)

The Scanning Tunneling Microscope (STM) [1-3], the first of the SPMs was developed by G. Binnig and W. Rohrer at the IBM Research Laboratory in 1982 and they were awarded the Noble Prize in 1986 for the same. The STM has distinct advantage over two other techniques, used for surface and near surface modification studies: scanning electron microscopes [4] (SEM) and transmission electron microscopes [5] (TEM). The STM is capable of providing better resolution as compared to SEM. The TEM is capable of providing comparable resolution besides providing information about the inner layers of the sample. However, the STM can provide additional information about the local density of electronic states. Moreover, a STM provides images in real space, which is not possible with SEM and TEM, making it an important instrument for surface science studies of conducting surfaces in real space. The STM has an added advantage that it is possible to obtain the surface images not only in vacuum, but in air or other environments also.

The schematic diagram of a STM is shown in Fig 2.1. In STM a sharp metallic tip is brought very close (within a few Å) to a conductive surface. When a bias voltage is applied between the tip and the sample a small electric current of the order of pA to nA can flow between the tip and the sample, even in the absence of a physical contact, due to quantum mechanical tunneling effect.

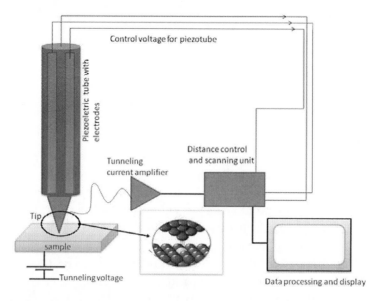

Figure 2.1. The schematic diagram of a STM.

This tunneling current has an exponential dependence on the separation between the tip and sample. The exponential variation of tunneling current with the tip surface separation facilitates a vertical resolution of up to 0.01Å, along with a lateral resolution of about 1Å. During surface imaging, the tip is moved across the surface and the resulting variation in the tunneling current is used to plot a map of the surface height. However, it should be noted that the obtained image is not a true picture of a topography, as the tunneling current is also dependent on the local electronic density of states of the surface.

The performance of an STM is affected by environment conditions such as a surface contamination. To take care of these problems and also to obtain stable tunneling current, it is preferable to operate it in vacuum [6].

2.1. Theory of STM

In classical treatment of physics, an electron cannot penetrate across a potential barrier, if its energy E is smaller than the barrier potential. However, according to the quantum mechanics, there is a finite probability for the event as it predicts an exponentially decaying electron wave function, across a finite potential barrier. For a rectangular potential barrier the wave function is found to be

$\psi(x)=\psi(0)\exp(-\kappa x)$, where $\kappa=\sqrt{[2m(\phi-E)]}/\hbar$

where m is the mass of electron, ϕ is the local barrier height for tunneling (generally approximated by the average work function of the tip and the sample)

Hence, the probability of finding an electron beyond a barrier of width x is given by the square of the wave function, showing an exponential decrease with inverse decay length κ i.e.,

$W(x)=|\psi(x)|^2=|\psi(0)|^2\exp(-2\kappa x)$,

When a bias voltage V is applied, this tunneling of electrons results in flow of tunneling current I between the tip and sample. If the applied voltage is much smaller than the work function i.e., $eV< \phi$, the tunneling current, which is proportional to the probability of all the electrons to tunnel through the barrier (and which is proportional to the square of the wave functions) can be represented as $I\alpha\exp(-2\kappa x)$.

This simplified formula shows that the tunneling current is proportional to the local density of states (LDOS) of the sample at a distance x, (the position of the tip) at the Fermi energy, and to separation between the tip and the sample. We can see that a separation increase from 1 Å to 2 Å will result in a decrease of tunneling current by 7 times and this high sensitivity results in a high vertical resolution for the STM. It should be noted that this is an approximate way of calculation and we have to solve Schrödinger's equation for square barrier potential in all three regions of interest, (before, inside and after the potential) for an exact calculation of current density and resulting tunneling current. Moreover, the observed tunneling current is a convolution of the tip and the sample state and would remain same if we interchange the electronic state of the tip and the sample. Hence, the observed corrugation amplitude in a STM image may be larger than that of the local density of states (LDOS) of the sample.

2.2. Lateral resolution of STM

The absence of focusing lenses ensures that the lateral resolution of the STM is not limited by the Fraunhofer diffraction limit with the few Å characteristic wave length for tunneling electron. The STM operates in the near-field regime and the 100 nm geometric radius for the tip would facilitate a lateral resolution of about 5 nm, in measurement. This actual atomic resolution is understood in a quantum mechanical framework, using the s-wave-tip model for STM. The tip is regarded as a metal tip with a Radius of curvature R. It is assumed that only the s-wave solutions of this quantum mechanical problem (spherical potential well) are important. Thus, at low bias the tunneling current is proportional to the local density of states at the center of curvature of the tip r_0. Experimental observations and calculations have shown that there is often a d_z like state near the fermi edge present at the apex atom and this state along with the p_z like states, predominantly contribute to the tunneling current and hence are advantageous for a sharp tip. In general Pt and W tips are preferred for STM operation.

2.3. Modes of Operation: Constant Height and Constant Current Mode

The STM is mostly operated in two modes. In the constant current mode, a feedback loop is used which adjusts the tip vertically so as to keep the current constant. Since the current is proportional to the local density of states, a constant current implies a contour of a constant density of states. Hence, recording the vertical position of the tip gives an approximate topographic image of the surface. In the second and rarely used mode of operation, called the constant height mode, the tip is kept at constant height and the variation in tunneling current plotted to get the surface profile.

2.4. Imaging Using STM: HOPG

HOPG surface as seen by STM at IUAC is shown [7] in Fig 2.2. The hexagonal lattice of HOPG has carbon atoms sitting at a separation of 1.42 Å . However with STM, we observe a triangular lattice with atom to atom separation of 2.46 Å, as STM image detects the higher density of states from overlapping carbon atoms from first two atomic planes.

The HOPG sample (Grade ZYB with grain size ~ 1mm) after irradiation with 150 MeV Au beam is shown in Fig 2.3. The values of electronic and nuclear energy loss are 19.6 keV/nm and 180 eV/nm respectively. The samples were irradiated with fluences varying from 1×10^{11} ions/cm^2, to 2×10^{13} ions/cm^2. Formation of hillocks and craters on the surface was observed. A typical hillock with diameter of 6.2 nm is shown in surface topographic image using STM.

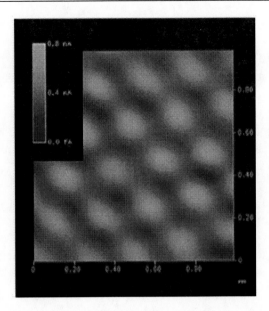

Figure 2.2. HOPG surface as seen by STM at IUAC. The triangular lattice with inter-atomic distance of ~0.246 nm is seen in picture.

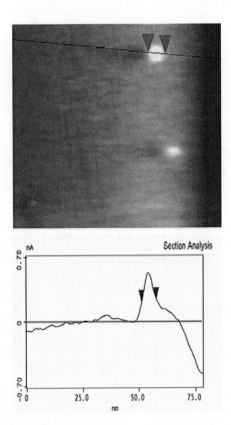

Figure 2.3. Formation of hillocks on HOPG surface after irradiation with 150 MeV Au ions at 1×10^{11} ions/cm^2 fluence [From Ref .7: A. Tripathi et al, *Nucl. Instru. Meth.* B. 2006, 244, 225 Copyright (2006) by Elsevier].

2.5. Scanning Tunneling Spectroscopy

The STM has a major advantage as it allows the measurement of local density of states (LDOS). This is due to the fact that the tunneling current results from the overlapping electron clouds of the tip and the sample. If we assume that the matrix element and the density of states of the tip are nearly constant, the tunneling current can be used to estimate the LDOS for the sample. Moreover, as the bias is increased it is possible to explore inner states for the sample. Experimentally the differentiation of the tunneling current yields the density of states and this can be deduced by two methods. In the first method, the bias voltage is modulated and a lock in amplifier is used for recording differentiated I-V characteristics. Alternatively, the tip is scanned in the constant current mode, thus maintaining a constant distance between the tip and the surface and during the scan, at desired points, the bias voltage is rastered to record current vs. voltage (IV) curve.

A typical I-V characteristic curve for the unirradiated HOPG sample is shown in Figure 2.4a. The sample has a semi-metallic character, displaying diode like I-V characteristics. One of the I-V curves after irradiation with fluence 1×10^{11} ions/cm^2, and 1×10^{13} ions/cm^2 is shown in Figures 2.8b and c. The curves show an increasing linear behavior as the ion fluence is increased, indicating an increase in metallicity of the HOPG surface.

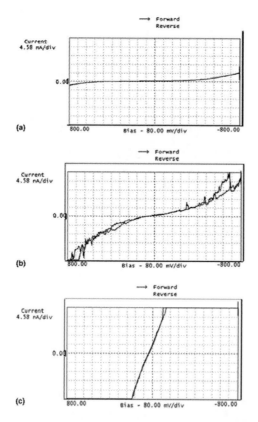

Figure 2.4 I–V characteristics of an unirradiated HOPG is shown in (a). An increase in linearity is seen with increasing fluence from (b) 1×10^{11} ions/ cm^2 and (c) 1×10^{13} ions/cm^2 fluence. The bias is varied from -800 mV to 800 mV in all the cases. [From Ref .7: A. Tripathi et al, *Nucl. Instru. Meth.* B. 2006, 244, 225, Copyright (2006) by Elsevier].

3. ATOMIC FORCE MICROSCOPE (AFM)

The first AFM developed in 1986 used a cantilever to examine insulating surfaces. The set up developed used a small hook at the end of the cantilever which touched the surface gently even as the sample was scanned below the tip. The instrument measures the Van der Walls force between the tip and the sample surface, which is very small and is of the order of 10^{-9} N. To measure this small force, the resulting deflection of the cantilever was measured by the tunneling current between the cantilever and a second tip, which was positioned above the cantilever. The tip-cantilever assembly is generally micro fabricated from Si or Si_3N_4. Nowadays in AFMs, the deflection of the micro cantilever is measured by the so called optical lever system. In this arrangement, the laser is reflected from the back side shining surface of the cantilever onto a position-sensitive photo-detector (see Fig 3.6). Using this arrangement, even a small deflection of the cantilever is measurable. A small bend of cantilever will tilt the reflected beam for a much larger measurable amount and change the position of the reflected laser beam on the photo detector. The force on the tip is initially set by pushing the cantilever against the sample surface with a piezoceramic based positioning element. The deflection of the cantilever is sensed and compared to some pre-set value of deflection, using a DC feedback amplifier. The feedback amplifier applies an additional voltage to the piezo to increase or decrease the separation of the tip and the sample to restore the pre-set value of deflection. This additional applied voltage gives a measure of the height of features on sample surface, and is displayed as a function of the lateral position of the sample, giving a height profile. The AFM has all the major advantages of STM as it is capable of imaging samples in air and under liquids with a resolution of the order of 100 pm. However, AFM has a major limitation that spectroscopic studies are not possible with AFM.

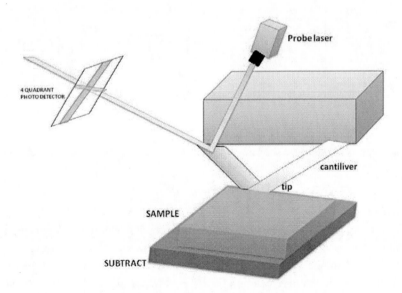

Figure 3.1. The schematic AFM with the concept of the optical lever showing a 100 μm long cantilever touching a sample.

The cantilevers are normally made of silicon oxynitride with a gold thin film for high reflectivity. Since the cantilever acts like a spring, the force of deflection can be calculated by Hookes Law $F = -kx$, where F = Force, k = spring constant, and x = cantilever deflection. The spring constants usually range from 0.01 to 1.0 N/m, resulting in force of the order of few nN, for nm size deflections. The spring constant decides the response time of the AFM and for the fast response time cantilever must have high resonance frequency. Since a cantilever with high spring constant k, will not respond easily to strong forces, a smaller cantilever with small mass and hence high resonance frequency is preferred.

3.1. Modes of Operation

As the distance between the tip and the surface is decreased, the interacting force can be attractive or repulsive. According to the interactive force between the tip and the sample surface, the AFM is classified as repulsive or Contact mode and attractive or Non contact mode. It is also possible to change the operating separation continuously by oscillating the tip, and the resulting tapping mode operation combines the advantages of both modes of operation.

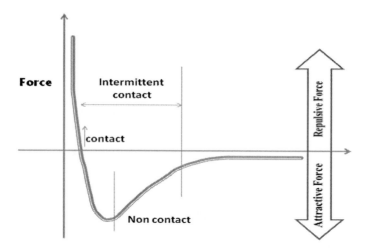

Figure 3.2. The force-distance curve showing the contact repulsive and non-contact attractive modes of operation.

3.1.1. Contact mode

In contact mode, the AFM measures hard-sphere repulsive force between the tip and the sample. The tip at the end of the cantilever lightly touches the surface of the sample and since the repulsive force-distance curve is very sharp, a very high resolution is possible in this mode. However, the disadvantage of operating the AFM in this mode is that the strong force may modify the surface itself, hence this mode is not ideal for soft surfaces like polymers. Besides that, this mode allows only topographic studies and the phase measurement studies are not possible, which are done in intermittent contact mode described later on.

Problems with contact mode are caused by excessive tracking forces applied by the probe to the sample. The effects can be reduced by minimizing the tracking force of the probe on the sample, but there are practical limits to the magnitude of the force, that can be controlled by the user during operation in ambient environments. Under ambient conditions, sample surfaces are covered by a layer of adsorbed gases

Under ambient conditions, sample surfaces may be covered by many contaminants such as water vapor and nitrogen. As the cantilever touches this layer, a meniscus is formed and the cantilever is pulled, toward the sample surface by up to 100 nun surface tension force. This meniscus force can be neutralized by operating with the probe and the sample immersed in liquid, a mode referred to as liquid mode.

3.1.2. Non-Contact Mode

In this mode the tip surface distance is kept 5-15 nm, above the surface, in such a way that the Van der Waals attractive forces are dominant and the tip does not touch the sample. Since the attractive Van der Waals forces are substantially weaker than the attractive forces used in contact mode, the force detection is more difficult. In this technique, the tip is given a small oscillation and AC detection methods are used to detect force gradient dependent changes in amplitude, phase, or frequency of the oscillating cantilever. However, it should be noted that for optimum resolution, it is necessary to measure force gradients from Van der Waals forces which are effective only up to a few nanometers from the sample surface, whereas, the contaminant layer is substantially thicker. Hence, the imaging of the true surface with non-contact AFM becomes difficult as the oscillating probe gets trapped in the fluid layer or oscillates above the Van der Waals force limits.

Many types of samples, including semiconductors and insulators, trap electrostatic charge which can result in additional attractive forces between the probe and sample and effectively create a frictional force as the probe scans over the sample. This frictional force can also damage the sample, slow the cantilever probe and distort the resulting image. Such samples and others which can not be immersed in liquid are to be studied in the Non-contact Mode or in tapping mode described below.

3.1.3. Intermittent Contact Mode (Tapping Mode)

In this mode the tip vibrates with a high frequency in such a way that it is in the repulsive force region for a short time, though remaining in the attractive force region for most of the time. This method facilitates the measurements of soft surfaces and allows phase measurement related applications, while retaining the accuracy of contact mode measurements. With the Tapping mode technique (as shown in Figure 3.3), the cantilever, primarily made of silicon, is oscillated at or near its resonance frequency with amplitude ranging from 20 nm-100 nm. The frequency of oscillation could be on either side of the resonant frequency. The probe is then brought closer to the sample surface until it begins to tap intermittently.

A schematic for the AFM operation is shown in figure 3.4. The difference signal from the photo-diode is fed to the control software which enables the tip to maintain either a constant force or constant height above the sample. In the constant force mode the piezo-electric transducer maintains the height above the surface so as to maintain a constant force on the cantilever by keeping the distance between tip and sample constant and the resulting movement of the piezo describes the surface profile.

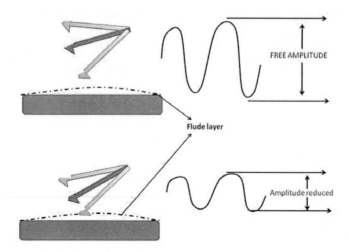

Figure 3.3. Tapping mode AFM where the amplitude and phase of the oscillations changes with force.

On the other hand, in the constant height mode the deflection force on the sample is recorded, while maintaining the piezo at a constant height. In this mode, the detection apparatus measures the vertical deflection of the cantilever, while the tip scans the surface of the sample, and that indicates the local sample height.

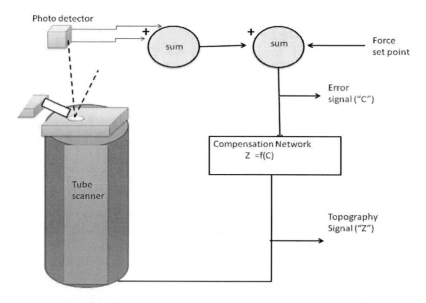

Figure 3.4. The constant force mode of operation where the feedback loop moves the piezo so as to keep the force on the cantilever constant.

The basic schematic diagram of AFM showing all the essential components is shown in Fig 3.5 below. Showing the continuous contact (dark lines) and tapping (light lines) mode AFM. A detector consisting of four photodiodes is also shown. Normal scanning is done perpendicularly to the long cantilever axis i.e., perpendicular to the plane of picture. In this arrangement the (A+ B) - (C+D) signal gives the topographic data. However, it is also possible to measure the frictional force from this arrangement as the (A+C) - (B+D) signal will vary due to the torsion of the cantilever and hence can provide lateral force information.

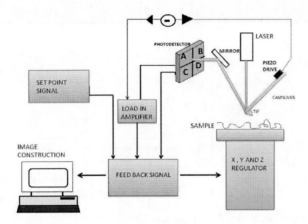

Figure 3.5. The basic schematic diagram of AFM showing all the essential component.

The tapping mode image of Si(100) surfaces after irradiation with 1.5keV Ar[+] beam irradiation at 45^0 incidence at fluence of 5.1 x 10^{17} ions/cm^2 is shown in Fig3.6. The image shows formation of ripples with wavelength of 17 nm on its surface[from Ref. 8].

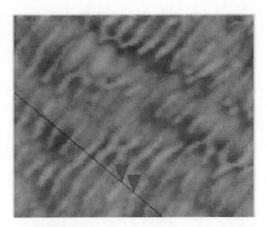

Figure 3.6. The tapping mode image (5μ x5μ) of Is(100) surfaces after irradiation with 1.5keV Are[+] beam irradiation (45^0 incidence at fluency of 5.1 x 10^{17} ions/cm^2.is shown in Figure The image shows formation of ripples with wavelength of 17 nm, on its surface as shown by red marks [From Ref. 8: P. Kulriya et al, *Ncul. Instr. Meth.* B. 2006, 244,958, Copyright (2006) by Elsevier].

4. FORCE-DISTANCE (F-D) STUDIES

The atomic force microscopy can also be used for characterizing the mechanical and adhesion properties of the sample surface. This is done in the force-distance or force-volume mapping mode, which is a very sensitive tool for measuring interaction forces, such as adhesion or compression with a lateral resolution of only nanometers. The typical force-distance curve is shown in Fig 4.1

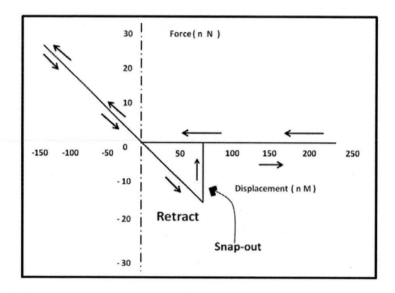

Figure 4.1. Typical force-distance curve using AFM piezo.

The retracting portion of the force curve may follow the approach curve in principle. However, practically, there is often a hysteresis and the most common type of hysteresis is due to the force of adhesion, which can be studied using F-D curve. The curve also gives information about the hardness of the surface.

A typical force volume plot for PET film irradiated with 200 MeV Ag ions at fluence 5 × 10^{12} ions/cm^2, is shown in fig 4.2a. The image includes the maps of FD measurements at all the points on source. Fig 4.2b shows such a plot for point 1.

a)

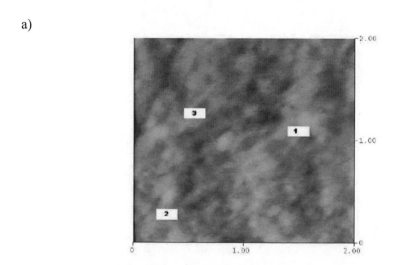

Figure 4.2. Continued on next page.

b)

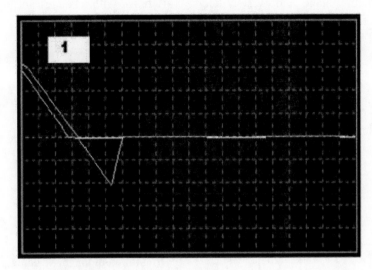

Figure 4.2. Force volume plot for PET film irradiated with 200 MeV Ag ions at fluence 5×10^{12} ions/cm^2. The image (a) includes the maps of FD measurements at all the points on source, whereas (b) shows such a plot for point 1. The X axis represents the force and Y axis represents the value (Z).

5. MAGNETIC FORCE MICROSCOPY (MFM)

The MFM is an effective tool for investigating magnetic signals from a sample with a lateral position resolution on submicron scale, thus facilitating magnetic domain structure and reversal process studies among others. In MFM the usual silicon or silicon nitride cantilever is coated with a magnetic (e.g. Co/Cr) thin film. For magnetic imaging at submicron scale, it is necessary to separate the magnetic image from the topographic effects. For this purpose, scanning is done in two steps. In the first scan normal topographic image is taken. In the second scan the cantilever is lifted for such a height that Van der Wall's forces are negligible and the cantilever is affected only by the long-range magnetic forces.

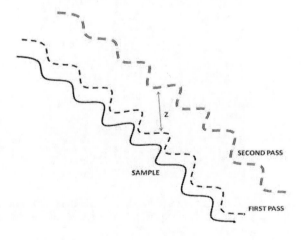

Figure 5.1. The principle of the MFM scan after lifting the tip.

The magnetic image shows step height variations with changes in magnetic field direction as is shown below in Fig 5.2

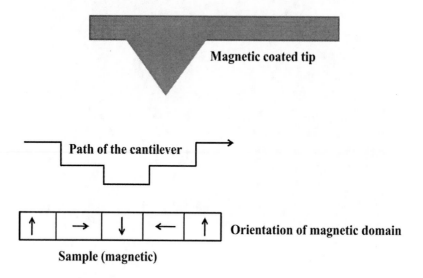

Figure 5.2 Magnetic image shows step height variations with changes in magnetic field direction.

Figure 5.3 shows MFM image of 92 MeV Si ion irradiation induced magnetization in C_{60} samples for fluences (a) pristine, (b) 1×10^{13}, (c) 3×10^{13}, and (d) 5×10^{13} ions/cm^2. The unirradiated sample shows no contrast, whereas irradiated films show clear magnetic signal, showing magnetization of the samples. The magnetization has been attributed to the formation of amorphous carbon network and incorporation of oxygen in the irradiated films. [9]

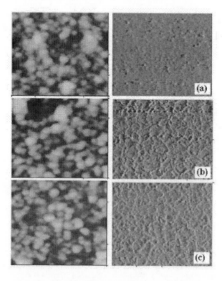

Figure 5.3. MFM image of 92 MeV Si ion irradiation induced magnetization in C_{60} samples for fluences (a) pristine, (b) 1×10^{12} , (c) 1×10^{13} ions/cm^2 [From Ref 9: A. Kumar et al, *Phys. Rev.* B. 2007, 74, 153409, Copyright (2007) by American Physical Society].

6. CONDUCTING ATOMIC FORCE MICROSCOPY

Conducting atomic force microscopy (C-AFM) facilitates measurement of localized conductivity variations for samples with medium conductivity. As a suitable bias (up to a few volts) is applied to the tip, the C-AFM allows the user to measure current, which may vary from a few pA to the order of μA, while maintaining a lateral resolution available with AFM. As the topography and current are measured simultaneously, it is possible to make a direct correlation of a sample location with its electrical properties. In this mode, while scanning the sample, a DC bias is applied between the tip and the sample and a current amplifier measures the current passing through the sample even as the topographic image is simultaneously obtained (figure 8). This current provides the information about the local conductivity of the sample.

6.1 I-V Characteristics Using C-AFM

In addition to the imaging mode, C-AFM also allows one to measure local current-voltage (I-V) spectra. To obtain I-V spectra, the scanning is stopped and sample bias is increased while the tip is held in the desired location. It is also possible to obtain I-Z spectra, for which the scanner is moved in the Z-direction while keeping the sample bias constant and the resulting current through the sample is plotted.

7. CONDUCTING TRACKS IN SHI IRRADIATED FULLERENE FILMS

Ion beam irradiation induced effects on fullerenes have been studied by different groups [10-19]. The SHI irradiation induced surface modifications have been studied using STM and AFM. The dimerization, polymerization and damage of C_{60} films [10-12], as well as sputtering from C_{60} films has been observed [13,14]. Lebrun et al have studied 420-625 MeV Xe ions induced ionization and fragmentation of C_{60}[17]. In other studies, 189 MeV Ag, 110 MeV N and 50 MeV Si ion induced polymerization and damage of C_{60} film, besides an increase in conductivity in C_{60} bulk samples [11,16] is also observed. In a similar study in DLC film, Krauser et al [20] have shown formation of narrow conducting ion tracks. We have shown formation of conducting ion tracks in C_{60} films by conducting AFM. This result has been ascribed to the disintegration of the C_{60} units or their amorphization.

Fullerene thin films were deposited on Si(100) substrate by resistive heating of commercially available C_{60} (99.9%), in a Ta boat. The thickness of the film as measured by a quartz crystal thickness monitor was 150 nm. A thin layer of Au was first deposited on the Si substrate to provide a proper contact (Figure 9.1), that allows the measurement of transverse conductivity across the C_{60} layer.

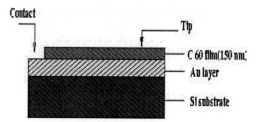

Figure 7.1. The arrangement for making the contact for C-AFM measurement. The arrangement allows the transverse measurement of current through C_{60} film only [from Ref. 21: A. Tripathi et al, *Nucl. Instru. Meth.* B. 2006, 244, 15, Copyright (2006) by Elsevier].

The samples were irradiated with 120 MeV Au ion beam from IUAC Pelletron with fluences varying from 2×10^{10} to 5×10^{11} ions/cm^2. The fluence was selected in such a way so as to enable single ion impact studies. The topographic and conductivity features are studied with Nanoscope IIIa SPM at IUAC, New Delhi, in the C-AFM mode. The measurements are done with doped diamond coated silicon nitride (DDESP) tip of 15 nm radius.

7.1. Surface Conductivity Study

For the pristine samples, no current through the sample was observed for sample bias up to 10V, which confirms the insulating nature of the fullerene film. On the other hand, the irradiated sample shows conductive tracks on the surface and 5 nA current is observed for a bias of 500 mV. The current image of conducting paths in the sample irradiated with a fluence of 2×10^{10} ions/cm^2, is shown in figure 7.2, where the impact sites are shown by regions of higher current separated by insulating zones. Figure 7.3 shows the 3D projection of the current image.

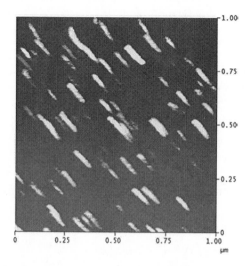

Figure 7.2. 1μ x 1μ two dimensional current image of a C_{60} film irradiated with 120 MeV Au ions (2×10^{10} ions/cm^2). The conducting impact sites are shown by high current bright zones. [from Ref. 21: A. Tripathi et al, *Nucl. Instru. Meth.* B. 2006, 244, 15, Copyright (2006) by Elsevier].

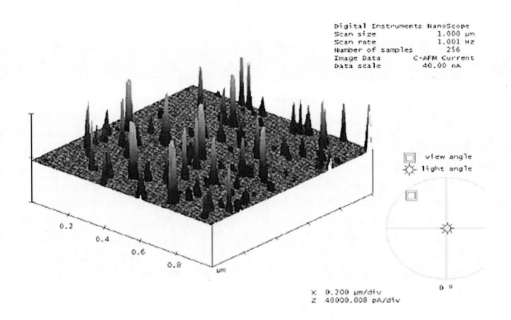

Figure 7.3. 1μ x 1μ 3dimensional current image of a C60 film irradiated with 120 MeV Au ions (2x10^{10} ions/cm^2). Different heights for current peaks are attributed to very close/ overlapping ion impacts. [from Ref. 22: A. Tripathi et al, *Nucl. Instru. Meth*. B. 2005, 236, 186, Copyright (2005) by Elsevier].

The current image of sample irradiated with a fluence of 2x10^{11} ions/cm^2, is shown in Figure 7.4, where many more impact zones are seen, commensurate with increased fluence.

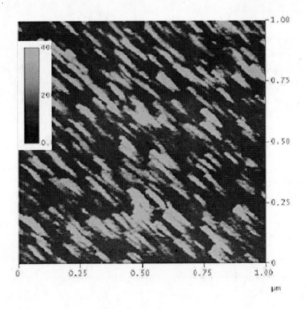

Figure 7.4 1. μ x 1 μ three dimensional Current image of a C 60 film irradiated with 120 MeV Au ions (2x10^{11} ions/cm^2). Many more impact zones are seen.

As the fluence is further increased to 5×10^{11} ions/cm^2, there is an overall increase in conductivity, with average current increasing to 10 nA.

7.2. Conducting Tracks Formation:

The increase in conductivity after irradiation is attributed to electronic energy loss induced transformation from insulating C_{60} to more conducting graphite like carbon. In crystalline form fullerene balls are well separated and weakly bonded to each other by van der walls force, which makes the material highly insulating. Under the ion impact fullerene cages break up into carbon atoms which disperse and serve as centers for hopping conductivity. These carbon atoms lying along the ion tracks provide conducting paths in the insulating fullerene film. The formation of conducting nano tracks is also facilitated by the polymerization of the fullerene molecules around the ion track. The polymerization occurs in the electronic energy loss induced high temperature and pressure region surrounding the ion path. This polymerized fullerene exhibits increased conductivity. The effect is shown in Figure 7.5, where the current image shows a larger dimension of high conducting zone, as compared to the topographical image.

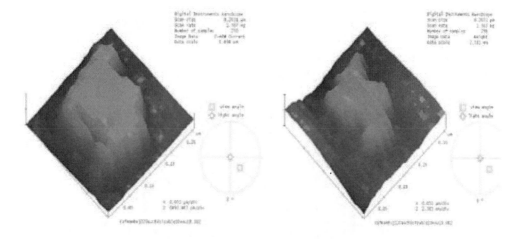

Figure 7.5. Topography (left) and current (right) image of a single impact zone. The current image shows a larger size of the conducting zone as compared to topographical image. [from Ref .21: A. Tripathi et al, *Nucl. Instru. Meth.* B. 2006, 244, 15, Copyright (2006) by Elsevier].

The number density of conducting zones does not match with the incidence ion fluence and instead a ratio of 0.4 conducting zones per ion impact is observed. Besides this, the height of current peaks shows that some of the tracks have higher conductivity than others. This observation has been attributed to the observation of overlapping conducting zones around ion tracks as shown in Fig 7.6. The ion impact sites have statistically random distribution and some of them are very close to each other. The tip, with a relatively large tip radius (~15 nm), images few tracks simultaneously resulting in observation of a conducting zone with a dimension larger than that of a single track. It is clear that the image of impact zone as seen consists of three overlapping tracks.

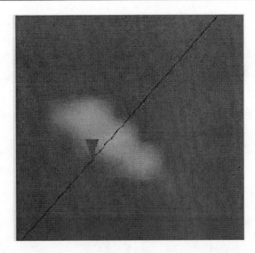

Figure 7.6. Section analysis of current image of a conducting ion track in two different directions. The image shows three overlapping tracks. [from Ref. 21: A. Tripathi et al, *Nucl. Instru. Meth.* B. 2006, 244, 15, Copyright (2006) by Elsevier].

7.3 I-V Characteristic Using C-AFM

The I-V characteristics of the irradiated fullerene films at different fluences is shown in Fig 7.7. The conductivity along the ion tracks increases with increasing ion fluence. The increase in conductivity with increasing fluence, is due to the combination of single ion impacts as mentioned earlier.

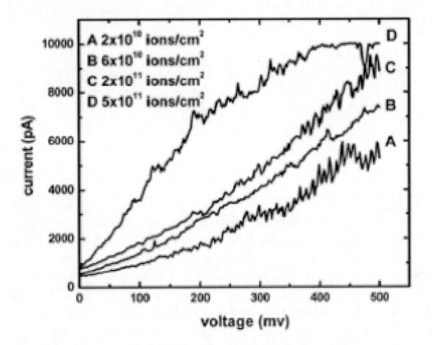

Figure 7.7. The current voltage characteristics recorded at an ion impact site after irradiation with 120 MeV Au ions. The plot shows an overall increase in current, with increasing fluence for the same bias. [From Ref 21: A. Tripathi et al, *Nucl. Instru. Meth.* B. 2006, 244, 15, Copyright (2006) by Elsevier].

7.4. Field Emission Characteristics of CNWS

These conducting tracks are linear and since they are aligned and have an effective high aspect ratio, they have a potential application from a field emission perspective. Their field emission properties of these CNWs are shown in Figure 7.8 [23]. We have observed a threshold field of about 9 V/μm for the irradiated films with CNWs whereas the unirradiated pristine films show a breakdown field at 51 V/μ m.

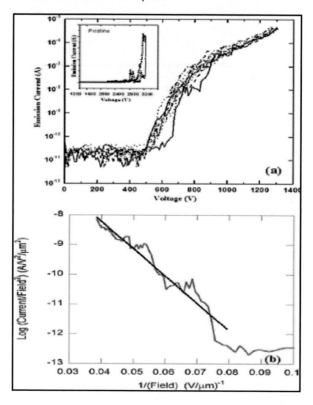

Figure 7.8. The emission current versus applied voltage for the CNWs. the curves show four measurements with good reproducibility of emission. Inset curve shows emission from an unirradiated fullerene film. In figure (b), the Fowler–Nordheim representation of one of the curves. [From Ref. 23 A. Kumar et al, J. Appl, phys, 2007, 102, 044305, Copyright (2007) by American Institute of Physics].

The field emission properties of pristine film, repeated four times is shown in the inset of Figure 7.8a. The Fowler–Nordheim representation of one of these field emission characteristic curves is shown in Figure 7.8b . From the linear fitting of these curves, we can estimate field enhancement factor. If we assume the nanowires work function of 5 eV, we estimate the value as 429. At the threshold applied field of 9 V/μ m, the average local electric field is 3.8 V/nm, which is of the order of emission from carbon nanotubes [24]. Lower values of applied field, corresponding to higher enhancement factors, are sometimes reported from ideal aligned nanowires and nanotubes. [24,25]. However, at high areal densities inter nanowire proximity screening becomes a significant factor. According to Nilsson et al. [25], the ideal average separation between nanowires should be about twice the length of nanowire. Since the typical nanowire lengths is 500 nm (same as film thickness), and the average separation between impacts sites approximately 710 nm, there is a possibility of proximity screening. The conductivity of the SHI irradiated fullerene thin film shows large increase which has been attributed to the fact that the swift heavy ions break the fullerene cages within the track to form nanocrystalline graphite embedded in a -C carbon, which is electrically more conducting than the parent fullerene molecule.

CONCLUSION

A brief introduction of the scanning probe microscopy (SPM) techniques (such as STM, AFM, MFM, C-AFM, and associated IV and FV studies), which are widely used in characterization of ion beam induced nanostructures is given. We have demonstrated the fabrication of conducting carbon nanowires in fullerene matrix by heavy ion irradiation. The conductive AFM measurements show that the nanowires are parallel to each other and perpendicular to substrate. The electrical and field emission properties of these carbon nanostructures are studied. These CNWs may be useful for better field emitters and large scale applications. The keV atom beams induce the formation of ripples and nanodots on InP surface and their structures depends on the ion incident angle and atom beam fluence.

ACKNOWLEDGMENTS

I would like to thank all my collaborators/scholars whose work has been included in this contribution, namely, Dr Amit Kumar, Dr. D. Kabiraj, Mr. P. Kulriya, Dr. J.D. Carey, Dr. J.C. Pivin, Dr D.K. Avasthi and others mentioned in references.

10. REFERENCES

[1]   Binnig, G.; Rohrer, H.; Gerber, Ch. and Weibel, E. *Phys. Rev. Lett.* 1982, 49,57.

[2]   Eigler, D.M.; Lutz C.P. and Rudge, W.E. *Nature*, 1991, 352, 600.

[3]   Eigler, D.M.; Weiss, P.S. and Schweizer, E.K.; *Phys. Rev. Lett.,* 1991 66, 1189.

[4]   Watanabe, H.;Fujita, J.;Ochiai, Y.;Matsui, S. and Ichikauo, M. *Jpn. J. of Appl. Phys.* 1995, 34, 6950.

[5]   Banhart, F. *J. Appl. Phys.* 1997, 81, 3440.

[6]   Tripathi, A.; Singh, J.P.; Ahuja, R.; Dutt, R.N.; Kanjilal, D.; Guha, A.; Biswas, A.; Roychaudhary, A.K. *Rev Sci Instru.* 2001, 72, 3884.

[7]   Tripathi, A.; Khan, S. A.; Kumar, M.; Baranwal, B.; Krishna, R.; Pnadey, A.C. *Nucl. Instru. Meth.* B. 2006, 244, 225.

[8]   P. Kulriya, P.; Tripathi, A.; Kabiraj, D.; Khan, S.A.; Avasthi, D.K. *Nucl. Instru. Meth.* B. 2006, 244,95.

[9]   Kumar, A.; Avasthi, D.K.; Pivin, J.C.; Tripathi, A.; Singh, F. *Phys. Rev.* B. 2007, 74, 153409.

[10]   Itoh, A.; Tsuchida, H.; Miyabe, K.; Imai, M.; Imanishim, B. Nucl. Instru. And Meth. B. 1997, 129, 363.

[11] Bajwa, N.; Ingale, A.; Avasthi, D.K.; Kumar, R.; Tripathi, A.; Dharamvir , K. and Jindal, V.K. J. Appl. Phys. 2003, 94, 326. Bajwa, N.' Ingale, A.; Avasthi, D.K.; Kumar, R.; Tripathi, A.; Dharamvir , K. and Jindal, V.K. *J. Appl. Phys.* 2008, 104, 1.

[12] Lotha, S.; Ingale, A.; Avasthi, D.K.; Mittal, V.K.; Mishra, S.; Rustagi, K.C.; Gupta, A.; Kulkarni, V.N. and Khathing, D.T. Solid State commun. 1999, 111, 55.

[13] Ghosh, S.; Avasthi, D. K.; Tripathi. A.; Srivastavta, S. K.; Nageswara Rao, S.V.S; Som, T.; Mittal, V.K.; Fruner, F.; Assman, W. *Nucl. Instru. And Meth. B.* 2002, 190,169.

[14] S. Ghosh, S.; Avasthi, D.K.; Tripathi. A.; Srivastavta, S.K.; Nageswara Rao, S.V.S.; Som, T.; Mittal, V.K.; Fruner, F.; Assman, W. *Nucl. Instru. And Meth.* B. 2003, 212, 431.

[15] Papaléo, R.M.; Hérino, R.; Hallén, A.; Demirev, P.; Sunquist, B. U. R. *Nucl. Instru. and Meth.* B. 1996, 152, 274.

[16] Tripathi, A.; Kabiraj, D.; Kumar, A.; Khan, S.A.; Baranwal, V.; Avasthi, D.K. et al, Proc. of DAE Solid State Physics Symposium, 2004, 49, 412.

[17] LeBrun, T.; Berry, H.G.; Cheng, S.; Dunford, R.W.; Esbensen, H.; Gemmell, D.S. and Kanter, E.P. Phys. Rev. Lett. 1994, 72, 3965.

[18] Foerster, C. E.; Serbena, F. C.; Lepienski, M.; Baltista, D.L.; Zawislak, F. C. *Nucl. Instru. and Meth.* B. 1999, 148, 634.

[19] Zawislak, F.C.; Baptista, D.L.; Behar, M.; Fink, D.; Grande, P.L.; Jornada, J.A.H.da. *Nucl. Instru. and Meth.* B. 1999, 149, 336.

[20] Krauser, J.; Zollondz, J.H.; Weidinger. and Trautmann, C. *J. Appl. Phys.* 2003, 94, 1959.

[21] Tripathi, A.; Kumar, A.; Kabiraj, D.; Khan, S.A.; Baranwal, V.; Avasthi, D.K. *Nucl. Instru. Meth.* B. 2006, 244, 15.

[22] Tripathi, A.; Kumar, A.; Singh, F.; Kabiraj, D.; Avasthi, D.K.; Pivin, J.C. *Nucl. Instru. Meth.* B. 2006, 236, 186.

[23] Kumar, A.; Avasthi, D.K.; Tripathi, A.; Filip, L.D.;Carey, J.D.; Pivin, J.C. J. Appl, phys, 2007, 102, 044305.

[24] J. M. Bonard, J.M.; Gaal, R.; Garaj, S.; Thien-Nga, L.; Forro, L.; Takahashi, K.; Kokai, F.; Yudasaka, M. and S. Iijima, S. J. Appl. Phys., 2002, 91, 10107.

[25] Nilsson, L.; Groening, O.; Emmenegger, C.; Kuettel, O.; Schaller, E.; Schlapbach, L.; Kind, H. Bonard, J.-M. and Kern, K. *Appl. Phys. Lett.* 2000, 76, 2071.

In: Synthesis and Engineering of Nanostructures...   ISBN 978-1-62100-261-1
Editors: Devesh Kumar Avasthi & Jean Claude Pivin   © 2012 Nova Science Publishers, Inc

Chapter 16

STUDIES ON ION IRRADIATION INDUCED MODIFICATIONS OF OPTICAL PROPERTIES OF Ag-C$_{60}$, Ag-C$_{70}$ AND Ag/a-C NANOCOMPOSITE THIN FILMS

R. Singhal[*] and D. K. Avasthi

Inter University Accelerator Centre, Post Box No. 10502, New Delhi 110067, India

ABSTRACT

We report the swift heavy ion induced modifications of optical properties of nanocomposite thin films of silver-fullerene (C$_{60}$), silver-fullerene (C$_{70}$) and silver-amorphous carbon (a-C). Nanocomposite thin films of C$_{60}$, C$_{70}$ and a-C containing Ag nanoparticles (NPs) were irradiated by 120 MeV Ag ions at different fluences. A regular blue shift of surface plasmon resonance (SPR) wavelength of Ag nanoparticles was observed in all three matrices, C$_{60}$, C$_{70}$ and a-C with increasing ion fluence. The shift in case of fullerene C$_{60}$ and C$_{70}$ matrix is explained by the structural transformation of fullerene into a-C with ion irradiation whereas the shift in case of a-C matrix, is due to the ordering of a-C network with ion irradiation. In all studied matrices, a growth of Ag NPs with increasing ion fluence is observed by transmission electron microscopy. The growth of NPs is explained in the frame of thermal spike model. The present work demonstrates the possibility to locally excite the SPR of Ag NPs at desired wavelength, when they are synthesized in fullerene matrix. This could be important for developing more efficient optical sensors.

1. INTRODUCTION

Nanocomposite thin film that consists of small noble metal nanoparticles has attracted the attention of researchers due to their applications in chemical and biological sensors, optical

---

[*] Author to whom any correspondence should be addressed. Email: rahuliuac@gmail.com, dka@iuac.ernet.in.

waveguides or filters and many other devices [1-3]. Among noble metal NPs (Cu, Ag and Au), silver ones show strongest SPR. When electromagnetic light is incident on these NPs, they exhibit a strong absorption band which is known as SPR band of Ag NPs. The SPR frequency is a function of NPs shape, size, dipolar interactions and the refractive index of the surrounding matrix [4]. The nanocomposite of Ag with carbon is of interest due to wide range of the value of the refractive index (1.5 to 2.3, from a-C to fullerenes) [5,6] among different allotropes of carbon which provides the possibility to tune the SPR wavelength of Ag NPs as per the requirement in various applications. The transparency of fullerenes (C_{60} and C_{70}) in the visible region and their reduced reactivity with noble metals make nanocomposite of fullerenes and noble metals particularly interesting for plasmonic integrated devices. Fullerene is a functional material having applications in various fields such as memory devices, drug delivery, catalysis, electronic devices, and coatings and in biology [7-9]. By embedding Ag NPs in fullerenes, the optical properties of these NPs as well as the properties of fullerene co-exist and therefore can be used simultaneously. The main issue with Ag NPs is, their possible oxidation in oxide matrices (Al_2O_3 and SiO_2) at ambient conditions [10,11] when they are porous. Carbon based matrices may be more suitable to protect the Ag NPs against oxidation. Another interest in Ag- fullerene nanocomposite thin films is the tuning of SPR wavelength due to the transformation of fullerene into a-C by damage of fullerene with ion irradiation which significantly changes the refractive index of the matrix. The tuning of SPR frequency is useful in many fields, such as surface enhanced Raman spectroscopy and non linear optical properties of metal nanoclusters [12-16]. The use of high energy ions as a tool for the tuning of SPR is also interesting due to its spatial selectivity. The SPR frequency of noble metal NPs has been tuned in many ways, for example by annealing the composite material at different temperatures [17,18] or by varying the metal atomic fraction [19,20]. Nevertheless, using these means, it is not possible to excite multiple SPR bands in a single optical device. One can obtain two SPR bands from a single sample, for example, by introducing Cu NPs with Au/Ag NPs simultaneously in a given matrix, provided they don't form an alloy [21] or by depositing multilayer of different noble metals [22,23]. One may expect that ion beam induced tuning provides a possibility of exciting multiple SPR bands with desired frequencies in a single sample, simply by irradiating different areas of film with different fluences. The study of stability of these nanocomposite thin films under ion irradiation is also important for their application in radiation environment.

The stability of fullerene C_{60} under various perturbations such as high temperature, high pressure, laser irradiation and ion irradiation has been extensively studied by us and various other groups [24-33]. In a recent studies, we investigated the stability of fullerene C_{70} under 120 MeV Au and Ag ion irradiation [34,35]. In this chapter, we discuss the effect of 120 MeV Ag ion irradiation on optical properties of nanocomposite thin films of Ag-C_{70}, Ag-C_{60} and Ag/a-C.

2. SYNTHESIS OF SILVER-FULLERENE AND SILVER-CARBON NANOCOMPOSITES AND IRRADIATION DETAILS

Ag NPs in fullerene matrix (separately in C_{60} and C_{70}) were synthesized by thermal co-deposition of Ag and fullerene from two crucibles. Thin films were deposited on different substrates such as glass, Si and carbon coated Cu grids in a high vacuum chamber. Films of a-C containing Ag NPs were also synthesized by co-sputtering of Ag and graphite using the atom beam sputtering setup, designed and built at IUAC New Delhi [36]. Fast Ar atoms of 1.5 keV energy, delivered by a wide beam atom source were used for co-sputtering. The vacuum in the chamber before deposition was 3×10^{-6} mbar and during the flow of Ar gas was 1.5×10^{-3} mbar. The deposition was performed simultaneously on several pieces of Si and glass of 1×1 cm^2 and carbon coated Cu grids. The metal concentration and thickness for all types of films on Si substrates were measured by Rutherford Backscattering Spectroscopy (RBS). The detector was kept at an angle of 165° with respect to the direction of the incident 2.4 MeV He^{++} beam provided by ARAMIS accelerator at CSNSM. In order to quantify the film thickness and metal atomic fraction in the films, Rutherford backscattering spectra were simulated by Rutherford Universal Manipulation Program (RUMP) [37]. The Ag atomic fractions were estimated to be 28, 27 and 17% for the as deposited films of Ag-C$_{60}$, Ag-C$_{70}$ and Ag/a-C respectively. The film thickness was found to be ~ 45 nm for the Ag-C$_{60}$ /Ag-C$_{70}$ nanocomposites and ~ 22 nm for the Ag/a-C nanocomposite. No oxygen contamination was detected in other measurements with a He beam of 3.05 MeV, undergoing a non Rutherford scattering by O atoms with scattering cross section 45 times greater than that of Rutherford one. The Ag-C$_{60}$, Ag-C$_{70}$ and Ag/a-C nanocomposite films on glass substrates and TEM grids were irradiated with a beam of 120 MeV Ag ions delivered by 15 UD Pelletron accelerator at Inter University Accelerator Centre, New Delhi. The vacuum in the chamber during the irradiation was of the order of 10^{-7} mbar. The ion fluence was varied from 1×10^{12} to 3×10^{13} ions/cm^2. UV-Visible absorption spectra of pristine and irradiated films of Ag-C$_{60}$, Ag-C$_{70}$ and Ag/a-C nanocomposite on glass substrates were recorded using a dual beam U-3300 Hitachi spectrophotometer. Transmission Electron Microscope (TEM) images of pristine and irradiated films deposited on carbon coated Cu grids were taken using a FEI TECNAI 20 microscope equipped with a LaB$_6$ filament and a CCD camera. The microscope was operated at 200 kV. Raman spectra of pristine and irradiated films on glass substrates were recorded using a Renishaw in-Via Raman microscope. The Ar ion laser excitation at 514 nm and at very low power (< 1 mW, 20 x objective) was used to avoid any heating effect.

3. STUDY OF PRISTINE AND IRRADIATED NANOCOMPOSITE THIN FILMS

The absorption spectra of pristine and irradiated films of Ag-C$_{60}$, Ag-C$_{70}$ and Ag/a-C nanocomposite on glass substrate are shown in figure 1(a), (b) and (c) respectively [38,39]. The spectra of pristine Ag-C$_{70}$, Ag-C$_{60}$ and Ag/a-C films show a broad SPR band at 528, 522 and 430 nm respectively. The presence of SPR band indicates the formation of Ag NPs in all three cases, Ag-C$_{60}$, Ag-C$_{70}$ and Ag/a-C. The SPR positions are consistent with effective medium theories which predict that an increase in the refractive index of the matrix shifts the SPR at higher wavelength. The refractive index of fullerene C$_{70}$, C$_{60}$ and a-C are ~ 2.3, 2.1 and 1.6 respectively [5,6]. It appears from the figure 1(a), (b) and (c) that in the case of C$_{60}$ and C$_{70}$ matrices, the SPR band is broader than that in a-C. It is due to the fact that fullerenes (C$_{60}$ and C$_{70}$) show significant absorption in 400 – 700 nm region compared to a-C.

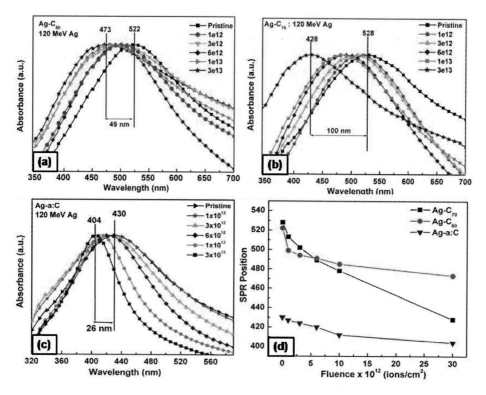

Figure 1. UV-Visible absorption spectra of pristine and 120 MeV Ag ions irradiated nanocomposite films of Ag-C_{60} (figure a), Ag-C_{70} (figure b) and Ag/a-C (figure c) showing a regular blue shift of SPR wavelength with increasing ion fluence. Figure (d) shows the behavior of change in SPR wavelength with ion fluence for Ag-C_{60}, Ag-C_{70} and Ag/a-C nanocomposite films. Figure a is reprinted from [38] R. Singhal et. al., Nuclear Instruments and Methods in Physical Research B 2009, 267, 1349., Copyright (2009) with permission from Elsevier. Figures b, c and d are reprinted from [39] R. Singhal et. al., J. Phys. D: Appl. Phys. 2009, 42, 155103., Copyright (2009) with permission from IOP Publishing Ltd.

In addition, it is clear that in all three cases, SPR band is blue shifted with a little decrease in FWHM with increasing ion fluence. The decrease in FWHM of SPR band is ascribed to the increase in Ag NPs size with ion irradiation, as shown later on the basis of TEM observations. In the case of Ag-C_{60} and Ag-C_{70} nanocomposites, the blue shift after ion irradiation at a fluence of 3 x 10^{13} ions/cm^2 is 49 nm and 100 nm, whereas in the case of Ag/a-C, the blue shift after ion irradiation at a fluence of 3 x 10^{13} ions/cm^2 is 26 nm. Here it is worth mentioning that the atomic concentration of Ag is ~ 27-28% in the case of Ag-C_{60} and Ag-C_{70} nanocomposite whereas it is ~ 17% in the case of Ag/a-C nanocomposite which makes it difficult to compare the magnitude of blue shift in case of fullerene and a-C matrix. Figure 1(d) shows the pattern of change in SPR wavelength with fluence of 120 MeV Ag ions for the Ag-C_{60}, Ag-C_{70} and Ag/a-C nanocomposites thin films. In order to understand the blue shift in SPR wavelength and its different magnitude in all three cases, we performed transmission electron microscopy and Raman spectroscopy on the pristine and irradiated films to observe the micro structural evolution of Ag NPs and structural change in host matrix with ion irradiation.

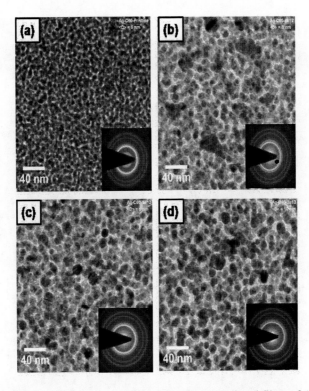

Figure 2. Bright field images of pristine and 120 MeV Ag ions irradiated films of Ag-C_{60} nanocomposite at the fluences of 6 x 10^{12}, 1 x 10^{13} and 3 x 10^{13} ions/cm^2. Selected area electron diffraction (SAED) pattern for the pristine and irradiated film is shown in the inset of each bright field image which confirms the fcc phase of Ag NPs. Reprinted from [38] R. Singhal et. al., Nuclear Instruments and Methods in Physical Research B 2009, 267, 1349., Copyright (2009) with permission from Elsevier.

Figures 2 and 3 show the bright field images of pristine and irradiated films of Ag-C_{60} and Ag-C_{70}, respectively at fluences of 6 x 10^{12}, 1 x 10^{13} and 3 x 10^{13} Ag ions/cm^2. In both cases, the TEM image of pristine film is labeled (a) whereas (b), (c) and (d) are for the films irradiated at fluences of 6 x 10^{12}, 1 x 10^{13} and 3 x 10^{13} ions/cm^2. Spherical Ag particles can be seen in the pristine and irradiated films, with average diameter <D> of 6 and 7 nm in the pristine films of Ag-C_{60} and Ag-C_{70} nanocomposite, respectively. Particles grow in size with ion irradiation and their average diameter were found to be 8, 9 and 10 nm for Ag-C_{60} and 9, 10 and 11 nm for Ag-C_{70} nanocomposites irradiated at fluences of 6 x 10^{12}, 1 x 10^{13} and 3 x 10^{13} ions/cm^2, respectively. Due to the film thickness (~ 45 nm), Ag NPs are seen to overlap to each other because in planer TEM imaging, projections of all NPs from different depth appear in the image. In such condition, it is difficult to measure the particle size distribution. Therefore arithmetical mean of particle sizes over the particles which are clearly distinguished from other nearby particles, is given as an average particle size. The selected area electron diffraction (SAED) pattern is shown in the inset of each bright field image of nanocomposites. The diffraction rings confirm the Ag metal in fcc phase in both pristine and irradiated films of Ag-C_{60} and Ag-C_{70} nanocomposite.

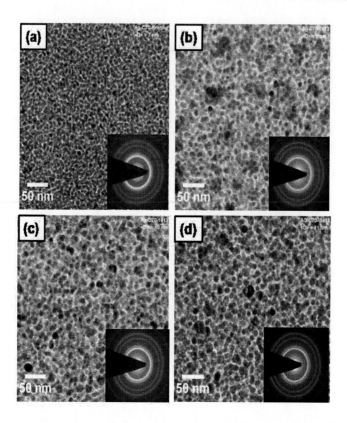

Figure 3. Bright field images of pristine and 120 MeV Ag ions irradiated films of Ag-C_{70} nanocomposite at the fluences of 6 x 10^{12}, 1 x 10^{13} and 3 x 10^{13} ions/cm^2. Selected area electron diffraction (SAED) pattern for the pristine and irradiated film is shown in the inset of each bright field image. Reprinted from [39] R. Singhal et. al., J. Phys. D: Appl. Phys. 2009, 42, 155103., Copyright (2009) with permission from IOP Publishing Ltd.

The crystallinity of thin film of C_{70} is usually poor and therefore no ring is seen in SAED pattern corresponding to C_{70} [40]. On the other hand, thin film of C_{60} on Si substrate is known to crystallize in fcc phase [41,42] but no ring was seen in the SAED pattern of pristine film of Ag-C_{60} corresponding to fullerene C_{60} which shows the poor crystallinity of C_{60} also in our films. It may be possible because Ag-C_{60} film was grown on glass substrate which is amorphous. Figure 4(a) and (b) show the bright field images of pristine and 120 MeV Ag ion irradiated film of Ag/a-C nanocomposite at a fluence of 3 x 10^{13} ions/cm^2 respectively. Spherical particles are easily seen in the TEM images for both pristine and irradiated films. In this case, the film thickness is small (~ 22 nm) and therefore well separated particles are seen in TEM images. The average diameter <D> was found to be 6.5 and 8.7 nm for the pristine and the film irradiated at a fluence of 3 x 10^{13} ions/cm^2. It is clear from these figures that in the case of Ag/a-C, the size distribution of Ag NPs is not as uniform as for the Ag-fullerene nanocomposite.

Figures 5(a) and (b) show the Raman spectra of pristine films of Ag-C_{60} and Ag-C_{70} nanocomposites. High intensity Raman active modes of fullerene C_{60} and C_{70} are visible in Raman spectra of pristine films of Ag-C_{60} and Ag-C_{70} and are marked by their wavenumbers.

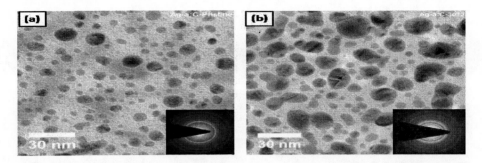

Figure 4. Bright field images of pristine and 120 MeV Ag ions irradiated films of Ag/a-C nanocomposite at a fluences of 3×10^{13} ions/cm^2. Selected area electron diffraction (SAED) pattern for the pristine and irradiated film is shown in the inset of each bright field image. Figure a is reprinted from [39] R. Singhal et. al., J. Phys. D: Appl. Phys. 2009, 42, 155103., Copyright (2009) with permission from IOP Publishing Ltd.

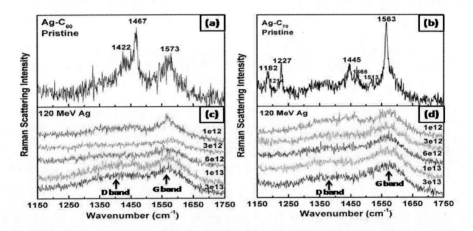

Figure 5. Raman spectra of pristine nanocomposite films of Ag-C$_{60}$ (figure a) and Ag-C$_{70}$ (figure b) showing high intensity Raman active vibrational modes of fullerene C$_{60}$ and C$_{70}$. Figures (c) and (d) show the Raman spectra of 120 MeV Ag ions irradiated nanocomposite films of Ag-C$_{60}$ and Ag-C$_{70}$ respectively at different fluences, showing the transformation of fullerene C$_{60}$ and C$_{70}$ into a-C. Figures (a) and (c) are reprinted from [38] R. Singhal et. al., Nuclear Instruments and Methods in Physical Research B 2009, 267, 1349., Copyright (2009) with permission from Elsevier. Figures (b) and (d) are reprinted from [39] R. Singhal et. al., J. Phys. D: Appl. Phys. 2009, 42, 155103., Copyright (2009) with permission from IOP Publishing Ltd.

Figures 5(c) and (d) show the Raman spectra 120 MeV Ag ion irradiated films of Ag-C$_{60}$ and Ag-C$_{70}$ nanocomposite at different fluences. At a fluence of 1×10^{12} ions/cm^2, the intensity of vibrational Raman modes of two fullerene matrices (C$_{60}$ and C$_{70}$) decreases and the peaks become broad. It is because of the damage of fullerene molecules with ion irradiation. At a fluence of 3×10^{12} ions/cm^2, the vibrational Raman modes of these fullerenes have almost vanished and two broad peaks in the range of 1350 to 1575 cm^{-1} start appearing which are the D and G bands of a-C [43,44]. With further increase in ion fluence, the intensity of these two broad peaks increases. At a fluence a 3×10^{13} ions/cm^2, the D and G peaks of typical a-C network are clearly evolved in the Raman spectrum and it confirms the complete transformation of host fullerene matrix into a-C network in both cases.

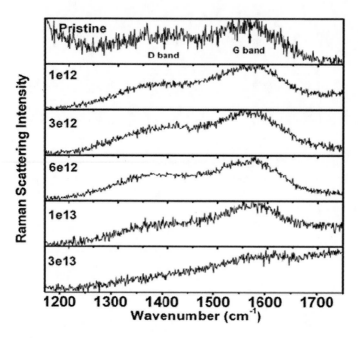

Figure 6: Raman spectra of pristine and irradiated nanocomposite thin films of Ag/a-C at different fluences.

Figure 6 shows the Raman spectrum of pristine and irradiated Ag/a-C nanocomposite films synthesized by co-sputtering. These spectra are fitted by two Gaussian curves and the background is subtracted. The spectrum of pristine film of Ag/a-C shows widespread asymmetric band formed by the superposition of the broad D (as disorder) and comparatively sharp G (as graphite) band, which are the characteristic of an a-C structure with a significant degree of sp^2 hybridization [43,44]. The peak position of D and G bands in pristine film of Ag/a-C is ~1355 and ~1566 cm^{-1}, respectively. When these films are subjected to 120 MeV Ag ion irradiation, an increase in the intensity of D band is observed with increase in ion fluence, whereas G band is almost unaffected. The intensity of D peak arises only from clusters of sp^2 sites in six fold aromatic rings. Its very broad nature in pristine film indicates that in-plane graphitic ordering is very poor in pristine film. The dominance of D peak (increase in intensity) with increasing fluence shows the increase in number of 6 fold aromatic rings in the a-C network, which in turn shows the ordering of a-C. The intensity ratio of D and G bands, i.e. $I(D)/I(G)$, determined using area of D and G peak, of pristine sample is ~ 0.3 and increases with fluence. The intensity ratio of D to G bands, i.e. $I(D)/I(G)$, is significant parameter to analyze the ordering in various forms of a-C. It is proportional to the number of ordered rings and cluster diameter. It is clear that cluster diameter (or net sp^2 content in the film) increases with the increase of fluence. Since the ordered a-C is having conductivity higher than disordered a-C, we expect a decrease in refractive index of the film with increasing fluence.

A growth of Ag NPs from 6 to 10 nm for Ag-C_{60} and 7 to 11 nm for Ag-C_{70} was observed by 120 MeV Ag ion irradiation at a fluence of 3×10^{13} ions/cm^2, whereas in the case of Ag/a-C nanocomposite, a growth from 6.5 to 8.7 nm was observed at a fluence of 3×10^{13} ions/cm^2. The growth of Ag NPs with irradiation, reported above, can be explained in the frame of thermal spike model. In nanocomposite films, Ag metal is present mainly in the form of NPs with some size distribution and a small amount of metal is also expected to present in form of solid solution. Carbon matrix (C_{60}, C_{70} and a-C) and Ag NPs are expected to undergo a phase transition to fluid state during some picoseconds as a result of the transient temperature increase in the ion track. There are several evidences, among which Raman spectra shown in figures 5 (c) and (d), that fullerene (C_{60} or C_{70}) is transformed into a-C after quenching of the temperature spike while in the case of a-C and diamond like carbons, a change in nanocrystalline graphitic cluster size, due to the conversion of sp^3 bonds to sp^2 bonds with ion irradiation has been well studied [45-46]. On the other hand, it has been shown by calculations that the noble metal particles, with sizes of 1-10 nm, in insulator melts due to the transient temperature increase in the ion track [47,48]. Since it is well known that the melting temperature of metal NPs is usually lower than that of bulk metal and this melting temperature decreases with the decrease in particle size [49], we expect that the smaller particles have a larger probability to dissolve in the matrix. Our recent experiments [50-52] indicate that due to the ion beam induced molten state diffusivity, the diffusion of atomic species occurs in transient molten state within the ion track. Since the smaller particles are expected to dissolve more easily in the matrix, the Ag atoms from these particles should contribute to growth of bigger particles. In this way bigger particles grow at the expenses of smaller particles. With the increase in ion fluence, the overlapping of latent tracks occurs which leads to further growth of Ag NPs due to enhanced diffusivity within overlapped ion tracks.

The SPR position of metal NPs can be tailored by controlling several factors such as shape, size, and concentration of NPs and also by the refractive index of the host medium. According to basic calculations, a decrease in the refractive index of the medium induces a blue shift to SPR wavelength for a same size, shape and concentration of the NPs. On the other hand, an increase in the size of the NPs for the same host medium and same shape of the NPs gives a slight red shift to the SPR wavelength of Ag NPs [4]. Here in all cases, we observe the growth of Ag NPs with ion irradiation. According to the calculations, a growth of NPs by 2 – 4 nm induces a red shift in SPR wavelength, only by few nm, whereas the decrease in refractive index of fullerene matrix, from ~ (2.3 to 1.6) for C_{70} and from ~ (2.1 to 1.6) for C_{60} [5,6] due to its transformation in a-C gives a large blue shift to SPR wavelength. So the large blue shift observed in fullerene matrices (induced by their transformation into a-C with a smaller refractive index) dominates the small red shift due to increase in the particle size. The higher blue shift in the case of Ag-C_{70} compared to that of Ag-C_{60} can be due to the higher refractive index value of C_{70} (~ 2.3) than that of C_{60} (~ 2.1).

CONCLUSION

Spherical Ag NPs were synthesized in different carbon based matrices namely C_{60}, C_{70} and a-C. These nanocomposite thin films on glass substrate were irradiated by 120 MeV Ag ions at different fluences ranging from 1 x 10^{12} to 3 x 10^{13} ions/cm^2. The SPR of Ag particles showed a regular blue shift of ~ 49 and 100 nm in C_{60} and C_{70} matrices, respectively with 120 MeV Ag ion irradiation at a fluence of 3 x 10^{13} ions/cm^2 whereas it is ~ 26 nm in the case of Ag/a-C nanocomposite film. In all cases a growth of Ag NPs was observed which is attributed to the occurrence of thermal spikes. Despite the growth of Ag NPs, a blue shift of SPR wavelength was obtained by ion irradiation. This blue shift is explained in terms of transformation of fullerene matrices into a-C networks with ion irradiation in the case of Ag-C_{60} and Ag-C_{70} nanocomposites, whereas the smaller blue shift in the case of Ag/a-C nanocomposite is explained by the increase in the size of graphitic clusters with ion irradiation.

ACKNOWLEDGMENTS

We are thankful to Dr. D. C. Agarwal, Dr. F. Singh, Dr. D. Kabiraj from Inter University Accelerator Centre, New Delhi for their help in carrying out these studies. We are also thankful to Dr. A. K. Chawla and Prof. R. Chandra from IIT Roorkee for TEM measurements. The help received by Dr. J. C. Pivin, CSNSM France is also gratefully acknowledged. We are also thankful to the Department of Science and Technology (DST), New Delhi for the financial support under the projects "Intensifying Research in High Priority Areas" (IRHPA) and "Nano Mission". The Author (R.S.) also acknowledges the financial support received from University Grant Commission, New Delhi is in terms of CSIR-UGC-JRF/SRF fellowship.

REFERENCES

[1]   Ozbay, E. *Science* 2006, *311*, 189-193.
[2]   Lezec, H. J.; Degiron, A.; Devaux, E.; Linke, R. A.; Martin,-Moreno, K.; Garcia-Vidal, F. J.; Ebbeson, T. W. *Science* 2002, *297*, 820-822.
[3]   Roldan, M. V.; Frattini, A.; De, Sanctis, O.; Troiani, H.; Pellegri, N. *Applied Surface Science* 2007, *254*, 281-285.
[4]   [4] Kreibig, U.; Vollmer, M. *Optical Properties of Metal Clusters;* Springer Series in Material Science; Berlin 1995.
[5]   Kataura, H.; Endo, Y.; Achiba, Y.; Kikuchi, K.; Hanyu, T.; Yamaguchi, S. *J. Phys. Chem. Solids* 1997, *58*, 1913-1917.
[6]   Lee, T.; Min, N.-K.; Lee, H. W.; Jang, J. N.; Lee, D. H.; Hong, M. P.; Kwon, K. H. *Thin Solid Films* 2009, *517*, 3999-4002.
[7]   Jensen, A. W.; Wilson, S. R.; Schuster, D. I. *Bioorganic and Medicinal Chemistry* 1996, *4*, 767-779.
[8]   Mohamad, A. A.; Allaf, A. W. *Synthetic Metals* 1999, *104*, 39-44.
[9]   Chen, K. M.; Wu, K.; Chen, Y.; Jia, Y. Q.; Jin, S. X.; Li, C. Y.; Gu, Z. N; Zhou, X. H. *Appl. Phys. Lett.* 1995, *67*, 1683-1685.
[10] Hillenkamp, M.; Domenicantonio, G. D.; Eugster, O. *Nanotechnology* 2007, *18*, 015702 (4pp).
[11] Mcmahon, M. D.; Lopez, R.; Meyer, V.; Feldman, L. C.; Haglund, R. F. JR. *Appl. Phys. B* 2005, *80*, 915-921.
[12] Campion, A.; Campion P. *Chem. Soc. Rev.* 1998, *27*, 241-250.
[13] Weaver, M. J.; Zou, S.; Chan, H. Y. *Anal. Chem.* 2000, *74*, 38A-47A.
[14] Medda, S. K.; De, S.; De, G. *J. Mater. Chem.* 2005, *15*, 3278-3284.
[15] Hache, H.; Ricard, D.; Flytzanix, C. *J. Opt. Soc. Am. B* 1986, *3*, 1647-1655.
[16] Tokizaki, T.; Nakamura, A.; Kaneko, S.; Uchida, K.; Omi, S.; Tanji, H; Asahara, Y. *Appl. Phys. Lett.* 1994, *65*, 941 (3pp).
[17] Mishra, Y. K.; Mohapatra, S.; Singhal, R.; Avasthi, D. K.; Agarwal, D. C.; Ogale, S. B. *Appl. Phys. Lett.* 2008, *92*, 043107 (3pp).
[18] Mohapatra, S.; Mishra, Y. K.; Avasthi, D. K.; Kabiraj, D.; Ghatak, J., Verma, S. *Appl. Phys. Lett.* 2008, *92*, 103105 (3pp).
[19] Su, G.; Tazawa, M.; Jin, P.; Nakao, S. *Appl. Phys. A* 2005, *80*, 1535-1540.

[20] Takele, H.; Greve, H.; Pochstein, C.; Zaporojtchenko, V.; Faupel, F. *Nanotechnology* 2006, *17*, 3499-3505.

[21] Kohler, J. M.; Held, M.; Hubner, U.; Wagner, J. *Chem. Eng. Technol.* 2007, *30*, 347.-354

[22] Roy, R. K.; Mandal, S. K.; Pal, A. K. *The European Physical Journal* B 2003, *33*, 109-114.

[23] Huang, Y.; Yang, Y.; Chen, Z.; Li X.; Nogami, M. *J. Mater Sci.* 2008, *43*, 5390-5393.

[24] Vaughan, G. B. M.; Heiey, P. A.; Luzzi, D. E.; Ricketts,-Foot, D. A.; Mcghie, A. R.; Fischer, J. E.; Hui, Y.-W.; Smith, A. I.; Cox, D. E.; Romanow, W. J.; Allen, B. H.; Coustel, N.; Mccauley, J. P.; jr., and Smith, A. B.; *Science 1991, 254*, 1350-1353.

[25] Verheijen, M.A.; Meekes, H.; Meijer, G.; Bennema, P.; Boer, J.L. De; Smaalen, S. V.; Tendeloo, G. V.; Amelincks, S.; Muto, S.; Landuyt, J.; *Chem. Phys.*1992, *166*, 287-297.

[26] Ghosh, G.; Sastry, V.S.; Sundar, C.S.; Sengupta, S.; Radhakrishnan, T.S.; *Phys. Rev.* B 1998, *58*, 14094-14097.

[27] Heiney, P.A.; Fischer, John, E.; McGhie, A. R.; Romanow, W. J.; Denenstein, A. M.; McCauley, John, P. Jr.; Smith Amos B.; Cox David E. *Phys. Rev. Lett.* 1991, *66*, 2911-2914.

[28] Y. Lwasa, et al. Science 1994, *264*, 1570-1572.

[29] Regueiro, M. N.; Marques, L.; Hodeau, J.L.; Bethoux, O.; Perroux, M. *Phys. Rev. Lett.* 1995, *74*, 278-281.

[30] Bajwa, N.; Dharamvir, K.; Jindal, V.K.; Ingale, A.; Avasthi, D.K.; Kumar, R.; Tripahti, A. *J. Appl. Phys.* 2003, *94*, 326-333.

[31] Prawer, S.; Nugent, K.W.; Biggs, S.; McCulloch, D.G.; Leong, W.H.; Hoffman, A.; Kalish, R. *Phys. Rev.* B 1995, *52*, 841-849.

[32] Kumar, A.; Singh, F.; Avashti, D.K.; Pivin, J.C. *Nucl. Instr. and Meth.* B 2006, *244*, 221-224.

[33] Tripathi, A.; Kumar, A.; Kabiraj, D.; Khan, S.A.; Baranwal, V.; Avasthi, D.K. *Nucl. Instr. and Meth.* B 2006, *244*, 15-18.

[34] Singhal, R.; Singh, F.; Tripathi, A.; Avasthi, D. K. *Radiation Effects and Defects in Solids* 2009, *164*, 38-48.

[35] Singhal, R.; Kumar, A.; Mishra, Y. K.; Mohapatra, S.; Pivin, J. C.; Avasthi, D. K. *Nucl. Instr. and Meth.* B 2008, *266*, 3257-3262.

[36] Kabiraj, D.; Abhilash, S. R.; Vanmarcke, L.; Cinausero, N.; Pivin, J. C.; Avashti, D. K. *Nucl. Instr. and Meth. in Phys. Res.* B 2006, *244*, 100-104.

[37] Doolittle, L. R.; *Nucl. Instr. and Meth. in Phy. Res.* B 1985, *9*, 291-300.

[38] Singhal, R.; Agarwal, D. C.; Mishra, Y. K.; Mohapatra, S.; Avasthi, D. K.; Chawla, A. K.; Chandra, R.; Pivin, J. C; *Nuclear Instruments and Methods in Physics Research* B 2009, *267*, 1349-1352.

[39] Singhal, R.; Agarwal, D. C.; Mishra, Y. K.; Singh, F.; Pivin, J. C.; Chandra, R.; Avasthi, D. K.; *J. Phys. D: Appl. Phys.* 2009, *42*, 155103 (7pp).

[40] McKenzie, D. R.; Davis, C.A.; Cockaynet, D.J.H.; Muller, D.A.; Vassallo, A.M. *Nature* 1992, *355*, 622-624.

[41] Tycko, R.; Dabbagh, G.; Fleming, R.M.; Haddon, R.C.; Makhia, A.V.; Zahurak, S.M. *Phys. Rev. Lett.* 1991, *67*, 1886-1889.

[42] Lu, J.P.; Li, X.-P.; Martin, R.M. *Phys. Rev. Lett.* 1992, *68*, 1551-1554.

[43] Ferrari, A. C.; Robertson, J. *Phys. Rev.* B 2001,*64*, 075414 (13pp); Ferrari, A. C.; Robertson, J. *Phys. Rev.* B 2000,*61*, 14095 (13pp).

[44] Mishra, S.; Ingale, A.; Ghosh, S; Avasthi, D. K. *Diamond and Related Material* 2005, *14*, 1416-1425.

[45] Zollondz, J. H.; Krauser, J.; Weidinger, A.; Trautmann, C.; Schwen, D.; Ronning, C.; Ronning, H.; Schultrich, B. *Diamond and Related Materials* 2003, *12*, 938-941.

[46] [46] Zollondz, J. H.; Schwen, D.; Nix, A. K.; Trautmann, C.; Berthold, J.; Krauser, J.; Hofsass H. *Material Science and Engineering C- Biometric and Supramolecular Systems* 2006, *26*, 1171-1174.

[47] Singh, F.; Mohapatra, S.; Stoquert, J. P.; Avasthi, D. K.; Pivin, J. C. *Nucl. Instr. and Meth. in Phys. Res.* B 2009, *267*, 936-940.

[48] Pivin, J. C.; Singh, F.; Mishra, Y.; Avasthi, D. K.; Stoquert, J. P. *Surface and Coatings Technology* 2009, *203*, 2432-2435.

[49] Pol, V. G.; Wildermuth, G.; Felsche, J.; Gedamken, A.; Morino, J. C. *J. Nanosci. Nanotechnology* 2005, *5*, 975-979.

[50] Srivastava, S. K.; Avasthi, D. K.; Pippel, E. *Nanotechnology* 2006, *17*, 2518-2522.

[51] Srivastava, S. K.; Avasthi, D. K.; Assmann, W.; Wang, Z. G.; Kucal, H.; Jacquert, E.; Carstanjen, H. D.; Toulemonde, M. *Phys. Rev* B 2005, *71*, 193405 (4pp).

[52] Avasthi, D. K.; Ghosh, S., Srivastava, S. K., Assmann, W. *Nucl. Instr. and Meth. in Phys. Res.* B 2004, *219*, 206-214.

In: Synthesis and Engineering of Nanostructures…   ISBN 978-1-62100-261-1
Editors: Devesh Kumar Avasthi & Jean Claude Pivin   © 2012 Nova Science Publishers, Inc

Chapter 17

ION INDUCED SYNTHESIS OF COMPOSITE OF Si NANOPARTICLES IN SILICON OXIDE FOR MOS DEVICES

S.V.Bhoraskar[a], Tejashree Bhave[b], Prajakta Chaudhari[a] and D. Kanjilal[c]

[a]Department of Physics, University of Pune, Pune,411007, India.
Defence Institute of Advanced Technology, Girinagar, Pune-411025, India.
[c]Inter-university Accelerator Centre, New Delhi-110067, India.

ABSTRACT

A nano-composite layer of silicon nanoparticles embedded in silicon oxide was prepared by swift heavy ion irradiation of silicon oxide film. The composite layer was characterized to prove that it consisted of uniformly distributed nanocrystalline silicon ranging in size from 2-5 nm in diameter. Photoluminescence spectroscopy was used to understand the optical behavior of the nano-composite in terms of the crystallite size dependence on the fluence of irradiation. The size of nano-silicon clusters increased with increasing fluence of radiation. MOS structures were fabricated from the irradiated nano-composite, forming the oxide layer. By frequency dependent C-V measurements and the hysterisis effects in the C-V plots, the charge storage properties of the oxide layer, useful for the memory devices, is demonstrated.

1. INTRODUCTION

Memory cell devices, using metal-oxide-semiconductor (MOS) structures containing silicon nanocrystals, are one of the most promising applications of the nanocomposites of silicon with silicon oxide. In such kind of devices, the oxide layer contains silicon nanoparticles, as floating gates[1]. As the floating gate is not electrically continuous, contrary to the standard floating gate in flash memory devices, the charge loss through lateral path is suppressed. This allows thinner injection oxides and, hence a smaller operating voltage. This results in important advantages, such as better endurance, and faster write/erase speeds, and better compatibility with ultra-large scale integration [2,3]. A long retention time and nonvolatility are, therefore, expected in these MOS structures. The memory function of these devices has been attributed to the charge exchange between the nanocrystals and the inversion layer at the interface of the semiconductor. An inversion layer results from the accumulation of minority carriers at the surface which is larger than the majority carriers in the bulk of the semiconductor [4].

Nano-composits can be prepared by variety of techniques such as by recrystallizing silicon from sol gel [5],forming the colloidal suspension of nanocrystalline silicon [6] or by suspending silicon nanoparticles in zeolite matrix [7].Alternatively porous silicon can be partially oxidized, to obtain a thin layer of nanocrystalline silicon, surrounded by silicon oxide[8]. However neither of these techniques is suitable for making a MOS device, with controlled properties of the composite layer. There are a few other methods of fabricating such devices, which include the chemical vapour deposition [9], pulsed laser ablation [10], laser pyrolysis[11], and electrochemical anodization [12]. Ion beam assisted synthesis is one of the most promising methods for fabricating stable silicon nanocrystals. A large number of reports are available on the synthesis of silicon nanoclusters by ion implantation [13,14], however relatively a few reports [15,16,17] on swift heavy ion (SHI) irradiation induced synthesis of silicon nanocrystals are found. In the latter method, desired amount of energy, can be deposited into a substrate/material, through swift heavy ion irradiation process. SHI irradiation leads to large deposition of energy into the films, which leads to intensive local heating and structural phase separation in metastable systems. Unlike other methods, no further post annealing is necessary. With this technique, one can achieve a low temperature recrystallization of silicon since SHI produces thermal spikes and, therefore, no post annealing treatment is required. Another important advantage of this technique lies in the flexibility, in the process parameters such as total fluence, energy, and the mass of the ions, available for controlling the local energy input.

In this chapter, the use of SHI irradiation is demonstrated for preparing the nano composite of silicon with silicon oxide. Sub-oxide of silicon, deposited on single crystal wafer of silicon, was used as the starting material. 100 MeV Ni, 100 and 150 MeV Ag and 100 MeV Au ions were used for irradiating these substrates. The resulting growth of nanocrystalline silicon was studied as a function of fluence, ranging between 10^{12} to 10^{13} ions/cm^2. Supportive evidence for the growth of nanocrystalline silicon was obtained from the Photoluminescence (PL) measurements as was also discussed in the earlier communication [15,16]

The results have been discussed on the basis of interesting changes in the PL peak positions, observed in the nano-composite samples, when the fluence of irradiation was changed. This was also associated with the shifts in the Infrared (IR) absorptions frequencies and refractive index properties of the composites.

For studying the charge storage applications of these composite layers the MOS structures were fabricated using 100 MeV Au ions. Subsequently the C-V measurements were carried out to study the suitability of the structures for the charge storage devices. From the hysteresis properties in the C-V curves, the trapped charge density of the order of 10^{10} couls/cm^2 was obtained after irradiation.

2. EXPERIMENTAL

The swift heavy ion irradiation experiments were performed at Inter University Accelerator Centre, New Delhi. The irradiated films were characterized, using various analytical techniques. The optical properties were studied with the help of photoluminescence studies. Grazing angle X-ray diffraction studies were performed to obtain the structure of the nanoparticles and to calculate the average size. Transmission electron microscopic studies were carried out to study the morphology of the films. Various other techniques, in conjunction with the above techniques namely, Energy Dispersive X-ray analysis (EDAX), Fourier Transform Infra Red spectroscopy (FTIR), refractive index measurements, were also used. The SiO_x films were irradiated with three different ions namely Ni, Ag and Au. The electronic and nuclear energy loss parameter associated with these ions, and the fluence of irradiations are expected to play a key role in the growth of silicon nano-crystals in the host matrix. A proper choice of these parameters may allow a better control over the growth of these nano-crystals. Thus to study the effect of each of these parameters and to obtain the optimal conditions for the control over the growth, different experiments with varying parameters (dE/dx and φ) were performed. Apart from changing the type of ions, the energy of irradiations was also varied. The fluence of irradiation was varied from 10^{11} ions/cm^2 to 10^{13} ions/cm^2 for separate runs. The amount of the energy loss and the projected range of the ions, utilized for different experimental runs, were calculated using a Monte Carlo simulation code of the stopping power and ranges of ions in matter (SRIM 2003) [18]. These are tabulated in Table 1.

It is inferred from the tabulated data that the energy loss associated with each ion is dependent on the mass of the ion as well as the energy of irradiation. In the present experiments, in each case, the electronic energy loss is much larger than the nuclear energy loss. The projected range of the ions, in all the four cases, is around 20 microns and is much larger than the thickness of the oxide layer which is around 200 nm. It has also to be noted that the electronic energy loss, for 100 MeV Au ions, is approximately the same as that of 150 MeV Ag ions.

Table 1. The energy loss and the projected range for the different ions used

Ion	Energy (MeV)	Electronic Energy Loss (eV/A)	Nuclear Energy Loss (eV/A)	Projected Range(μm)
Ni	100	753.6	1.376	23.8
Ag	100	1133.6	6.002	18.5
Ag	150	1269.1	4.296	23.6
Au	100	1294.0	2.490	17.5

The MOS structures were fabricated on an n-type semiconductor by depositing the different layers of Si rich oxide and metal (Au) on it and subsequent SHI irradiation of the same. The commercially available SiO powder was used as the source, for making SiO_x film. The steps involved in the fabrication of MOS structures were as follows:

[87]Ohmic contact (by Au deposition) to the n-type wafers was formed using vacuum evaporation.

[88]SiO$_x$ was deposited on the front side of Si wafer by vacuum evaporation of Au.

[89]About 40 nm thick gold layer was coated on top of SiO$_x$ layer, by vacuum evaporation, to form series of MOS capacitors. This was incorporated using masks having circular holes with 1 mm diameter.

[90]These MOS structures were then irradiated with SHI ions at different fluence

The steps are schematically represented in Figure 1.

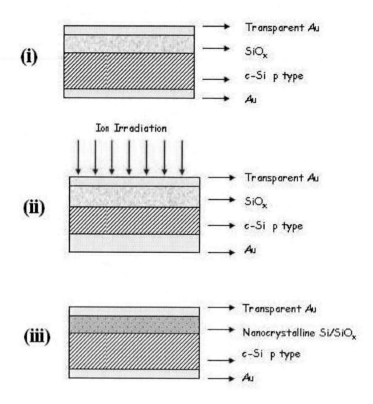

Figure 1. Steps involved in the fabrication of MOS structures using Swift Heavy Ion Irradiation.

3. RESULTS AND DISCUSSIONS

3.1 Photoluminescence Measurements

3.1.1. (a) Ni Ion Irradiation

The films of SiO$_x$, when deposited (typically on glass substrates) appeared bluish green in color. After irradiation, a change in the color of the films was observed, turning to less bluish in colour. This phenomenon is related to the change in the optical properties of the films.

Photoluminescence studies were performed for all the films of SiO$_x$ before and after irradiation. This was intended to reveal the signature of the formation of nanoclusters of silicon, in silicon oxide, since Si nanocrystals exhibit a PL by radiative recombination of exciton and the emission wavelength is sensitive to the size of the nanoparticles. Before irradiation, the SiO$_x$ films did not show any kind of photoluminescence. However, after irradiation the films exhibited clear peaks in the photoluminescence (PL) spectra. The PL spectra for the samples irradiated with 100 MeV Ni ions, with fluence ranging from 5x10^{12} to 5x10^{13} ions/cm^2, are shown in Figure 2(a). Two luminescence peaks in the visible region are observed in each of this spectrum. One peak (P1) is centered around 350 nm and the other peak (P2) around 610 nm. It is observed that the position of the peak at 350 nm, is unaffected by the fluence of irradiation and is known to originate from the defects in silicon oxide [19].

The peak at 610 nm, however is seen to exhibit a small red shift with increasing fluence. The origin of this peak is associated to the luminescence from Si nanoclusters, embedded in the matrix of SiO$_x$. PL in such systems can arise from the generation of carriers inside the nanocrystalline silicon and recombination via interface states [16].The position of the peak can therefore be correlated to the size of the crystallites as well as to the position of the interface states. No sensible excitonic transition is observed in such systems for the sizes studied here (2 to 5nm), since Si remains an indirect gap-semiconductor .The blue shift of the effective band gap closely mimic that of bulk Si.

The red shift, observed in this peak (P2) with increasing fluence, can be thought of arising from the irradiation-assisted growth of silicon nanocrystals, resulting from an increased phase separation. However for the highest fluence of irradiation the peak is observed to shift to 840 nm, informing about an unusually large size of the crystallite .Same has not been observed by irradiation with other ions. This might be expected to occur on account of the generation of shallow interface states

Figure 2(b) shows the change in the ratio of the intensities (I_{P2}/I_{P1}) of the two peaks and the shift of the second peak, corresponding to nanocrystalline silicon, with the fluence of irradiation. It can be seen from the figure that the ratio of the intensities of the two peaks, does not vary synchronously with the fluence of irradiation. The variation in the PL intensity indicates that, apart from the re-crystallization, heavy ion irradiation also generates defects. These defects may act as non-radiative recombination centers, thereby altering the intensity of the PL emission. Similar effects were discussed in view of PL emission by porous silicon in the our earlier studies [20].

3.1.2 b) Ag Ion Irradiation

The photoluminescence spectra of the SiO$_x$ samples irradiated with 150 MeV and 100 MeV Ag ions, with varying fluence, are presented in Figure 3(a) and (c) respectively. Similar effects as seen in case of the Ni ions, were observed. The values of the peak positions and their shifts were slightly modified. The analysis in terms of the shift in the peak position and intensities are grouped in Figure 3(b and d).

3.1.3 c) Au Ion Irradiation

The effects of irradiation in terms of the PL spectra were similar. However the values of the intensity ratios and the peak intensities were different as indicated in Figure 4 for comparison.

a)

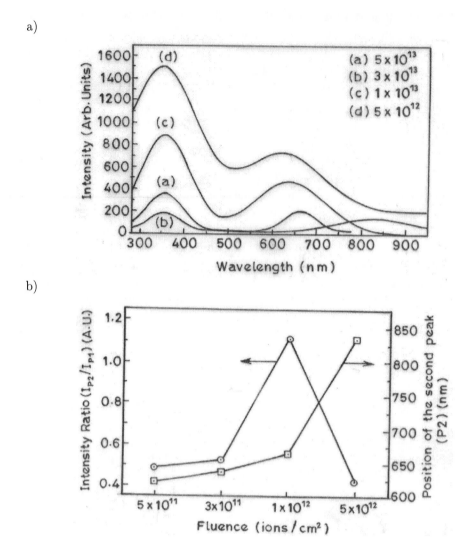

b)

Figure 2 (a) PL spectrum of SiO_x films irradiated with 100 MeV Ni ions at different fluence (from ref. 16, REPRINTED WITH PERMISSION FROM P.S.Chaudhari et.al. J.Appl. Phys. 93, 3486.2003, COPYRIGHT 2003,AMERICAN INSTITUTE OF PHYSICS.) (b) The change in the position of the PL peak related to nanocrystalline silicon and the ratio of the integral intensities of the two peaks with the change in fluence.

3.2 Structural and Morphological Analysis

The morphology of the ion irradiated SiO_x films was studied with the help of Transmission Electron Microscopy (TEM). Before irradiation, the films of SiO_x were seen to be completely amorphous and no specific pattern was observed. Figure 5(a) shows the TEM picture of a typical film irradiated with a fluence of $1x10^{13}$ ions/cm^2 of Ag ions. The figure exhibits nano-clusters between 2 to 5 nm diameters. The structural features of the nanocrystalline silicon clusters were further confirmed by the grazing angle XRD analysis, as shown in Figure 5 (b) by the appearance of a broad peak around $2\Theta=29^0$ which correlates to the (111) plane of crystalline Si [20].

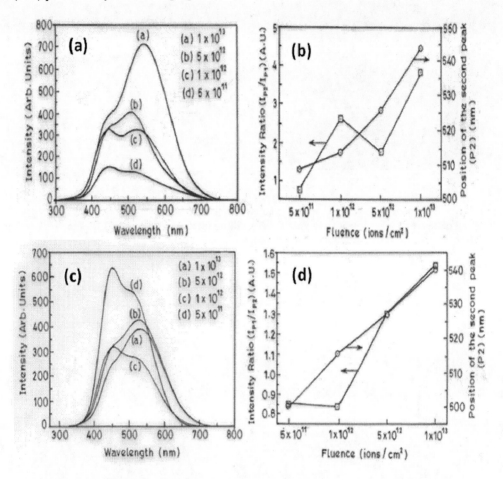

Figure 3(a) and (c) PL spectra of SiO_x films irradiated with 150 and 100 MeV Ag ions at different fluence. (b) and (d) Change in the position of the PL peaks related to nanocrystalline silicon and the ratio of the integral intensities of the two peaks with the change in fluence.

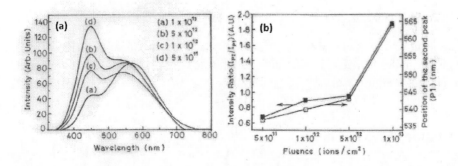

Figure 4 (a) PL spectrum of SiO_x films irradiated with 100 MeV Au ions at different fluence (b) The change in the position of the PL peak related to nanocrystalline silicon and the ratio of the integral intensities of the two peaks with the change in fluence.

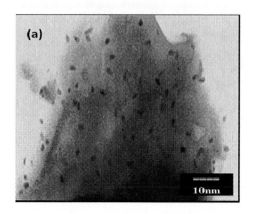
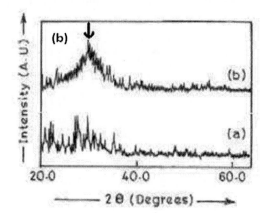

Figure 5 (a) TEM image of 150 MeV Ag ion irradiated film at a fluence of 10^{13} ions/cm2 (b) X-Ray Diffraction pattern of the composite showing the crystalline features of silicon (111) planes in curve at $2\theta \sim 290$ (b). Curve (a) refers to the un-irradiated film and curve (b) refers to the irradiated film.

c)

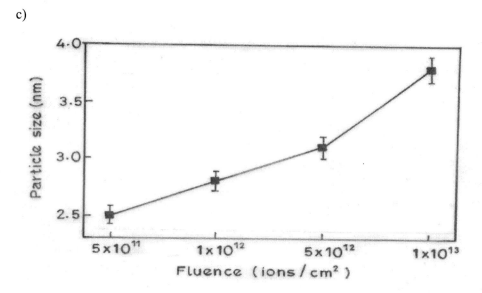

Figure. 5(c) Variation of average particle size with fluence as inferred from the XRD line width.

The variation in the particle size derived from the line broadening in the XRD measurements for samples irradiated with different fluence of irradiation using Scherrer formula [20] is shown in Figure 5(c).

3.3 Refractive Index Measurements

The variation of the refractive index n with x is well-known, in case of single phase SiO_x films. The value of n in SiO_x film is a decreasing function of x. Its value for Si, SiO and SiO_2 are 4 , 2.3 and 1.46 respectively [21]. Thus looking to the trend one can estimate the value of x in SiO_x films, before and after irradiation; since the presence of nanocrystallites in the host matrix can modify the refractive index of the silicon oxide film.

The refractive index measurements were carried out, typically, for the 100 MeV Ni ion irradiated samples. The values of n measured for all the samples before and after irradiation, are tabulated in Table 2.The values of n close to 1.6, in the as deposited films of SiO_x (before irradiation), sets the value of x to 1.7 in these films. For the films irradiated with fluences of 5×10^{12} and 1×10^{13} ions/cm^2, the value of n is close to 1.9 which assigns the value of x in the Si- SiO_x composite films to 1.3 .However we find that increasing the fluence beyond 1×10^{13} ions/cm^2 has not helped in further increasing the value of n, probably on account of the other processes like formation of defects at the interfaces or inside the silicon nano-crystallites.

Table 2.The refractive indices of films irradiated with 100 MeV Ni ions at different fluences

Fluence Ions/cm^2	Before irradiation		After irradiation	
	Refractive Index (n)	x in SiO_x	Refractive Index	x in SiO_x
5×10^{13}	1.6	1.78	1.82	1.5
3×10^{13}	1.6	1.78	1.87	1.5
1×10^{13}	1.6	1.78	1.95	1.3
5×10^{12}	1.6	1.78	1.96	1.3

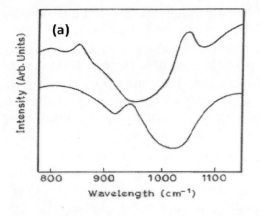 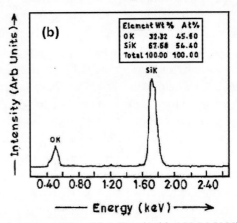

Figure 6 (a) FTIR spectrum for unirradiated SiOx film (upper curve) and irradiated with 100 MeV Ni ions with fluence of 10^{13} ions/cm^2 (lower curve). (b) EDAX spectrum for SiO_x films which remained unchanged before as well as after Irradiation. It is seen that the ratio of silicon to oxygen does not change. (from ref. 16, REPRINTED WITH PERMISSION FROM P.S.Chaudhari et.al. J.Appl. Phys. 93, 3486.2003, COPYRIGHT 2003, AMERICAN INSTITUTE OF PHYSICS).

3.4 Fourier Transform Infra-Red Spectroscopy

Amongst the various vibrational frequency domains of SiO_x, the absorption in the 1000 cm^{-1} is due to the asymmetric stretching vibrations of oxygen atoms in the Si-O-Si group. These vibrations are observed for all the SiO_x films but their frequency depends on the environment of Si atoms. The absorption frequency is an increasing function of x, because of the strong electro-negativity of oxygen atoms [22]. Figure 6 shows the FTIR spectrum for the SiO_x film before and after irradiation. Curve `a' corresponds to the film before irradiation and curve `b' to the film after irradiation at a fluence of $1x10^{13}$ ions/cm^2. Before irradiation, the absorption peak appears at 970 cm^{-1}, which is shifted to 1020 cm^{-1} after irradiation. This shows that sub-oxide of silicon has evolved into silicon dioxide (SiO_2) as an effect of irradiation.

3.5 Energy Dispersics X-Ray Analysis

Figure 6 (b) shows a typical EDAX spectrum of the unirradiated films of SiO_x. Peaks related to silicon and oxygen was obtained. An estimate of the atomic percentage shows the Si rich nature of the films. This percentage did not change after irradiation of these films, which confirms the fact that phase separation has taken place in the films, which can be formulated as:

$$2SiO = SiO_2 + Si$$

3.6 C-V Measurements with MOS Capacitors

The memory effect of a Si nanoparticles floating gate memory structure consisting of SiO_2 tunneling and control oxides can be investigated by means of high-frequency capacitance–voltage (C–V) measurements. C-V measurements in MOS devices provide useful information about the charge storage in the oxide capacitance, including those with the Si nanoparticles. The memory effect was observed by the hysteresis loop in the C-V curves. Generally, C-V measurements are very useful for studying the charge storage of the Si nano-particles by measuring the flat-band voltage of the MOS capacitors. Figure 7(a) shows the 1 MHz C-V curves measured at room temperature for the MOS capacitor without Si nano-particles. The sample without Si nano-particles shows a typical C-V curve with a hysteresis loop having a width of ~ 1 V, which means that the SiO_2 layer and the Si interface fabricated under these condition did originally contain some defect states. At the same time, the effect of mobile ions on the charge trapping cannot be ruled out. It is seen that the trapped charge density of the sample without Si nano-particles is 1×10^{10}/cm^2 at a bias voltage of 1V. The C-V measurements were recorded by scanning the voltage in a reverse (-6 v to + 5 v) and forward (+5 v to -6 v) direction, at different measuring frequencies. A significant shift of the C-V curves on the right during the forward scan was observed. Figure 7(b) shows the hysteresis curve for samples after irradiation at a fluence of $5x10^{11}$ ions/cm^2 for a typical measurement carried out at a frequency of 1 MHz It can be seen that this hysteresis behavior is observed for samples before as well as after irradiation. The origin of this hysteresis in the samples before irradiation, can be assumed due to the interface states between the silicon oxide film and the silicon substrate [23]. The shift, ΔV_{FB}, for all the samples before and after irradiation is calculated and the values are tabulated in Table 3.

Table 3. The change in the ΔV_{FB} for different frequencies after irradiation with a fluence of 5×10^{11} ions/cm^2

Frequency (Hz)	ΔV_{FB} before irradiation (Volts)	ΔV_{FB} after irradiation (Volts)	Change in ΔV_{FB}	Change in Trapped charge density (cm^{-2})
500 K	0.97	3.87	2.90	6.21×10^{11}
1 M	0.88	3.92	3.04	7.29×10^{11}
10 M	1.02	4.33	3.31	7.58×10^{11}

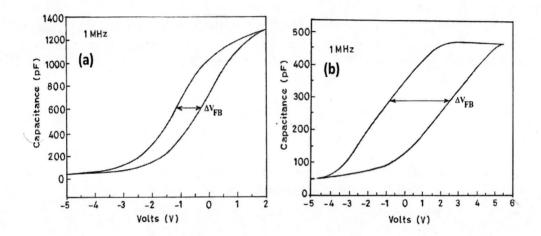

Figure 7. The hysteresis curves for unirradiated samples (a) and for samples after Irradiation (b) at a fluence of 5×10^{11} ions/cm^2 (measurements were carried out at different frequencies; however the results corresponding to 1 MHz are only indicated).

It is seen that after irradiation, the magnitude of the ΔV_{FB} increases. Moreover this increase in ΔV_{FB}, is sensitive to the frequency and increases with increase in the frequency. The increased area under the hysteresis loop can be attributed to the electron trapping mechanism in the structure. Generally this can be explained on the basis of various factors. These factors include the variation in the interface state density, the traps, charge storage in nanocrystals, and the polarization of the insulator. In addition to these factors, the three dimensional quantum confinement and the Coulomb charge effects are also expected to affect the width of the hysteresis curve. Usually mixed phenomena are responsible for such kind of memory effects. Moreover the slopes of the C-V curves are seen to have changed for the sample before and after irradiation. The change in the slope of C-V hysteresis curve is attributed to the variation in the interface state density. This makes it difficult to differentiate the influence of interface traps in the observed charge storage behavior. The magnitude of trapped charge density is calculated from the observed shift in the hysteresis curve, using the formula[4]

$$\Delta V_{FB} = \frac{Q_f}{C_i}$$

where Q_f is the total charge density in the oxide layer , Ci is the MOS capacitance and ΔV_{FB} is the observed shift in the hysteresis curve, of trapped oxide charges. The values of these trapped charge densities are tabulated in the last column of Table 1. For the lower frequency the magnitude of the stored charge density is obtained to be equal to 4×10^8 /cm^2. The density of nanoparticles, as estimated from the TEM micrograph (Figure 5a), is approximately of the order of 10^{12} /cm^2. A lower value of the charge density as calculated from the C-V measurements can be expected since only those nanoparticles which are near to the semiconductor surface will contribute towards the charge storage.

CONCLUSIONS

In conclusion, the composite of nano-silicon with silicon oxide, synthesized by the SHI irradiation, has charge storage property. The C-V hysteresis behavior of MOS structures alters after the heavy ion irradiation thus, confirming the effect. Width of the hysteresis loop was found to be sensitive to the fluence of irradiation and measuring frequency.

ACKNOWLEDGMENT

SVB acknowledges CSIR , New Delhi , for awarding her the ES Scheme.TB wishes to thank IUAC, New Delhi for providing the research funding.

REFERENCES

[1]   Ostraat, M. L.; De Blauwe, J. W.; Green, M. L.; Bell, L. D.; Brongersma, M. L.; Casperson, J.; Flagan, R. C.; Atwater, H. A. *Appl. Phys. Lett.* 2001, *79*, 433-435. b) Lu, T. Z.; Shen, J.; Mereu, B.; Alexe, M.; Scholz, R.; Talalaev, V.; Zacharias, M. *Appl. Phys. A* 2005, *80*, 1631-1634.

[2]   Skorupa, W.; Yankov, R. A.; Tyschenko, I. E., Frob, H. ; Bohme, T. ; Leo, K. *Appl. Phys. Lett.*1996, *68*, 2410-2412.

[3]   Fernandez, B. G. ; Lopez, M. ; Garcia, C. ; Perez-Rodriguez, A.; Morante J. R.; Bonafos, C.; Carrada, M.; Claverie, A. *J. Appl. Phys.* 2002, *91*, 798-807.

[4]   Sze, S.M.; *Physics of Semiconductor Devices*; Ed 2; *Wiley Eastern Limited*:New Delhi,IN,1985; pp.366.

[5]   Savin, D.P.; Gevelyuk, S.A.; Roizin,Ya.O.; Mugeski, E.; Sokolska, I. *Appl.Phys.Lett.*1998,*72*,3005-3007.

[6]   Beard, M.C.; Knutsen, K .P.; Yu, P.; Luther, J. M.; Song, Q.; Metzger, W. K.; Ellingson, R. J.; Nozik, A. J. *Nanoletters* 2004, *7*, 2506-2512

[7]   Ba,Y.; He, J.; Ratcliffe,C .I .; Ripmeester, J. A. *J.Am.Chem.Soc.* 1999, *121*, 8387-8388.

[8]   Muller, F.; Herino, R.; Ligion, M.; Gaspard, F.; Romestein, R.; Vial, J.C. *J. Lummin.* 1993, *57*, 111-115.

[9]   Edelberg,E.; Bergh,S.; Naone,R.; Hall,M.; Aydil,S.; *Appl. Phys. Lett.*.1996 *, 68*,1415 - 1417

[10] Patrone,V.I.;Nelson,D.; Safarov,V.I.;Sentis,M.;Marine,W.;Giorgio,S.;*J.Appl.Phys*.2000, *87*, 3829-3837.

[11] Ledoux,G.; Gong, J.; Huisken F.; *Appl.Phys.Lett.* 2001, *79*, 4028-4030.

[12] Shih, S.; Jung, K.; Hsieh, T.; Sarathy, J.; Campbell, J.; Kwong, D. *Appl. Phys. Lett.* 1992, *60*, 1863-1865.

[13] Pivin, J.C.; de Castro, M.J.; Hofmester, H.; Vassileva, M.S. *Mat.Sc. and Engineering B.*, 2003, *97*, 13-19.

[14] Iwayana, T. S.;Kurumado, N.;Hole, D. E.; Townsend, P. D. *J. Appl. Phys.* 1998, *83*, 6018-6022.

[15] Chaudhari, P. S.; Bhave, T. M.; Pasricha,R.; Singh,F.; Kanjilal, D.; Bhoraskar, S. V. *Nucl. Instr. and Meth.B* 2005, *239*, 185-190.

[16] Choudhari,P. S.; Bhave,T. M.; Kanjilal,D.; Bhoraskar, S. V. *J. Appl. Phys.* 2003, *93*, 3486-3489.

[17] Pivin, J. C.; Vassileva, M. S.; Nikolaeve, M.; Malinovska, D.D.; Martucci, A. *Appl.Phys.A*, 2002, *75*, 401-410.

[18] Zeiler, J. F.; Biersack, J. P.; Littmark, U. *Stopping and Range of Ions in Solids*, Pergamon : New York, US,1985;

[19] Dusane, S.; Bhave, T. M.; Hullavarad, S.; Bhoraskar, S. V.; Lokhare, S. *Solid State Comm.*,1999, *111*, 431-435.

[20] Bhave, T. M.; Bhoraskar, S. V.; Singh, P.; Bhoraskar, V. N. *Nucl. Instr.and Meth.*B, 1997, *13*, 409-417.

[21] Pi, X. D.; Colemana, P. G.; Harding, R.; Davies, G.; Gwilliam, R. M. *J. Appl. Phys.* 004, *95*, 8155-8159.

[22] Lin, S. Y. *J. Appl. Phys.*, 1997, *82*, 5976.-5982. b) Lucovsky, G.; Wang, J.; Chao, S.S.; Tyler J. E.; Czubatyj, W. *Phys. Rev. B*, 1983, *28*, 3225-3233.

[23] Carlotti, J. F.; Touboul, A. D.; Ramonda, M.;Caussanel, M.; Guascha, C.; Bonnet, J.; Gasiot,J. *J. Appl. Phys. Lett.*, 2006, *88*, 041906(1-3).

In: Synthesis and Engineering of Nanostructures…   ISBN 978-1-62100-261-1
Editors: Devesh Kumar Avasthi & Jean Claude Pivin   © 2012 Nova Science Publishers, Inc

Chapter 18

SURFACE NANOSTRUCTURING OF OXIDE THIN FILMS UNDER MEV HEAVY ION IRRADIATION

D.C. Agarwal[1] and R.S. Chauhan[2]

[1]Inter-University Accelerator Centre, New Delhi-110067, India
[2]R.B.S. College, Agra-282002, India

ABSTRACT

Nano-structure materials have received global interest due to their particular properties and variety of interesting applications. Ion irradiation of solid surface results in the spontaneous self-organization of surface and control the surface morphology. In addition, the ballistic sputtering and diffusion of surfaces atoms allows the growth of nanodots, nanoripples and nanoholes on surfaces depending on the ion beam parameters. The self-affine nano-patterns produced on the surface of ZnO thin film under swift heavy ion (SHI) irradiation, are different types of nanostructures in linear array followed by nanodimensional grains. XRD and Raman results showed the improvement in crystallinity of the ZnO films at low fluences and disordering was induced at higher fluences. The absorption edge was blue shifted upto fluence 3 x 10^{12} ions/cm^2 and beyond this band gap was decreased. No change in stoichiometry and resistivity of the films was observed after irradiation. The 2D-Power spectral densities (PSD) of the irradiated ZnO thin films have been evaluated for each image to determine the process responsible for surface nanostructuring. The value of growth factor (β) and roughness exponent (α) has been extracted from PSD analysis. The exponent, n, increases from 2.2 to 4.0 up to a critical value of fluence and beyond which it decreases. These values suggest that ion assisted/induced diffusion process plays a crucial role in the evolution of self-affine nanostructures on ZnO surface. We show that the long-term damage in ZnO under ion irradiation is resisted by defect annihilations. Surface of NiO thin film on different substrates (SiO$_2$, Si and Al) is also self-organized in well-defined periodic lamellae structures due to the plastic deformation induced by swift heavy ion irradiation at LN$_2$ temperature and at an incidence angle of 75° with the beam axis. The quite regular lamellae with width, height and average distance of hundreds of nm are oriented perpendicular to the beam direction. Section analysis of the AFM images reveal that the width of the lamellae, at the same irradiation condition, is less in case of NiO films deposited on SiO_2 substrate in comparison to Al substrate. The cracking and development of lamellae structures are seen at higher fluence in the case of Al substrate.

1. INTRODUCTION

One of the fundamental problems in materials science is to understand the effects of ion irradiation on solid surfaces. Nanoscale surface morphologies spontaneously develop from uniform ion irradiation of an initially flat surface in a non-equilibrium self-organization process termed "sputter patterning". The spontaneous self-organization processes have no fundamental throughput limitations and have been used to create patterns with lateral feature sizes as small as 15 nm, and good short-range order. The ion interaction with the atoms leads to different phenomena, e.g. topographical modification of the sample surface. It has long been known that under some conditions of uniform ion irradiation of a solid surface, spontaneously sputtering pattern topography arises, that often takes the form of one-dimensional ripples or two-dimensional arrays of dots. The periodicity is understood to arise as a result of a kinetic competition between the surface roughening effect of the ion beam and the morphological relaxation.

These competing processes are responsible for the creation of characteristic surface features like quasiperiodic ripples [1-4] and self-affine topographies [4-7]. The ion bombardment is known to enhance the surface diffusion and affect the surface morphology. The morphological evolution of ion-bombarded surfaces has generated much experimental and theoretical interest in recent years. The spontaneous rippling of surfaces under ion irradiation was first observed on glass [7]. Similar patterns have been produced on different materials, including semiconductors [8-11], metals [12] and insulators [13] mainly in the ballistic regime of ion slowing down. These entire patterns have been produced using low energy ion beam. One or two-dimensional nanopatterns on the surfaces with well-defined symmetry have been obtained by sputter rippling. Arrays consisting of small bumps or 'nano dots' have been fabricated on GaSb [13] surfaces, using normal incidence sputtering. These studies have been performed in the low energy regime, where sputtering is dominant and ion incidence is tilted to the surface normal. A lot of work has been carried out in the field of nanoscale patterning of the surfaces, using the low energy ion beam with different ion species and ion energies [8-13] while there are only a few works, which report the nanostructuring on the surface using high energy ion beams [14-15]. In the high-energy regime and at normal incidence, there are only a few studies of the scaling of the surfaces evolved under ion bombardment [16]. Bradley and Harper (BH) theory [17] and its refinement based on the surface instability, caused by local surface curvature dependent sputtering are frequently used to explain the formation of ordered structures. The BH theory describes the sputter process in terms of the energy, deposited by the ion, as it slows down through a series of collisions in the solid and comes to rest at an average range of a_0. The collision cross section actually increases as the ion slow down, resulting in greater energy deposition below the surface than at the surface. Considering the statistical result of a large number of ion collisions, the energy is deposited in 3-D ellipsoidal Gaussian contours around the end of the ion track. If the ion range is short enough, then there is sufficient energy deposited near the surface and consequently, atoms located at the bottom of the troughs gain more energy on average to cause sputtering of an atom as compared to those on the peaks of crests. This instability can be thought as a negative surface tension because the surface tends to maximize its area. To balance this negative surface tension, there exists a stabilizing mechanism called surface diffusion, which is always present in physical system at non-zero temperature. Bradley and Harper extended this theory to show how the surface can become unstable to small-amplitude periodic disturbances. If the interaction of the surface morphology with the energy deposition is considered, the local sputter yield is proportional to the curvature of the surface. The surface morphology then evolves according to

$$\frac{\partial h}{\partial t} = S_x \frac{\partial^2 h}{\partial x^2} + S_y \frac{\partial^2 h}{\partial y^2} \tag{1}$$

Where h is the height of the surface relative to the average height. x is defined as the spatial coordinate parallel to the projected direction of the ion beam on the plane of average surface orientation and y is the coordinate within this plane perpendicular to x. S_x and S_y are surface tension parameters, generated by the erosion process, calculated by BH, that depend on the ion beam, the angle of incidence and the material. S_x is negative for all incidence angles and S_y can change the sign with the angle of incidence ion. Balancing the roughening caused by the ion beam, there is mass transport induced by a driving force or diffusion to smoothen the surface in order to reduce surface energy. Using a continuum model of the surface [18-20], the chemical potential of atoms at the surface is proportional to the curvature. The variations in the surface morphology create a gradient in the curvature, driving mass away from convex regions of the solid towards concave. If the mass transport pathway is surface diffusion, this effect changes the height of the surface. But this theory fails to explain the saturation of the ripple amplitude, appearance of kinetic roughening and observation of rotated ripples.

To remedy the shortcoming of BH model, Cuerno and Barabasi [21] proposed non-linear terms that are consistent with the observed saturation of the ripple, at large amplitude. The non-linear equation is

$$\frac{\partial h}{\partial t} = K \frac{\partial h}{\partial x} + S_x \frac{\partial^2 h}{\partial x^2} + S_y \frac{\partial^2 h}{\partial y^2} + \eta_x \left(\frac{\partial h}{\partial x}\right)^2 + \eta_y \left(\frac{\partial h}{\partial y}\right)^2 - B\nabla^2\nabla^2 h + \Gamma(x,y,t) \tag{2}$$

where K, η_x and η_y are coefficients calculated by Cuerno and Barabasi and $\Gamma(x,y,t)$ is an uncorrelated noise term with zero mean. η_x and η_y describe the tilt-dependent erosion rate, proportional to the ratio between flux and penetration depth.

Transparent semi-conducting ZnO thin films have attracted considerable attention both for fundamental and application points of view, primarily because of their useful properties. Zinc oxide is n type semiconductor of wide interest exhibiting excellent optical, electrical, catalytic, gas sensing properties and has possible technological applications in various fields [22-27]. The notable properties of ZnO are its wide band gap of 3.3 eV at room temperature and high exciton binding energy (60 meV) compared to those of ZnS (20 meV) and GaN (21 meV) [28-32]. Due to its wide band gap, ZnO can be used for short wavelength light emitting devices such as light emitting diodes and laser diodes, surface acoustic wave (SAW) band pass filters etc. The extensive usage of ZnO and its nanostructures in device fabrication and the continued miniaturization of device structures have brought the issue of making good device in nanoscale, to the forefront.

NiO also have found wide application in different areas such as sensors [33], transparent electrodes [34], efficient control of energy inflow-outflow of buildings or automobiles and aerospace [33-35], large scale optical switching glazing and electronic information display [36].

The ion beams are extensively used for the modification of the properties of materials for device fabrication. Since the roughness of the surface can crucially affect the performance and reliability of device [37], it becomes necessary to characterize the surface roughness and to understand the corresponding fundamental processes influencing it. Therefore, the factors responsible for such modifications and the resulting surface morphology after ion bombardment, have received considerable attention [38]. Surface nanostructuring by SHI has been noticed in recent years [14,15, 39,40]. The aspects of nanostructuring by SHI in ZnO and NiO are discussed here in detail. The self-affine nanostructures have been produced on the surface of ZnO thin films via SHI irradiation, at normal incidence and atomic force microscopy (AFM) was used to investigate these structures. Evolution of these surface structures has been explained using scaling theory within the framework of existing model for surface evolution at low energy ion. Although the phenomena of sputtering and surface diffusion, involved in the surface evolution are same as in the case of low energy and that of BH theory. However the underlying mechanisms of surface evolution in present case is due to swift heavy ion bombardment. Our interest has also been to obtain the value of roughness exponent (α) for swift heavy ion beam induced smoothed surfaces because neither any theoretical prediction nor any experimental determination of α is available in the literature so far. Analysis of the change in structural and optical properties of ZnO thin films is also the topic of present investigation. We have shown that ZnO thin films are radiation hard and can be suitable for space application.

NiO thin films, deposited on different substrates, were also irradiated by 100 MeV Ag ions at LN_2 temperature and at an incidence angle of 75^0 with respect to the surface normal. We observed that after the application of high fluence, the surface of the NiO films is re-organized in the form of periodic lamellae structures. The results have been explained on the basis of Grinfeld instability of surface and plastic deformation of material under swift heavy ion irradiation.

2. IRRADIATION AND CHARACTERIZATION OF ZnO THIN FILMS

Experiment was performed on the ZnO films with a thickness of 120 nm, deposited on Si and quartz by electron beam evaporation of ZnO powder (Aldrich 99.9%) at the substrate temperature of 300°C. The distance between source to substrate and source to quartz crystal was 15 cm. The vacuum during the evaporation was 5 x 10^{-5} torr and the deposition rate was 0.1 to 0.4 nm/sec. The details of the synthesis of the ZnO film have been given in reference 41. The samples were irradiated with 100 MeV Ag ions using the 15 UD Pelletron tandem accelerator at Inter-University Accelerator Centre (IUAC), New Delhi. The samples were mounted on the sample holder, made of copper, in high vacuum irradiation chamber. In order to achieve homogeneous irradiation, the ion beam was carefully scanned over an area (1cm x

1cm). The films were irradiated at different ion beam fluences (ϕ) 1 x 10^{10}, 7 x 10^{10}, 1 x 10^{11}, 3 x 10^{11}, 7 x 10^{11}, 1 x 10^{12}, 3 x 10^{12}, 7 x 10^{12} and 1 x 10^{13} ions-cm^{-2}. The electronic and nuclear stopping powers of 100 MeV Ag ions in ZnO thin film are 20.39 keV/nm and 0.122 keV/nm respectively. Since the range of the ion was much greater than the film thickness, therefore, no ions were implanted into the film and modification was expected only due to the defects produced by ions passed through the film. The surfaces of the post-irradiated samples were characterized by AFM Nanoscope IIIa at IUAC, New Delhi. Elastic recoil detection analysis (ERDA) was used to determine the sputtering rate and UV-Visible spectroscopy was performed to study the modification in band-gap. Optical absorption spectra were recorded with the conventional two-beam method, using U-3300 UV-VIS spectrophotometer of Hitachi. In ERDA experiment the sample was tilted at 75° with the beam axis and the detector was placed at an angle of 45° with respect to the beam direction. The crystallographic modifications have been analyzed by X-ray diffraction (XRD) and Raman Spectroscopy at IUAC, New Delhi and at C2RMF, France respectively. Raman spectra were recorded using a Jobin Yvon Infinity micro-Raman setup with a Ar laser beam of wavelength 532 nm and intensity 4.5 mW focused over 3 μm.

3. RADIATION HARDNESS AND SURFACE NANOSTRUCTURING OF ZNO THIN FILM

The surface morphologies of the un-irradiated and irradiated films by Ag ions are shown in Figures 1 and 2 respectively. The AFM image of the pristine sample shows that the features on the surface are randomly distributed. The surface morphology of the ZnO films, irradiated at fluence up to 7 x 10^{12} ions-cm^{-2} is dominated by an almost uniformly distributed nanoscale self-affine structures. At fluences beyond 7 x 10^{12} ions-cm^{-2}, the surface patterns disappear. Formation of these self-affine nanostructures occurs due to the change in surface energy, induced by energy deposition by swift heavy ions in surfactant region. The shape (as well as size) of these structures transforms with the variation in ion beam fluence. The nanostructures possess spherical shape at a fluence of 1 x 10^{10} ions-cm^{-2}, which are transformed into ellipsoidal ones (nano-rod like) when the ion beam fluence reaches a value 7 x 10^{11} ions/cm^2. When the fluence is further increased upto 1 x 10^{12} ions-cm^{-2}, the nanostructures further retain the spherical shape. The size distributions of the obtained nanostructures are shown in Figure 3.

At certain fluence 3 x 10^{11} ions-cm^{-2}, some small spherical particles appear on top of the big ones. Although some of them have diameters more than 100 nm yet most of the nanostructures have diameters lower than 100 nm. It has been observed that the average diameter of nanostructures decreases from 75 nm to 50 nm upto the fluence 1 x 10^{12} ions-cm^{-2} and further increasing fluence beyond 1 x 10^{12} ions-cm^{-2} results in increase in the size of nanostructures. Density of the nanostructures has been calculated and it is noticed that the areal density of the nanostructures increases from 8 x 10^9 cm^{-2} to 3 x 10^{10} cm^{-2} upto the fluence of 1 x 10^{12} ions-cm^{-2} due to the reduction in the size of the nanostructures and after this critical fluence the density of nanostructures again decreases due to evolution of bigger structures.

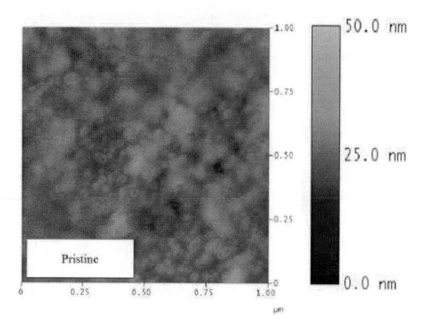

Figure 1. AFM micrograph of ZnO thin film (From ref. 42, REPRINTED WITH PERMISSION FROM D. C. Agarwal et.al. J.Appl. Phys. 104,02304,2008, COPYRIGHT 2008, AMERICAN INSTITUTE OF PHYSICS).

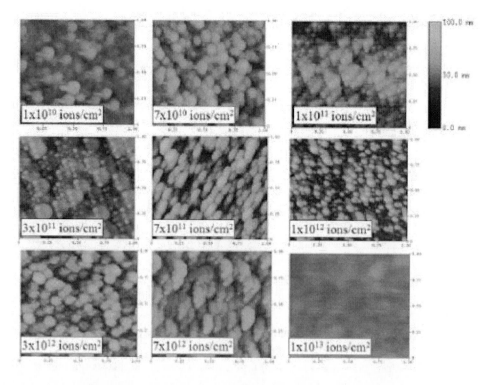

Figure 2. AFM micrograph of ZnO thin film irradiated at different fluence by 100 MeV Ag ions (From ref. 42, REPRINTED WITH PERMISSION FROM D. C. Agarwal et.al. J.Appl. Phys. 104,02304,2008, COPYRIGHT 2008, AMERICAN INSTITUTE OF PHYSICS).

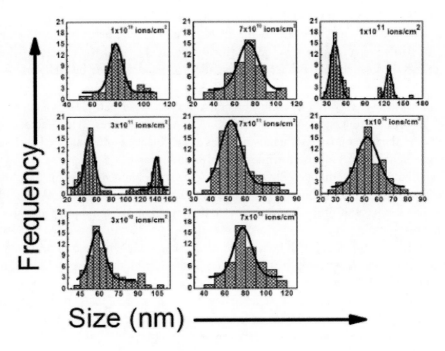

Figure 3. Size distribution of surface structures after the 100 MeV Ag ion irradiation at different fluence (From ref. 42, REPRINTED WITH PERMISSION FROM D. C. Agarwal et.al. J.Appl. Phys. 104,02304,2008, COPYRIGHT 2008, AMERICAN INSTITUTE OF PHYSICS).

From our work on irradiation of ZnO thin films [42], it is known that it does not amorphize and is radiation hard. The reduction in size and increase in areal density of the nanostructures up to a specific fluence may be explained in terms of stress generation by ion beam and change in surface energy due to total energy ($S_e x \phi$) deposited by ion beam. When SHI passes through the material, it deposits large amount of energy into the material. So far, two models, Coulomb explosion and thermal spike have been used to explain the strain development in particle. According to Coulomb explosion, a highly ionized zone of charged particles is created by ion along its trajectory. If target electrons on the time scale of lattice vibration do not neutralize charges, the electrostatic repulsion of ionized target atoms will force a rapid expansion of the material in the charged domain, resulting in the formation of a shock wave. These shock waves that are developed in the material cause strain in the nano size structures. According to the thermal spike model, the energy, which is deposited by the projectile ions in the electronic sub-system of the target, is shared among the electrons by electron–electron coupling and transferred subsequently to the lattice atoms via electron–lattice interactions, leading to a large increase in the temperature along and in the vicinity of the ion path. The pressure waves develop due to the temperature spike and cause strain in the nano size structure.

Since the creation of nanostructures typically of 80 nm in diameter is observed at low fluence of $1x10^{10}$ ions-cm^{-2}, it implies that each ion influences a zone of about 80 nm in diameter. The diffusion and erosion of atoms within this zone is responsible for creating the nanostructures at the surface. As the fluence is increased up to the $1x10^{12}$ ions-cm^{-2}, the fragmentation of these structures is supposed to occur due to the internal strain generated by ion impacts, which results in reduction of size and increase of the areal density of nanostructures. No further fragmentation of nanostructures is observed beyond the fluence of 1×10^{12} ions-cm^{-2}. This may be due to the increase in surface energy corresponding to a decrease in particle size. There may be a critical size of the nanostructures for which the surface energy is so high that further fragmentation of nanoparticles by SHI irradiation is prevented. Finally, at fluence larger than 1 x 10^{12} ions-cm^{-2} (deposition of more $S_e x \phi$), again increase in surface energy induces the agglomeration of these particles, which results in decrease in surface roughness and formation of bigger structures. This factor may be responsible for the lower density of nanostructures at the fluence more than 1 x 10^{12} ions-cm^{-2} and at much higher fluence; the self-affine structures disappear.

The similar nano-patterning of ZnO thin film were also obtained under the 100 MeV Au ion irradiation [42]. Formation of self-affine surface nanostructures by Au irradiation confirms that surface self-organize under the SHI irradiation and produce peculiar surface nanostructures.

The surface rms roughness will be insufficient to supply the complete information of the surface modifications; therefore, surface-scaling analysis via the power spectral density (PSD) evaluation can be utilized to determine the process dominating the surface evolution. The PSD can provide quantitative information about the surface roughness both in the vertical and lateral directions and also remains independent of scan size. The 2D-PSD function is a Fourier transform of the surface and is defined by equation [43]

$$PSD(\gamma) = \frac{1}{area} \left[\iint \frac{d^2 r}{2\pi} e^{-iq.r} <h(r)_t> \right]^2 ; r = (x, y) \tag{3}$$

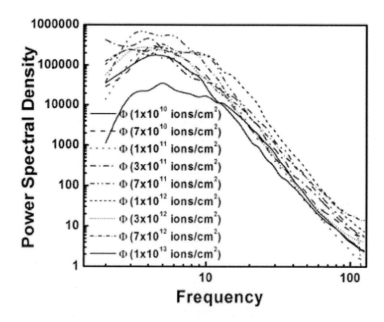

Figure 4. Plots of power spectral density (PSD) function versus spatial frequency q of ZnO surfaces at different fluences for Ag ions (From ref. 42, REPRINTED WITH PERMISSION FROM D. C. Agarwal et.al. J.Appl. Phys. 104,02304,2008, COPYRIGHT 2008, AMERICAN INSTITUTE OF PHYSICS).

Where q is the spatial frequency (nm^{-1}) and $h(r)$ is the surface height at a point r. Fig 4 shows the 2D-PSD curves of ZnO surfaces irradiated with 100 MeV Ag. These graphs have been acquired in the tapping mode with 256 x 256 data points with the image size of 1 x 1 μm^2. The power spectra of Figure 4 can be divided into two distinct regions: the horizontal low frequency part resembles the uncorrelated white noise, while the straight line in high frequency region represents the correlated surface features. PSD curves do not show any significant peak corresponding to the structures. It implies that no periodicity is present in the formed nanostructures or growth of nanostructures lacks the selection of wavelength [44]. No spatial wavelength selection of grown nanostructures confirms the self-affine nature of the nanostructures. At spatial frequency greater than the correlation length (k_o), the PSD displays the power-law dependence [45].

$$PSD = q^{-n} \tag{4}$$

The exponent 'n' is a real number and may define the mechanism contributing to the surface evolution. The value of 'n' can be obtained from the linear fit of the tail of the PSD curve in log-log plot. The slope of PSD function (n) has been found to 2.2 for un-irradiated ZnO thin films and it consistently increases from 2.2 to 4.0 with increasing the fluence up to 1 x 10^{12} ions-cm^{-2}, beyond which it decreases. Eklund et al. [45] studied the diffusion dominated surface structures, which led to a q^{-4} dependence for large spatial frequencies in PSD.

The roughness exponent is determined from the slope of the PSD function, using the relation:

$$\alpha = \frac{n-d}{2} \tag{5}$$

The value of roughness exponent (α) has been found between the 0.8 to 1 for the irradiated samples by Ag ions. The value of $\alpha = 0.90 \pm 0.1$ indicates the self-affine nature of the ion bombarded modified surface. Eklund et. al. [5] reported $\alpha = 0.2$-0.4 for graphite bombarded with 5 keV Ar ions at an angle 60° with respect to surface normal, consistent with the predictions of the Kardar-Parisi-Zhang (KPZ) equation in 2+1 dimension. This is reasonable in good agreement for ion induced roughening with the exponent for growth without surface diffusion. In scaling studies for non-equilibrium film growth by deposition, a value of $\alpha = 0.35$ [46-48] is expected when surface mobility of deposited particles is not allowed and $\alpha = 0.66$ is expected when surface mobility is allowed. Various other mechanisms that could lead to smoothing may provide different values of α.

The root mean square of surface roughness of the film versus ion beam fluence is shown in Figure 5. It is clear from the figure that the roughness exhibits in two different regions as a function of ion fluence. The value of roughness of the ZnO thin film increases up to fluence of 1 x 10^{12} ions-cm^{-2}, following the equation roughness $\alpha \ \Phi^\beta$ with $\beta = 0.24 \pm 0.01$ and at higher value of fluence the roughness decreases. β is known as growth exponent. The plateau height (w) of the PSD curves increases with the fluence up to 1 x 10^{12} ions-cm^{-2} and after this fluence plateau height decreases. The increase in w means that the roughness of the surface increases. The intensity of plateau height in PSD curves also support the variation of surface roughness with fluence. The value of dynamic exponent ($z = \alpha/\beta$) is determined to be 3.6. The measured value of growth exponent $\beta = 0.24 \pm 0.01$, is consistent with numerical simulation of the noisy Kuramoto and Tsuzuki (KS) equation [49-51]. Edwards-Wilkinson (EW) [52] equation also shows the same scaling properties. In this regime, nonlinear effects eventually stabilize the surface and the surface relaxes by surface diffusion with the EW value of growth exponent (β). The value of $\beta = 0.3$ was found to be strongly dependent on the diffusion relaxation mechanism of the Wolf-Villain [47] type to study the surface smoothing effects and to demonstrate the values $z = 3.2$ to 4, characteristic for the diffusion process.

In case of ion bombardment, surface diffusion may be activated by thermal effect and radiation enhanced diffusion processes. Since silver epoxy has been used to paste samples on sample holder (Copper), the heat generated, during ion bombardment is transferred from sample to sample holder. So, the rise in sample temperature is negligible during the ion bombardment and also the ZnO thin films were deposited at the substrate temperature of 300^0C, hence no role of thermally activated surface diffusion is expected. In order to be sure that there is no role of thermally activated surface diffusion in evolution of surface nanostructures, ZnO thin films have been annealed at different temperatures (AFM micrograph not shown here) and no surface structuring has been observed. Therefore, in the present case, the swift heavy ion beam induces the surface diffusion.

Figure 6 shows the absorption spectra of pristine and irradiated ZnO thin films. It is noticed from the spectra that band edge is shifted towards the shorter wavelength at low fluences up to 3 x 10^{12} ions-cm^{-2} and beyond this fluence value, the band edge again comes to its original position. The blue shift in the band-edge indicates the formation of nanostructures. From the optical absorption spectra, the band gap of ZnO films are determined, using the Tauc's procedure of plotting $(\alpha h v)^2$ versus $h v$ and extrapolating the linear portion of absorption edge to the energy axis. These values show that the band gap increases from 3.18 eV to 3.24 eV up to the fluence value 3 x 10^{12} ions-cm^{-2} due to the decrease in the average size of nanostructures and beyond that fluence, band-gap decreases on increasing the ion fluence.

Since sputtering is one of the factors to be considered in understanding the nanostructures, created by energetic ions, the sputtering yield and stoichiometry of the ZnO thin film, under the 100 MeV Ag ion bombardments are determined using the on-line ERDA techniques [53]. The results of ERD analysis are shown in Figure 7 (a) and 7 (b). It is clear from Figure 7 (a) that there is reduction in areal concentration of both zinc and oxygen with ion fluence, which is a clear indication of sputtering under the ion bombardment.

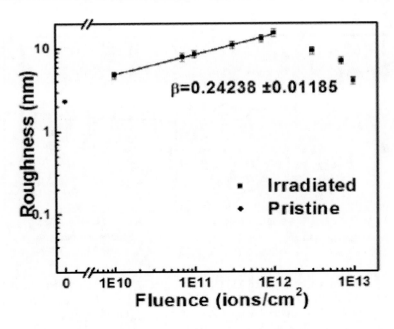

Figure 5. Variation of rms roughness of ZnO surfaces with fluence for Ag ions (From ref. 42, REPRINTED WITH PERMISSION FROM D. C. Agarwal et.al. J.Appl. Phys. 104,02304,2008, COPYRIGHT 2008, AMERICAN INSTITUTE OF PHYSICS).

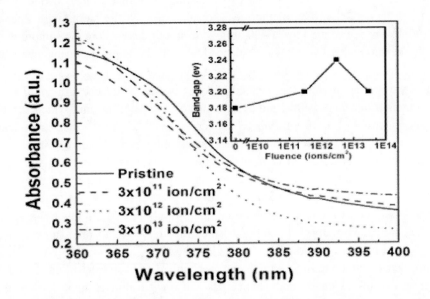

Figure 6. Absorption spectra of ZnO thin film at different fluences (From ref. 42, REPRINTED WITH PERMISSION FROM D. C. Agarwal et.al. J.Appl. Phys. 104,02304,2008, COPYRIGHT 2008, AMERICAN INSTITUTE OF PHYSICS).

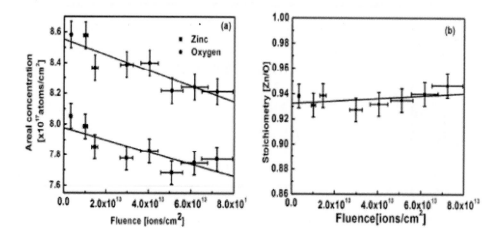

Fig 7(a). Plots of areal concentration of Zn and O with fluence .7(b.). Plot of stoichiometry of ZnO with fluence ((From ref. 42, REPRINTED WITH PERMISSION FROM D. C. Agarwal et.al. J.Appl. Phys. 104,02304, 2008, COPYRIGHT 2008, AMERICAN INSTITUTE OF PHYSICS).

The sputtering at this energy regime is dominantly due to electronic energy loss. From transport and range of ions in matter (TRIM), a Monte Carlo based ion induced damage calculation software [54], the sputtering due to nuclear stopping is indeed found to be negligible or less than 0.3 atom/ion. The experimental sputtering yield is deduced from the linear fit (with in the 3% error), of the areal concentration of the atoms with fluence. The sputtering yield has been found to be 400 atoms/ion in our case where the sample is tilted at 75° with the beam axis. K. M. Gibbs et. al. [55] studied the angular dependence sputtering yield of condensed O_2 and found that yield varies as $(\cos\theta)^{-1.6}$. On the basis of this angular dependence, the sputtering yield for normal incidence is estimated to be around 40 atoms/ion. The total sputtered thickness is 0.05 nm at a fluence of 1×10^{13} ions/cm^2, which is much less than low energy case (~5 to 10 nm) where fluence is very high (~10^{16} ions/cm^2). Therefore, the role of sputtering yield in creation of surface nanostructures for irradiated ZnO thin film at normal incidence can be assumed to be negligible or very less. In case of BH theory, the sputtering occurs due to nuclear stopping of low energy ions, which is affected by curvature at the surface due to smaller penetration depth. In the present case, the swift heavy ions (100 MeV Ag ions) are used which have penetration depth of about ~10 μm much larger than that of the low energy ions to form the surface nanostructures. Due to their larger penetration depth and normal incidence irradiation (perpendicular to the sample surface), there is no role of curvature dependent sputtering. Further the mechanism of sputtering in our case is totally different from that of low energy ions, hence, also different from BH theory. In present case, sputtering is due to electronic effect and no model exists as on today to explain it exactly, except some possible explanation [56]. In low energy regime sputtering is due to elastic collision and subsequent cascade collision. According to Sigmund's theory nuclear sputtering is proportional to S_n whereas electronic sputtering is proportional to $(s_e)^b$ and b is different for different materials.

The electronic sputtering of ZnO thin film under the swift heavy ion irradiation is clear evidence that the ions impart enough energy to the atoms in the films to make them mobile and even leave the surface. Atoms, which have energies greater than the surface binding energy, escape the surface. However, if the energy of the atoms is smaller than the surface binding energy, they contribute to the surface diffusion. The role of these atoms is important in surface smoothing. The stoichiometry of the ZnO thin film almost remains same under the irradiation, as revealed by Figure 7 (b).

From the above discussion, one can infer that the sputtering and ion induced surface diffusion; both play a role in determining the surface features of swift heavy ion irradiated ZnO thin film. The specific features making the difference in the surface evolution at high energy from that of low energy ion beam, are listed in Table-I.

Table-I

A Comparison of different parameters affecting surface evolution at low and high ion energies (From ref. 42, REPRINTED WITH PERMISSION FROM D. C. Agarwal et.al. J.Appl. Phys. 104,02304,2008, COPYRIGHT 2008, AMERICAN INSTITUTE OF PHYSICS.)

S. No.	Parameters	Low energy ion	Swift heavy ion	Comments
1	Energy loss	S_n dominant	S_e dominant	In low energy case, the ion looses energy via the elastic collision with target nuclei whereas in the case of SHI, it is due to the ionization and excitation of electronic system.
2	Fluence	10^{16}-10^{18} ion/cm^2	10^{10}-10^{12} ion/cm^2	Fluence is ~10^6 order of magnitude less in case of SHI irradiation.
3	Sputter yield	less than 5 atoms/ion	40 atoms/ion in our case	Sputtering is one order of magnitude greater in case of SHI irradiation.
4	Range of the ion	few nm	~10 μm	Due to the normal angle irradiation and larger penetration depth, no dependence on surface curvature in the case of SHI sputtering.

From the value of scaling exponent (α, β and z), it is concluded that the large number of atoms contribute in surface diffusion and may be responsible for the formation of self-affine surface nanostructures, induced by swift heavy ion irradiation. Although there is sputtering of the ZnO during ion bombardment, the ion induced surface diffusion is more dominant in the formation of self-affine surface nanostructures.

Figure 8 shows the XRD spectra of pristine and irradiated films. The (100), (002) and (101) reflections of wutzite phase are observed at 31.7°, 34.5° and 36.4° respectively in the figure and the ratio of their intensities accounts for a preferential growth of the ZnO crystals, with the c axis of the hexagonal cell perpendicular to the surface. This fiber texture is usual for ZnO films, grown by physical vapor deposition techniques [57]. After low fluence irradiation, the intensity of the (100) and (002) peaks increases and full width of half maxima (FWHM) of these peaks decrease, while the intensity of (101) peak decreases, indicating that crystals with a or c axis perpendicular to the surface, grow at the expense of others, with a less favorable interface energy. This implies that the irradiation at low fluence increases the texturing along lower energy states and enables the atoms to move to their stable orientation [58]. On the point of view of some applications like for dilute magnetism, the quality of the film is improved. At higher fluences (1×10^{12} and 1×10^{13} ions/cm^2), a significant decrease of peaks intensity but little broadening of all peaks is observed. This result indicates that crystals do not become subdivided by dislocations but are instead amorphized. Taking that, the ZnO films were deposited on Si substrates, which has a large lattice mismatch with ZnO, and therefore inflict a high strain in the films, irradiation at low fluences may help to reduce the strain by further texturing, under the effect of transient heating within tracks through electron-phonon coupling, known as thermal spikes [59]. It is worth noting here, that similar texturing and amorphization induced by SHI irradiation has been reported in various systems of ferrites and magnetites [39,60,61].

The space group of the hexagonal wurtzite ZnO belongs to C^4_{6v}, with two formula units per primitive cell. According to the group theory, single-crystalline ZnO has eight sets of optical phonon modes at Γ point of the Brillouin zone, classified as $A_1+E_1+2E_2$ modes (Raman active), $2B_1$ modes (Raman silent) and A_1+E_1 modes (infrared active) [62,63]. Moreover, the A_1+E_1 modes split into LO and TO components. Typical Raman spectra of the ZnO films irradiated at different ion fluences are shown in Figure 9. The observed phonon frequencies are E_2 (high) = 436 cm^{-1}, slightly shifted towards low wavenumber, with respect to bulk ZnO, as usual for nanocrystals [63]. Other than the characteristic mode of ZnO, few second order modes are also observed. The modes at 233 cm^{-1} and 299 cm^{-1} are related to B_1(high)-B_2(low) and mode at 822 cm^{-1} is related to the B_1(high)+B_1(low) phonon mode frequencies [64].

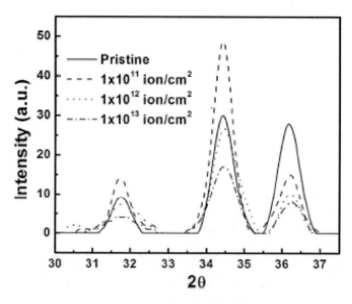

Figure 8. XRD spectra of un-irradiated and irradiated ZnO films.

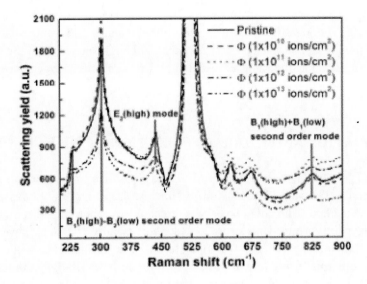

Figure 9. Raman spectra of pristine and irradiated ZnO films.

The peak at 630 cm^{-1} has been assigned to E_1-LO mode [65]. E_1-LO mode at phonon frequency 630 cm^{-1} was theoretically calculated by Zaoui et. al. using the atomistic calculations based on an inter atomic pair potential, within the shell model approach. Since the light penetration depth is larger than the thickness of the ZnO films, a pronounced mode E_2 (high), of the Si substrate is also observed at 521 cm^{-1}. It was noticed that the intensity of the characteristic E_2 mode of ZnO decreased at high fluences. This result corroborates the loss of crystallinity observed by XRD.

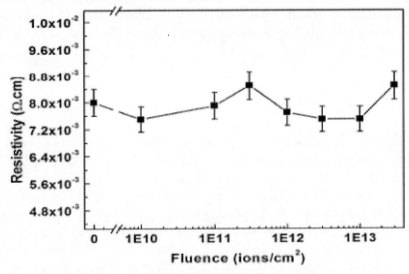

Figure 10. Variation of resistivity of ZnO thin films with ion fluence.

ZnO films deposited on any substrate, exhibits n-type conductivity [66], in which the electrical conductivity is due to the excess zinc presumably, located interstitially within the lattice and oxygen vacancies. Electrical resistivity of all films was measured using the Vander

Pauw four-probe method, at room temperature. The variation in resistivity with ion fluence is shown in fig 10. The resistivity of the ZnO films remains almost constant under the irradiation. This result can be related to the fact that, although sputtering of the films occurs, their stoichiometry remains the same as revealed by ERD spectra. Oxygen vacancies, which contribute in the conduction, are not formed during the irradiation.

4. IRRADIATION AND CHARACTERIZATION OF NiO THIN FILMS

NiO thin films were deposited on Si, Al/Si and SiO_2/Si by rf-magnetron sputtering at Stuttgart University, Germany. The Al film of thickness 250 nm on Si was deposited by resistive heating method. The SiO_2 layer was prepared by annealing the Si substrates in presence of oxygen at Inter-University Accelerator Centre (IUAC), New Delhi. The irradiation has been performed at LN_2 temperature and at an incidence angle of 75^0 with respect to surface normal using the 100 MeV Ag ions from 15 UD Pelletron accelerator at IUAC, New Delhi. The samples were mounted on the irradiation ladder in high vacuum irradiation chamber. In order to do homogeneous irradiation, the ion beam was carefully scanned over an area (5mm x 5mm). The films were irradiated at different fluences 1x 10^{13}, 3 x 10^{13}, 7 x 10^{13}, 1 x 10^{14}, 3 x 10^{14}, and 6 x 10^{14} ions/cm^2. The electronic stopping power of 100 MeV Ag ions in NiO thin film is 20.17 keV/nm while nuclear stopping power is 0.12 keV/nm. Since the range of the 100 MeV Ag ions (9.22 μm) was much greater than the film thickness, no ions were implanted in to the film and modification was expected only due to the S_e.

Surface morphology of irradiated and pristine samples was studied by Atomic force microscopy (AFM). The sputtering of Ni and O from the films is determined by on-line elastic recoil detection analysis (ERDA) measurement. The sample was kept at LN_2 temperature and tilted at 75^0 with respect to the surface normal for ERDA measurement. The recoils were analyzed by large area position sensitive detector telescope (LAPSDT) placed at a scattering angle of 45°.

5. SURFACE RESTRUCTURING OF NiO THIN FILM

The irradiation at small angles of incidence with surface or large angle of incidence with surface normal results in restructuring of crystalline NiO films. The AFM study shows that the continuous film of NiO starts to crack at low fluence perpendicular to the beam direction and after the application of high fluence the material between the cracks begins to shrink and self-organize into the periodic lamella structures. Figure 11(a) to fig 11(c) show the AFM micrograph of the NiO thin film on different substrates irradiated at fluence of 6 x 10^{14} ion/cm^2. The width of the lamellae is less in the case of NiO thin film deposited on SiO_2 substrate while width is greater in the case of Al substrate. The width and separation of lamellae is given in Table-II.

It is also observed that the cracking and development of lamellae structure occurs at higher fluence in the case of Al substrate. The development of lamellae structure on SiO_2 and Al substrates, with fluence is shown in Figure 12 and Figure 13 respectively. The possible mechanism of self-organization of NiO thin film can be understood by visco-elastic model followed by thermal spike model.

Table-II

Change in the width, height and distance between lamellae at different ion fluence

Sample	Fluence (ions/cm^2)	Width of Lamellae	Distance between Lamellae	Height of Lamellae
NiO/Al/Si	1×10^{14}	1.3 μm	450 nm	150 nm
NiO/Al/Si	3×10^{14}	1.0 μm	600 nm	220 nm
NiO/Al/Si	6×10^{14}	0.9 μm	700 nm	310 nm
NiO/SiO$_2$/Si	1×10^{13}	Lamellae are not appeared at this fluence		
NiO/SiO$_2$/Si	3×10^{13}	1.2 μm	300 nm	55 nm
NiO/SiO$_2$/Si	7×10^{13}	1.1 μm	410 nm	62 nm
NiO/SiO$_2$/Si	1×10^{14}	1.0 μm	475 nm	175 nm
NiO/SiO$_2$/Si	3×10^{14}	0.95 μm	605 nm	250 nm
NiO/SiO$_2$/Si	6×10^{14}	0.80 μm	800 nm	620 nm

When swift heavy ion passes through the material, it looses energy via electronic excitation or ionization and produces a cylindrical zone of few nm. The electronic subsystem come in to equilibrium by electron-electron collision and electron-phonon coupling and produces the Gaussian like temperature profile in the vicinity of ion path in the material [67-69]. High temperature causes the transient local melting of the lattice within a cylindrical zone. The energy rapidly dissipates into the cold surroundings resulting in the solidification. The melting and subsequent re-solidification of materials generates the uni-axial tensile stresses along the ion track [70,71]. When the tensile stresses along the beam direction overcome the fracture strength of the NiO surface, it shows periodic cracking perpendicular to the beam direction due to Grinfeld instability [72,73]. Grinfeld showed by the linear surface stability analysis that the competition between elastic strain energy and surface energy leads to the amplification of perturbation of specific periodicity on such stressed surface. The elastic energy releases with the formation of cracked surface. The formation of cracks release elastic stress energy and consumes energy for the creation of the crack surface. For each stressed surface there is an optimum cracking distances, which minimizes the total free energy. The theory of lamellae formation can be explained by hammering effect, which was discovered by Klaumuenzer [74-76]. When fluence increases, the material between cracks shrinks and develops the lamellae structure. The width of the lamellae decreases and the separation between them increases with the increase of fluence. The possible reason for higher width and lack of periodicity of lamellae in case of Al substrate can be understood on the basis of the energy transferred from the film to the substrate through interface. Since the resistivity of the Al is less than Si and SiO$_2$, the energy deposited by SHI in the film can be easily transferred to Al substrate.

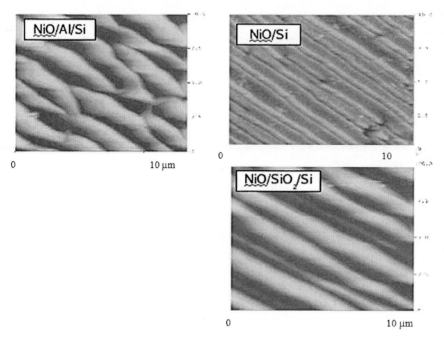

Figure 11. AFM images of NiO film on different substrate irradiated at 6x10^{14} ions/cm^2 (a) on Al/Si (b) on Si (c) on SiO$_2$/Si.

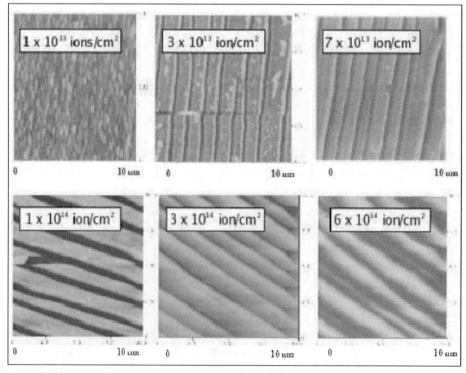

Figure 12. AFM images of NiO/SiO$_2$/Si irradiated at different fluences.

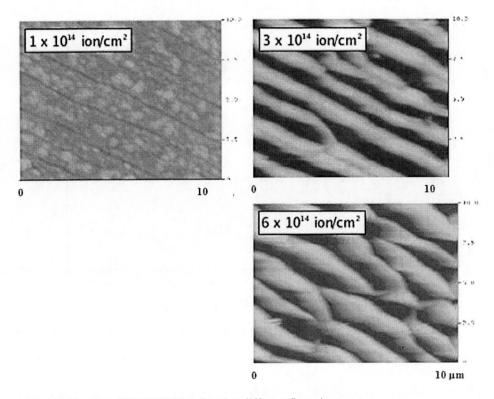

Figure 13. AFM images of NiO/Al/Si irradiated at different fluencies.

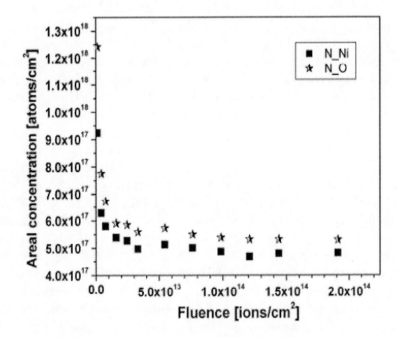

Figure 14. Areal concentration O and Ni in NiO on Si at different fluences.

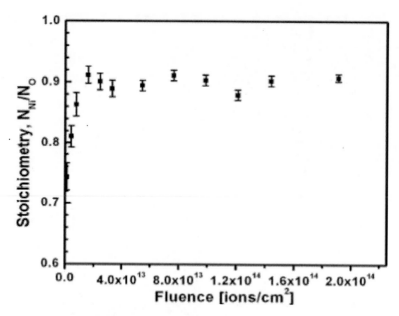

Figure 15. Stoichiometry (ratio of areal concentration of Ni to O) of NiO on Si at different fluences.

Since the surface structures induced by ion bombardment are formed due to the interplay between sputtering and surface diffusion, we measure the sputtering of NiO thin film under the swift heavy ion bombardment. The sputtering yield and stoichiometry of the NiO thin film under 100 MeV Ag ions bombardment are determined using the on-line ERDA technique. Areal concentration of O and Ni and the ratio of areal concentration of Ni to O or stoichiometry were calculated from recoil spectra of individual elements by usual ERDA formulae at every fluence step [77,78]. The results of ERD analysis are shown in Figure 14 and 15. It is clear from Figure 14 that there is reduction in areal concentration of both Nickel and oxygen with ion fluence, which is a clear indication of sputtering under the ion bombardment. The sputtering at this energy regime is mainly caused by electronic energy loss, which is referred as electronic sputtering. From TRIM, a Monte Carlo based ion induced damage calculation software, the sputtering due to nuclear stopping is indeed found to be less than 2 atoms/ion. Electronic sputtering of NiO thin film under swift heavy ion irradiation is clear evidence that the ions impart enough energy to the atoms in the films to make them mobile and even leave the surface. It is clear from Figure 14 that the sputtering takes place up to the fluence 1×10^{13} ions/cm^2 and beyond this fluence the surface cracks and reorganization of NiO surface starts as seen in Figure 13(a) and 13(b). The stoichiometry (Ni/O) of the film increases from 0.74 to 0.91 up to 1×10^{13} ions/cm^2 and beyond which it remains constant with fluence as shown in Figure 15. As stoichiometry approaches to 0.9, the sputtering of the NiO film ceases or material becomes resistive to sputtering. However, the energy received by atoms is large enough for surface diffusion. This surface diffusion leads to the plastic deformation of the material, which results in self-organization of the surface in the periodic lamellae structure. This implies that once plastic deformation starts; there is no loss of NiO material. The possible reason for this kind of reorganization is that initially the sputtering of NiO thin film is taking place under the ion bombardment and whenever ion imparted so much energy into the film so that the tensile stress generated by ion beam exceeds the fracture strength of the NiO surface, the plastic deformation of film occur after a certain fluence. The surface stresses induced by swift ion beam are given by Trinkaus model [70,71]:

$$\sigma_{xx}(\theta) = -0.58 \frac{E}{1-\nu} \alpha T (\cos^2 \theta - \sin^2 \theta) = \sigma(1 - 2\sin^2 \theta) \tag{6}$$

$$\sigma_{yy}(\theta) = -0.58 \frac{E}{1-\nu} \alpha T \cos^2 \theta = \sigma \cos^2 \theta \tag{7}$$

$$\sigma_{zz}(\theta) = 0 \tag{8}$$

Where E, ν, α, θ and T are the Young's modulus, Poisson's number, coefficient of linear thermal expansion, angle of incidence and freezing temperature respectively. σ_{xx}, σ_{yy} and σ_{zz} are the stresses along the X, Y and Z-axis respectively. From these equations the coordinates are: z-axis points towards the surface normal and x-axis points to the projection of ion beam. It is clear from equation (1) and equation (2) that the dependence of σ_{xx} and σ_{yy} on incident angle show two components of stresses, compressive and tensile, which point along the y and x direction respectively. For $\theta = 0^\circ$, $\sigma_{xx} = \sigma_{yy}$ with negative sign indicating the uniaxial compressive stresses. At $\theta < 45^\circ$ the compressive and at $\theta > 45^\circ$ tensile stress is dominant. It is clear from above equation that if angle approaches 90^0, then σ_{yy} tends to zero. At large angle, only tensile stress exists along the direction of the sample layer thickness and due to the energy transferred by SHI; the sample is under uniform tensile stress. Thin film shows cracking when the applied tensile stress exceeds the critical fracture stress σ_c [79], which is expressed as

$$\sigma_c = \frac{K_c}{\Omega_c d^{1/2}} \tag{9}$$

Where K_c, Ω_c and d are the fracture resistance, decohesion number and film thickness respectively. When the value of σ_{xx} for 100 MeV Ag in NiO overcomes the fracture strength of the NiO surface (σ_c), the surface cracks and their penetration into larger depths of the NiO layer, until the SiO_2 layer is reached and further irradiation then leads to shrinking of the NiO "stripes" in between the cracks and an increase of their height i.e. the material shrinks parallel to the ion beam and expands perpendicular to the beam direction. Finally at high fluence, the lamellae structures have formed and there is no material loss during the development of lamellae structures. The lamellae formation itself can be understood in terms of the so-called hammering effect or ion beam induced plastic flow first observed by Klaumünzer, et al., in metallic glasses because the characteristics of lamellae formation is same as ion beam induced plastic flow in the form of anisotropic growth, which can be explained by viscoelastic model given by H. Trinkaus. According to viscoelastic model the intense electronic excitations and efficient electron-phonon coupling, a cylindrical region around the track of ion may become fluid in sense that any thermally induced shear stress would relax in this region. The region has virtually cooled down to ambient temperatures with in the 100 ps generally in a modified state due to the relaxation of shear stress during the spike. The extremely fast heating and quenching process may, however, results in local reduction of viscosity and the frozen in of stress relaxation. This induces the anisotropic growth or plastic flow of the material.

CONCLUSION

In this chapter, we have review the work on surface nanostructuring of metal oxide thin films under the application of swift heavy ion irradiation. ZnO films, deposited by thermal evaporation, were used to study the irradiation effect on structural and optical properties. In conclusion, we report the evolution of self-affine nanostructures on the surface of ZnO film, under the swift heavy ion irradiation. However the changes in other properties of ZnO thin films are not significant. The shape and density of the nanostructures depends upon the ion fluence and there is a critical fluence beyond which the structures are agglomerated due to the overlapping of damaged zones and finally disappear. Blue shift in the band-edge of UV-Visible spectra also supports the formation of nanostructures. Both the sputtering rate (40 atoms/ion), and scaling exponent have been calculated for ion beam evolved surfaces. The value of roughness exponent (α= 0.90±0.1), and growth exponent (β= 0.24±0.01), reveal that surface diffusion is more dominant and plays major role in the evolution of surface structures, which is induced by swift heavy ion beam. XRD and Raman spectroscopy results reveal that at low fluence, the film quality is improved as larger grains can be observed due to increase in the intensity of the XRD peaks and decrease in FWHM in the irradiated films due to the strain relaxation between the substrate and film. However, at higher fluence, little disordering of the film has been observed. We have concluded from absorption spectra and ERD analysis that the basic lattice and stoichiometry of the ZnO thin films is not modified due to the irradiation. Four-probe resistivity measurement shows that the electrical property has not been modified.

NiO thin film on different substrates shows very interesting self-organization phenomena under the oblique ion bombardment at LN_2 temperature. We propose that the cracking of the surface of the film is due to the Grien-feld instability and after that the well-known plastic flow of the material play important role in the formation of periodic lamellae structure. We conclude from the AFM study that the self-organization of the film depends on substrate. We can control the shape and size of the lamellae using different substrates. We infer from ERDA data that at low fluence, the sputtering is dominant and at higher fluences beyond the 1 x 10^{13} ions/cm^2, the surface diffusion play crucial role in the self-organization of NiO surface. It is observed that low fluence is required for development of lamellae structure and good periodicity occur in the case of insulator substrate.

ACKNOWLEDGMENT

We are thankful to Department of Science and Technology (DST), New Delhi for providing financial assistance to procure AFM under the Intensifying the Research in High Priority Areas (IRHPA) project. Authors are also thankful to W. Bolse, Stuttgart University Germany, J. C. Pivin, CSNSM, Orsay France for fruitful discussions and help in film deposition and RBS experiment. Authors are also highly grateful to Dr. D. K. Avasthi, IUAC

New Delhi for his valuable guidance and inputs in this work. Experimental help received from material science group Inter University Accelerator Centre is also acknowledged. Further DCA and RSC would like to thank again DST, New Delhi for financial support under the project Swift Heavy Ion Induced Nanostructures Formation of Oxide Thin Films.

REFERENCES

[1]   Chason E.; Mayer T. M.; Kellerman B. K.; McIlroy D. T. and Howard A. J.; *Phys. Rev. Lett.,* 1994, *72,* 3040-3043

[2]   Carter G. and Vishnayakov V.; *Phys. Rev., B,* 1996, *54,* 17647-17653

[3]   Wittmaack, in Practical Surface Analysis, Vol.2 *Ion and Neutral Spectroscopy*, edited by Briggs D. and Seah M. P. *(Wiley, Chichester, 1992) chap.3,* p.122.

[4]   Habenicht S.; Bolse W.; Lieb K. P.; Reimann K. and Geyer U.; *Phys. Rev., B* 1999, *60,* 2200-2203

[5]   Ekland E. A.; Bruinsma R.; Rudnick J. and Williams R. S.; *Phys. Rev. Lett,* 1991, *67,* 1759-1762

[6]   Krim J.; Heyvart I.; Haesendonck D. V. and Bruynseraede Y.; *Phys. Rev. Lett,* 1993, *70,* 57-60

[7]   Navez M.; Chaperot D. and Sella C.; *Comptes Rendus Academie des Sciences,* 1962, *254,* 240

[8]   Erlebacher J. D. and Aziz M.J.; *Mater. Res. Soc. Symp. Proc.* 1997, *440,* 461 (7p)

[9]   Facsko S.; Dekorsy T.; Koerdt C.; Trappe C.; Kurz H.; Vogtand A. And Hartnagel H. L.; *Science* 1999, *285,* 1551-1553

[10]   Frost F.; Schindler A. and Bigl F.; *Phys. Rev. Lett.,* 2000, *85,* 4116-4119

[11]   Gago R.; Vazquez L.; Cuerno R.; Varela M.; Ballesteros C. and Albella J.M.; *Appl. Phys. Lett.* 2001, *78,* 3316-3318

[12]   Rusponi S.; Boragno C. and Valbusa U.; *Phys. Rev. Lett.,* 1997, *78,* 2795-2798

[13]   Mayer T. M.; Chason E. and Howard A. J.; *J. Appl. Phys.* 1994, *76,* 1633-1643

[14]   Bolse W.; *Nucl. Instr. and Meth. B,* 2006, *244,* 8-14

[15]   Bolse W.; Schattat B. and Feyh A.; *Appl. Phys. A 2002, 77,* 11-15

[16]   Goswami D. K. and Dev B. N.; *Phys. Rev. B,* 2003, *68,* 33401 (4p)

[17]   Bradley R. M. and Harper J. M.; *J. Vac. Sci. Technol. A,* 1988, 6, 2390-2395

[18]   Herring C. In and Kingston W E, *editor. Physics of powder metallurgy. New York: McGraw-Hills;* 1951;

[19]   Herring C.; *J. Appl. Phys.,* 1950, *21,* 301-303.

[20]   Mullins W W.; *J. Appl. Phys.,* 1959, *30,* 77-83

[21]   Cuerno R and Barabasi A. L.; *Phys. Rev. Lett.,* 1995, *74,* 4746-4749

[22]   Pang Z. W.; Dai Z. R. and Wang Z. L.; *Science,* 2001, *291,* 1947-1949

[23]   Rensmo H.; Lindstrom K. K.; Wang L. N. and Muhammed M.; *J. Phys. Chem. B,* 1997, *101,* 2598-2601

[24]   Huang M. H.; Wu Y. Y.; Feick H.; Tran N.; Weber E. and Yang P. D.; *Science,* 2001, *292,* 1897-1899

[25]   Muhr H. J.; Krumeich F.; Schonholzer U. P.; Bieri F.; Niederberger M.; Gauckler L. J. and Nesper R.; *Adv. Mater. (Weinheim, Ger.),* 2001, *12,* 231-234

[26] Liu C. H.; Yiu W. C.; Au F. C. K.; Ding J. K.; Lee C. S. and Lee S. T.; *Appl. Phys. Lett.*, 2003, *83*, 3168 (3p)

[27] Liu C. H.; Zapien J. A.; Yao Y.; Meng X. M.; Lee C. S.; Fan S. S.; Lifshitz Y. and Lee S. T.; *Adv. Mater. (Weinheim, Ger.)*, 2003, *15*, 838-841

[28] Hvam J. M.; *Phys. Rev. B*, 1971, 4, 4459-4464

[29] Klingshirn C.; *Phys. Status Solidi B*, 1975, *71*, 547-556

[30] Service R. F.; *Science*, 1997, *276*, 895-897

[31] Huang M. H.; Mao S.; Feick H.; Yan H.; Wu Y.; Kind H.; Weber E.; Russo R. and Yang P.; *Science*, 2001, *292*, 1897-1899

[32] Chen Y. F.; Bagnall D. M.; Koh H.; Park K.; Hiranga K.; Zhu Z. and Yao T.; *J. Appl. Phys.*, 1998, *84*, 3912-3918.

[33] Mutschall D.; Berger S.A. and Obermeier E.; Proc. of 6th international meeting on chemical sensors, Gaithersburg, 1996, *28*

[34] Fantini M. and Gorenstein A.; *Solar Energy Materials*, 1987, *16*, 487-500

[35] Carpenter M. K.; Conell R. S. and Corrigan D. A.; *Solar Energy Material.*, 1987, *16*, 333-346

[36] Yu P. C.; Nazri G. and Lampert C.M.; *Solar Energy Materials.*, 1987, *16*, 1-17

[37] Dimaria D. J. and Kerr D. R.; *Appl. Phys. Lett.*, 1975, *27*, 505-507

[38] Carter G.; Nobes M. J.; Katardjiev I. V. and Whitton J. L.; *Defect Diff. Forum*, 1988, *57/58*, 97-126

[39] Mohanty T.; Satyam P. V. and Kanjilal D.; *J. of Nanosci. and Nanotechnol.*, 2006, *6*, 2554-2559

[40] Singh J. P.; Singh R.; Mishra N. C.; Ganesan V. and Kanjilal D.; *J. Appl. Phys.* 2000, *87*, 2742 -2746

[41] Agarwal D. C.; Chauhan R. S.; Kumar A.; Kabiraj D.; Singh F.; Khan S. A.; Avasthi D. K.; Pivin J. C.; Kumar M.; Ghatak J. and Satyam P. V.; *J. Appl. Phys.*, 2006, *99*, 123105 (6p)

[42] Agarwal D.C.; Kumar A.; Khan S. A.; Kabiraj D.; Singh F.; Tripathi A., Pivin J. C.; Chauhan R. S. and Avasthi D.K.; *Nucl. Instrum. Meth. B*, 2006, *244*, 136-140, Agarwal D.C.; Chauhan R. S.; Avasthi D. K.; Khan S. A.; Kabiraj D. and Sulania I.; *J. Appl. Phys.*, 2008, *104*, 024304 (8p)

[43] Petri R.; Brault P.; Vatel O.; Henry D.; Andre E.; Dumas P. and Salvan F.; *J Appl. Phys.*, *1994, 75*, 7498-7506

[44] Liu Z. J.; Jiang N.; Shen Y. G. and Mai Y. W.; *J. Appl. Phys.*, 2002, *92*, 3559-3563

[45] Eklund E. A.; Snyder E. J. and Williams R. S.; *Surf. Sci.*, 1993, 285, 157-180

[46] Kardar M.; Parisi G. and Zhang Y.; *Phys. Rev. Lett.*, 1986, *56*, 889-892

[47] Wolf D. E. and Villain J.; *Europhys. Lett.*, 1990, *13*, 389-394

[48] Lai Z. W. and Sarma S. Das; *Phys. Rev. Lett.*, 1991, *66*, 2348-2351

[49] Sneppen K.; Krug J.; Jensen M. H.; Jayaprakash C. and Bohr; *Phys. Rev. A*, 1992, *46*, 7351-7354

[50] Hayot F.; Jayaprakash C.; Josserand Ch.; *Phys. Rev. E*, 1993, *47*, 911-915

[51] Zaleski S.; *Physica D*, 1989, *34*, 427-438

[52] Edwards S. F. and Wilkinson D. R.; *Proc. R. Soc. London A*, 1982, *381*, 17-31

[53] Avasthi D. K.; Assmann W.; Huber H.; Mieskes H. D. and Nolte H.; *Nucl. Instrum. Meth. B*, 1998, *142*, 117-121

[54] Ziegler J. F. and Biersack J. P.; *SRIM-2003. 20: The Stopping and the Range of Ions in Matter*, [www.srim.org] .

[55] Gibbs K. M.; Brown W. L. and Johnson R. E.; *Phys. Rev. B.,* 1988, *38*, 11001-11007

[56] Toulemonde M.; Assmann W.; Trautmann C. and Grüner F.; *Phys. Rev. Lett.,* 2002, *88*, 057602 (4p)

[57] Fujimura N.; Nishihara T.; Goto S.; Xua J. and Ito T.; *J. Cryst. Growth,* 1993, *130*, 269-279

[58] Kim Y. J.; Kin Y. T.; Yang H. J.; Park J. C.; Han J. I.; Lee Y. E. and Kim H. J.; *J. Vac. Sci. and Technol. A,* 1997, *15*, 11031107

[59] Toulemonde M.; Costantini J. M.; Dufour Ch.; Meftah A.; Paumier E. and Studer F.; *Nucl. Instr. and Meth. B,* 1996, *116*, 37-42

[60] Kumar Ravi; Choudhary R. J.; Patil S. I.; Hussain S; Srivastava J. P.; Sanyal S. P. and Lofland S. E.; *J. Appl. Phys,,* 2004, *96*, 7383-7387

[61] Dogara A.; Kumar Ravi; Khan S. A.; Kumar V. V. S.; Kumar N.; Singh M.; *Nucl. Instrum. Methods B,* 2004, *225*, 283-290

[62] Bundesmann C.; Ashkenov N.; Schubert M.; Spemann D.; Butz T.; Kaidashev E. M.; Lorenz M. and Grundmann M.; *Appl. Phys. Lett.,* 2003, *83*, 1974-1976

[63] Khan A. A.; Vladimir A. F.; Manu S. and Alexander A. B.; *J. Appl. Phys.,* 2005, *97*, 124313 (5p)

[64] Serrano J.; Romero A. H.; Manjoen F. J.; Lauck R.; Cardona M. and Rubio A.; *Phys. Rev. B,* 2004, *69*, 094306 (14p)

[65] Zaoui A. and Sekkal W.; *Phys. Rev. B,* 2000, *66*, 174106 (6p)

[66] Minami T.; Sato H. and Takata S.; *Jpn. J. Appl. Phys., Part 2,* 1985, *24*, L781-L784.

[67] Seitz F. and Koehler J. S.; *Solid State Phys.* 1956, *2*, 305-448

[68] Wang Z. G.; Dufor Ch.; Paumier E.; and Toulemonde M.; *J. Phys.: Condens Matter,* 1994, *6*, 6733

[69] Toulemonde M.; Dufor Ch.; Wang Z. G. and Paumier E.; *Nucl. Instr. and Meth. B,* 1996, *112*, 26-29

[70] Trinkaus H. and Ryazanov A. I.; *Phys. Rev. Lett.,* 1995, *74*, 5072-5075

[71] Trinkaus H.; *Nucl. Instr. and Meth. B,* 1998, *146*, 204-216

[72] Grinfeld M. A. and *Nauk D. A.; SSSR,* 1986, *290*, 1358-1363

[73] Srolovitz D. J.; *Acta Metall.* 1989, *37*, 621-625

[74] Klaumuenzer S. and Schumacher G.; *Phys. Rev. Lett.,* 1983, *51*, 1987-1990

[75] Klaumuenzer S.; Hou M. and Schumacher G.; *Phys. Rev. Lett.,* 1986, *57*, 850-853

[76] Klaumuenzer S. and Benyagoub A.; *Phys. Rev. B,* 1991, *43*, 7502-7506

[77] Avasthi D. K.; Assmann W.; Huber H.; Mieskes H. D. and Nolte H.; *Nucl. Instr. and Meth. B,* 1998, *142*, 117-121

[78] Kumar M.; Khan S. A.; Singh F.; Tripathi A.; Avasthi D. K. and Pandey A. C.; *Nucl. Instr. and Meth. B,* 2007, *256*, 328-332

[79] Evans A. G.; Drory M. D. and Hu M. S.; *J. Mater. Res.,* 1988, *3*, 173110-

In: Synthesis and Engineering of Nanostructures…   ISBN 978-1-62100-261-1
Editors: Devesh Kumar Avasthi & Jean Claude Pivin   © 2012 Nova Science Publishers, Inc

Chapter 19

ION BEAM INDUCED RESIZING OF SEMICONDUCTING OXIDE NANOSTRUCTURES

Tanuja Mohanty[1]

School of Physical Sciences, Jawaharlal Nehru University,
New Delhi, India – 110 067

ABSTRACT:

Tin oxide (SnO_2) nanocrystalline thin films are grown on amorphous and crystalline substrates by electron beam evaporation method, followed by ion bombardment. Grain size of as-deposited films were estimated from atomic force microscopy and glancing angle X-ray diffraction studies and were found to be varying from 7nm to 15nm. To achieve narrow size distribution, these nanocrystalline SnO_2 thin films were bombarded by 100 MeV Au ions at a fluence varying from $1x10^{11}$ ions.cm^{-2} to $5x10^{11}$ ions.cm^{-2}. After ion bombardment, nanocrystalline grains are found to have acquired size of ~10nm radius with narrow size distribution. In case of crystalline sapphire substrates, the nanocrystalline grains are aligned in periodic manner. It is expected that the stress induced due to mismatch in thermal expansion coefficient between film and sapphire matrix leads to self organization of nanocrystlline grains, along a particular orientation.

1. INTRODUCTION

Combination of low electrical resistance with high optical transparency in the visible range of electromagnetic spectrum leads tin oxide (SnO_2) to have wide optoelectronic applications [1-2]. These properties are sought in number of applications: as electrode materials in solar cells, light emitting diodes, flat panel displays, other optoelectronic devices and gas sensors. Crystalline tin oxide, with cassiterite structure, is a wide band gap (3.6 eV) semiconductor. Tin oxide nanostructures are prepared by different techniques, using dry processes, e.g. sputtering from a tin oxide target or from a metallic target followed by oxidation [3], laser ablation [4] and chemical vapor deposition (CVD) [5], electron beam evaporation[6], and wet processes, e.g. spray pyrolysis, decomposition and oxidation of tin (II) amides, sol-gel related methods [7].

In recent years, a lot of efforts have been made to control the size and shape of the nanostructure because these parameters affect their properties. It is very important to organize nanoscale building blocks into complex nanostructure especially periodic ones. Ion beam bombardment technique has been used as an important tool for the fabrication, modification and self-organization of nanostructures [8]. It plays important role in reorganization and resizing of nanostructures. Control on the size distribution of nanocrystals can be achieved by ion irradiation. In this work, application of ion bombardment for modification and self organization of tin oxide nanostructures is reported.

2. EXPERIMENT

Thin films of SnO_2 (~100 nm thick) were deposited on amorphous and crystalline substrates by e-beam evaporation in a high vacuum chamber, at a base vacuum of 10^{-6} torr. Quartz and sapphires were chosen as amorphous and crystalline substrates. During deposition, the substrate temperature was maintained at 200°C to enhance surface diffusion of atoms on the substrate. These as-deposited thin films were characterized by atomic force microscope (AFM), Glancing Angle X-Ray Diffraction (GAXRD) and UV-visible absorption spectroscopic techniques for structural, morphological and optical characterization. Wide variation in morphology of these as-deposited films was observed. To reorganize these nanostructures, these films were bombarded by 150 MeV Au beams at a fluence of 5×10^{11} ions.cm^{-2} using 15 MV tandem accelerator. The range of the ion beam was ~19 μm which is much more than thickness of the film (~100nm). The ion bombarded tin oxide thin films were also characterized by AFM, GAXRD and UV-visible spectroscopy techniques.

3. RESULT AND DISCUSSION

3.1 Atomic Force Microscopy (AFM) Studies

Atomic Force microscopy studies were carried out using nanoscope III. Figures 2 and 3 show the morphology of as-deposited thin films of tin oxide on quartz and sapphire substrates. These nanostructures show wide variation in size. After ion bombardment, the morphology of nanostructure is modified.

When bombardment was done at 1×10^{11} ions.cm^{-2}, the morphology and reorganization in both quartz and sapphire substrates were found to be similar. But when the fluence was 5×10^{11} ion.cm^{-2}, the reorganization on both the substrates were quite different. Figures 3 and 4 show the morphology of ion bombarded tin oxide thin films on quartz and sapphire

---

[1]   Dr. Tanuja Mohanty, School of Physical Sciences, Jawaharlal Nehru University New Delhi -110 067, India, e-mail: tmohanty@mail.jnu.ac.in .

substrates after a fluence of 5×10^{11} ions.cm^{-2}. The nanocrystalline grains are arranged periodically along one dimension.

Figure 1. AFM scan of as-deposited SnO$_2$ thin films on quartz substrate.

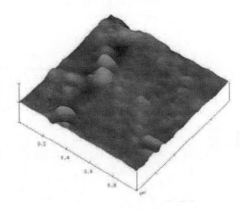

Figure 2.AFM scan of as-deposited SnO$_2$ thin films on sapphire substrate.

Figure 3. AFM scan of 150 MeV Au bombarded SnO$_2$ thin films on quartz at $\varphi = 5 \times 10^{11}$ ions.cm^{-2}.

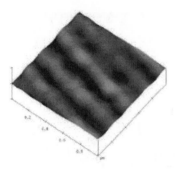

Figure 4. AFM scan of 150 MeV Au bombarded SnO_2 thin films on sapphire at $\varphi = 5 \times 10^{11}$ ions.cm^{-2}.

Alignment along the orientation of crystalline substrate was observed in earlier work [9] on tin oxide thin films grown on Si-substrate. The crystalline substrates are found to orient the films in particular direction during ion bombardment by high energy heavy ion. Depending on ion beam fluence, desired orientation and periodicity in nanostructure can be achieved.

For structural study, Glancing angle X-Ray Diffraction (GAXRD) studies were carried out on all thin films. GAXRD plot for both unirradiated and ion bombarded thin films grown on sapphire substrate are shown in figures 5. It is observed that the crystallinity has been increased in thin films bombarded at a ion fluence of 5×10^{11} ions.cm^{-2} showing similar results as in our previous observation in case of Xe ion irradiation but with higher intensity [9].

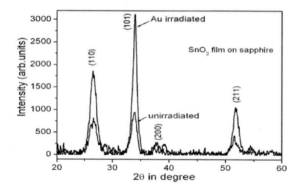

Figure 5. GAXRD plot of 150 MeV Au bombarded ($\varphi = 5 \times 10^{11}$ ions.cm^{-2}) SnO_2 thin film on sapphire substrate (from Ref. 9).

The size of the nanocrystalline grains were calculated from XRD peaks and were found to be about 10 nm after ion bombardment. UV-visible characterization was carried out for both as-deposited and 150 MeV Au ion bombarded thin films using Hitachi 3300 spectrophotometer. Figure 6 shows the variation of UV/visible absorbance of both as-deposited and ion bombarded SnO_2 thin films with energy. Red shift of optical band edges in case of ion bombarded ($\varphi = 5 \times 10^{11}$ ions.cm^{-2}) thin films as compared to as-deposited thin films indicates quantum confinement effect as well as grain growth effect.

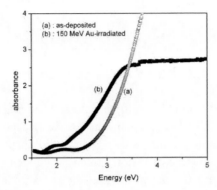

Figure 6. UV/visible absorption plot of SnO_2 thin films grown on sapphire substrate (a) as-deposited (b) 150 MeV A-irradiated ($\square = 5 \times 10^{11}$ ions.cm^{-2}).

The observed changes in morphology, structural and optical properties of the nanocrystalline grains are attributed to the effect of substrates and ion beam interaction with the target material which are discussed below.

4. DISCUSSION

4.1 Ion Beam Interaction

The passage of SHI in materials mainly produces electronic excitation of the atoms in the materials. It deposits electronic excitation energy of ~1 to 10keV/A in the materials. Electronic excitation produces tracks when its value crosses a threshold value (S_{eo}) for track formation [10]. SHI interaction with target material is important at ion energies $\geqslant$1 MeV/u leading to generation of hot electron gas around the straight ion trajectory. Coupling between the electron gas and the atoms of the target material, leads to very high temperatures spike so that the target material within a few nm around the trajectory melts within a few picoseconds [11]. Rapid re-solidification ($\sim$10–100 ps) can lead to a trail of defects or modified material, the ion track having radius of few nanometers. Below S_{eo} the track structure deviates more and more from a cylindrical shape. The temperature in a small volume of nano-metric length scale increases to $\sim 10^4$-10^3 K [10] within picoseconds. Thus, fast mean relaxation process ($\sim 10^{-12}$s in a single cascade) gives a typical quenching rate of $\sim 10^{15}$ K.sec^{-1}. Such a fast quenching rate in a thermal spike is probably the highest among currently available techniques for producing metastable phases. Meanwhile, such a short time of relaxation restricts the kinetic condition for the phase formation so that only amorphous or simple crystalline phases are obtained. Both the time scale and lengths favor the formation of nanostructures in the ion irradiation process.

Electronic energy loss thresholds (S_{eo}) for track generation in SnO_2 is ~ 6 keV/nm. During 150 MeV Au ion bombardment on SnO_2 nanocrystalline thin films, the electronic energy loss is 14 keV/nm and nuclear energy loss is 0.19 keV/nm as estimated by the SRIM 2003 code [12]. Since value of S_e is higher than S_{eo}, latent tracks get formed inside the film.

The radius of the track was estimated to be ~ 9 nm corresponding to S_e value of 14 keV/nm [13].

4.2 SELF ORGANIZATION

Self organization occurs through multiple interactions among the components [14] minimizing the free energy. In our experiment, during vapor deposition, when the atoms hit the substrate, their initial positions are random. The rapid shape relaxation of these solid particles is dominated by the surface diffusion. But when the temperature is changed during bombardment by suitable energetic ion, phase transitions take place, starting from so-called nuclei or clusters. The mobile atoms diffuse towards nucleated phase. There is a competition between the coarsening (due to phase boundary energy) and refining (due to the non-uniform surface stress) which defines the size of the phase [15]. The elastic field in the substrate leads to spatial ordering of the phase in the surface of the film. Surface energy of the deposit has to be higher than the combined surface energies of the substrate and interface to achieve a good control over the size of nanoclusters.

In our experiment, SHI ion bombardment leads to high rise of temperature of the nanocrystalline thin films locally for a very short period of the order of 10^{-12} seconds. This temperature rise is high enough to melt the nanocrystalline grains of tin oxide. The melting temperature of tin oxide thin films is ~1100°C. The melting point of nanocrystallites is much lower than bulk melting temperature [16]. Thus it is expected that 150 MeV Au ion bombardment creates local melting of SnO_2 nanocrystalline grains and hence a liquid medium is generated where all the atoms are more or less mobile. These mobile atoms get nucleated surrounding the point defects generated by ion bombardment. Defects like oxygen vacancies and tin interstitials are formed during ion bombardment. The nucleation and growth process of nanocrystallites are separated and the growth time is same for all the nanocrystallites leading uniformity in size distribution in both the host matrices. However the features observed after the same ion bombardment for same fluence is different in two different matrix. This is explained in the form the schematic below (Figure 7).

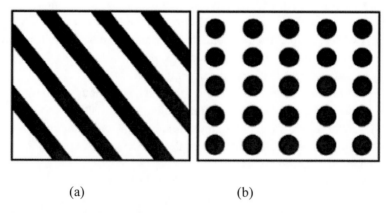

(a)   (b)

Figure 7. Schematics of experimentally observed nanoscale patterns on solid surfaces. (a) Alternating stripes. (b) A lattice of dots.

This schematic emphasizes that in solid state due to atomic diffusion from one site to another, atoms may self assemble into a periodic structure, such as nano array of stripes or dots. The feature size may be of nanoscale, small compared to bulk structures, but large compared to individual atoms. This may be due to the change in free energy which is affected by mass transport processes, such as diffusion. It is expected that long range inelastic interaction is the driving force for ordering in the matrix [17].

4.3 SHAPING OF TIN OXIDE NANOSTRUCTURES

The elongated shaping of tin oxide nanostructures may be due to the stress-induced preferential absorption or stress-induced preferential nucleation of radiation-induced vacancies and interstitials [18]. This stress is expected to arise from the thermal coefficient mismatch between the film and the lattice, particularly sapphire substrate. Thermal expansion coefficient of sapphire (8.4×10^{-6} K^{-1}) is much higher than that of SnO$_2$ (0.35×10^{-6} K^{-1}). The effect of mismatch in thermal expansion coefficient is much pronounced when the films are bombarded by ion beam and the local temperature rises above melting temperature. This lattice mismatch stress leads to periodic arrangements of nanodots in parallel stripes.

CONCLUSION

Ion beams provide a versatile means to modify materials on a nano-meter scale. It is a potential tool for formation of nano-phase and modification of materials, due to its non-equilibrium interaction. During dynamic annealing process, the self organization of nanograins takes place around the vacancies created, by ion bombardment. The periodic arrangement of nanostructures are dependent on stress induced in matrix as well as fluence of the ion beam.

ACKNOWLEDGMENTS

The author is thankful to Dr. D. Kanjilal of Inter University Accelerator Centre, New Delhi for fruitful discussions. TM is also grateful to Dr. Ambuj Tripathi and Pawan Kularia of IUAC for carrying out AFM and GAXRD characterizations.

REFERENCES

[1] Kim, T.W.; Lee, D.U. and Yoon, Y.S. *J. Appl. Phys.* 2000, *88*, 3759.
[2] Guangsheng, P.; Siguang, C.; Yuri, K.; Arie, Z.; Shouhua, F.; and Aharon, G. *Nano Lett.* 2001, *12*, 723.
[3] Minami ,T.; Nanto, H.; and T akata, S. *Jpn. J. Appl. Phys.* 1988, *27*,.L287.
[4] Chen, Z.W.; Lai, J. K. L. and Shek, C.H. *Phys. Rev. B* 2004, *70*,165314.
[5] Tarey, R. D. and Raju, T. A. *Thin Solid films* 1995,*128*,181.

[6]   Pan, X. Q.; Fu, L. and Dominguez *J. Appl. Phys.*2001, *89*, 6056.

[7]   Mohanta, S. K.; Soni, R. K.; Tripathy, S. and Chua, S. J. *Appl. Phys. Lett.* 2006, 88, 43101.

[8]   Wolfgang, B. *Nucl. Instrum. and Meth. B* 2006, *244*, 8.

[9]   Mohanty, T.; Batra, Y.; Tripathi, A. and Kanjilal, D. *J. Nanosci. Nanotechnol.* 2007, *7*, 2036.

[10]   Szenes, G *Phys. Rev. B* 1995, *51*, 8026.

[11]   Kanjilal, D. *Current Science* 2001, *80*,1560.

[12]   Zeigler, J. F.; Biersac, J. P. and Littmark, U. *Stopping and Range of Ions in Solids, Pergamon,* 1985, New York, Vol. 1.

[13]   Thakur, Desai M.; Mohanty, T. *J. Nanosci. Nanotechnol. 2008.*

[14]   Joydeep, D. and Hofmann, H. *Encyclopedia of Nanoscience and Nanotechnology, 2003, 10,* 1.

[15]   Suo, Z. and Lu, W. *J. of Nanoparticle Res.* 2000, *2*, 333.

[16]   Shrinyan, A. S.; and Waautelet *Nanotechnology* 2004, *15*, 1720.

[17]   Aggrawal, S.; Monga, A. P.; Perusse, S. R.; Ramesh, R.; Ballarotto, V.; Williams, E. D.; Chalamala, B. R.; Wei, Y.; Reuss, R. H. *Science* 2000,*287*, 2235.

[18]   Shchukin, V. A.; Ledentsov, N. N. and Bimberg, D. *Physica E* 2001, *9*,140.

D. Ion Beams in Biomaterails and Simulation of Ion Beam Processes

In: Synthesis and Engineering of Nanostructures…   ISBN 978-1-62100-261-1
Editors: Devesh Kumar Avasthi & Jean Claude Pivin   © 2012 Nova Science Publishers, Inc

Chapter 20

EFFECT OF SWIFT HEAVY ION IRRADIATION ON CALCIUM PHOSPHATE BASED BIOCERAMICS

S. Narayana Kalkura[1]
Crystal Growth Centre, Anna University,
Chennai- 600025, India

ABSTRACT

Calcium phosphate based biomaterials have been extensively used to treat bone defects, bone augmentation in arthrodesis, periodontal treatment. Moreover, they are also applied as a coating of metal implants to enhance the biocompatibility and bioactive properties. Almost all hard tissues of humans contain Hydroxyapatite [HAp, $Ca_{10}(PO_4)_6(OH)_2$] as the major inorganic component. The synthetic Hydroxyapatite is highly biocompatible and bioactive with an excellent affinity for natural tissue, which makes it an ideal material for bone and teeth replacement applications. This chapter describes the effect of irradiation of swift heavy ion (SHI), on hydroxyapatite ceramics, synthesized using different routes such as wet chemical, hydrothermal, silica gel, sol-gel and microwave techniques. The irradiated samples were characterized by glancing angle X-ray diffraction (GXRD), atomic force microscopy (AFM) and scanning electron microscopy (SEM). The bioactivity of the samples was tested using simulated body fluids (SBF). There was considerable reduction in particle size on irradiation leading to the formation of nanosized HAp (53 nm). The formation of pores due to irradiation could enable the ingrowths of bone tissues and the circulation of body fluids to improve the implant's biocompatibility and to gain cementless fixation. The irradiated samples exhibited better bioactivity than the pristine HAp. In addition, the samples exhibited enhanced photoluminescence on irradiation.

---

[1]   E-mail: kalkura@annauniv.edu/kalkura@yahoo.com.

1 INTRODUCTION

Hydroxyapatite (HAp,) is the main mineral constituent of bones and teeth. Bone contains carbonated-HAP crystals in the form of plates and needles, which are about 40–60 nm long, 20 nm wide, and 1.5–5 nm thick. Therefore, from the point of view of biocompatibility, synthetically prepared HAp seems to be the most ideal ceramic material for hard tissue replacement implants [1-4]. Implants are widely used in surgery to replace hard tissues such as knee, hip, teeth etc.; however, they are frequently prone to failure due to infection, inflammation and integration problems with the surrounding tissues [5, 6]. In order to overcome this disadvantage modification of the implant surface properties are attempted. HAp coating technology is now being applied widely to improve the longtime performance of prosthetic orthopedic and dental implants. However, HAp thin film coatings have inherent limitation such as poor mechanical strength, weak adhesivity, densification etc. To surmount this problem to a large extent, ion implantations have been used to modify the surface, where the bulk properties of the implant remain unaltered [7, 8]. Already, there are reports on implantation of metal ions on to the metallic biomaterials which hardened the surface and reduced friction. Sagari et.al had reported a reduction in contact angle when irradiated with low energy argon ions on HAp thin films [7]. Hardness and elastic modulus of the HAp films were found to increase when irradiated with N^+ and Ar^+ ions. [8]. There are also reports of low energy irradiation of hydroxyapatite composites [9], ion beam densification of HAp [10], and SHI modification of polymers [11]. Si ion implantation improves densification, hardness and scratch resistance of the films along with an enhancement of bioactivity [12]. Moreover, Apatites (mainly, fluoroapatite and HAp), could be used as matrix for storing nuclear waste elements like Sr, I, Np, Pu, etc. The effect of swift heavy ion irradiation on fluoroapatite pellets was carried out by Miro *et al.,* to explore its potential use for nuclear waste storage [12]. This chapter deals with the SHI irradiation of HAp synthesized by various techniques and their *in vitro* characterization.

2. IRRADIATION DETAILS OF HAP

The method of preparation of HAp plays a significant role in its bulk and surface properties. For this purpose, HAp was prepared using different routes like wet-chemical-hydrothermal (WCH), silica gel (SGM), sol-gel-hydrothermal (SGH), and microwave (MW) treatments [13-15]. Pellets of these HAp powders (8 mm in diameter and about 1 mm in thickness) were subjected to irradiation by oxygen ions of 7^+ charge state, at energy of 100 MeV (fluences 1 x 10^{12}, 1 x 10^{13}, 1 x 10^{14} ions/cm^2, current 4 pnA). Glancing angle X-ray diffraction (GXRD), atomic force microscopy (AFM), photoluminescence spectra (PL), scanning electron microscopy (SEM), dynamic light scattering (DLS), and in vitro bioactivity test using simulated body fluids, were carried out on the irradiated samples.

3. STUDY OF PRISTINE AND IRRADIATED HAP

A summary of the significant results and observations are discussed in this chapter .
Remarkable improvement in crystallinity and reduction in particle size was seen for irradiated samples prepared by SGM, WCH, SGH, MW and SGH. X-ray diffraction patterns

of silicon doped HAp by SGH (sintered to 300 °C), revealed excellent enhancement in crystallinity, when irradiated with a fluence of 1×10^{12} ions/cm^2 (Figure 1 a , b).

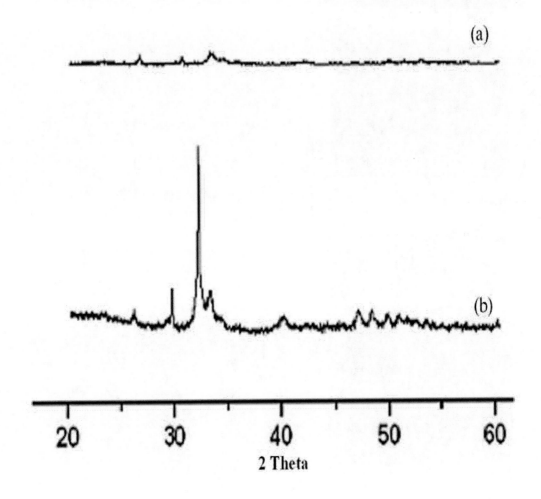

Figure 1. XRD patterns of sintered silicon doped HAp by SGH (a) Pristine and (b) 1×10^{12} ions/cm^2 irradiated samples.

AFM pictures (Figure 2 a,b) of Hap synthesized by WCH, confirmed the reduction in particle size from about 1 μm (pristine) to 53 nm (fluence 1×10^{14} ions/cm^2). Pores were induced in all samples due to irradiation. Their average size was in the range of 4-6 μm. The particle size reduction was also further confirmed by DLS analysis of these samples [13].

Surface analysis by SEM of some of the irradiated samples, revealed considerable changes in their morphology. HAp prepared by microwave method (MW) [14], showed plate-like morphology, when irradiated with a fluence of 1×10^{12} ions/cm^2 (Figure 3). There was also an increase in the aspect ratio of the particles, which would make them more protein adsorbent.

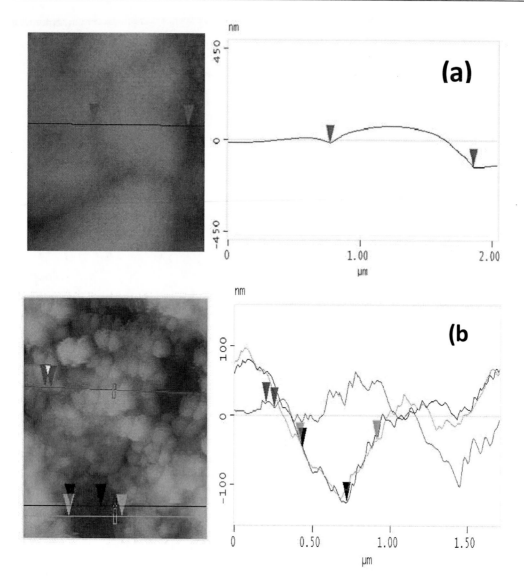

Figure 2. AFM of WCH showing particle size reduction (a) Unirradiated and (b) Irradiated with 100 MeV oxygen ions with a fluence of 1×10^{14} ions/cm^2 irradiated samples.

The bioactivity of the irradiated samples was tested by immersing them in SBF- a synthetically prepared fluid whose ion concentration is nearly equal to that of human blood plasma [15]. In general, when compared to unirradiated samples, all irradiated samples showed better bioactivity, as confirmed by the deposition of HAp on the irradiated surface (Figure 4 a ,b). The microwave treated sample surfaces showed unique bioactivity, forming spherical macro-porous apatite layer, which can enhance osteointegration and osteoconduction (Figure 4a). The formation of macro pores on the surface of the sample indicates the selective dissolution of the irradiated layers; this could lead to the biosorption of the samples *in vivo*. The hydrothermally grown samples irradiated with 10^{13} ions/cm^2 showed better bioactivity compared to pristine samples [13].

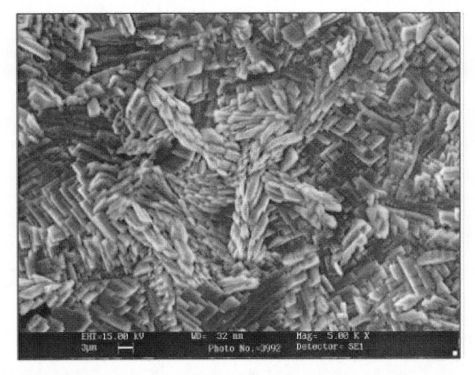

Figure 3. Surface morphology of MW sample after irradiation with 100 MeV oxygen ions with a fluence of 1×10^{12} ions/cm^2. Reprinted from J.Cer.Soc.Jp, Girija, E.K.; Parthiban, S. P.; Suganthi, R.V.; Elayaraja, K.; Kulariya, P.; Katharria, Y.S.; Singh, F.; Sulaniya, I.; Tripathi, A.; Asokan, K.; Kanjilal, D.; Narayana Kalkura, S.: High energy radiation- a tool for enhancing the bioactivity of the Hydroxyapatite: (2008), 116, 320-324, Fig.2b, with permission from the Ceramic Society of Japan.

Ionoluminescence was observed in all samples during irradiation. Presence of phosphorus in HAp is likely to be the origin of ionoluminescence. HAp synthesized by SGM, showed excellent ionoluminescence compared to other samples [16]. Photoluminescence spectra of the samples were analyzed to investigate the luminescent property. The PL spectra showed increase in intensity with an increase in fluence (Figure 5). The band gap energy was found to be 3.52 eV.

Figure 4. HAp deposit on the irradiated surface due to bioactivity; a) macroporous layers on MW, b) SGM after irradiating with a fluence of 1×10^{12} ions/cm^2. The average size of the nucleated HAp is 8 μm. :- Fig.4a is Reprinted from J.Cer.Soc.Jp, Girija, E.K.; Parthiban, S. P.; Suganthi, R.V.; Elayaraja, K.; Kulariya, P.; Katharria, Y.S.; Singh, F.; Sulaniya, I.; Tripathi, A.; Asokan, K.; Kanjilal, D.; Narayana Kalkura, S.: High energy radiation- a tool for enhancing the bioactivity of the Hydroxyapatite: (2008), 116, 320-324, Fig.3c, with permission from the Ceramic Society of Japan.

The enhancement of luminescence could be attributed to the combined effect of emissions from the surface states as well as from the defects caused due to SHI irradiation [17]. Reduction in the particle size and pore formation was observed in all most all the irradiated samples. Reduction in particle size leads to better bioactivity and biocompatibility. The pores formed should facilitate the circulation of physiological fluids and could further assist the cementless fixation of the implants by allowing the bone tissue ingrowths.

The bioactive deposition of the HAp could be explained as follows. The HAp surface has negative surface charges due to hydroxyl (OH^-) and phosphate (PO_4^{3-}) groups on its surface. On immersion, these negative ions attract the positive Ca^{2+} ions from the SBF, thereby forming a layer of positive charge i.e. calcium rich amorphous calcium phosphate (ACP) (Figure 6a). Subequently the Ca-rich ACP interacts with the negative phosphate ions in the SBF to form the Ca-poor ACP (Figure 6b). These processes repeats to form alternative layers of Ca-rich and Ca-poor ACP which lead to the formation of apatite on the surface (Figure 6c). This gradually crystallizes to form a complete layer of bone-like apatite Figure 6d [13].

High energy oxygen ion irradiation has modified the surface morphology of the irradiated HAp samples. Roughness, size of particles, all contribute to the enhanced bioactivity, as they can expose more negative charges to surface, thereby promoting more apatite deposition. Size of particles plays a significant role, because the surface area being high for nanostructures, it can expose more number of charges, which leads to excess apatite formation. The enhanced photoluminescence exhibited by the irradiated samples may possibly be made use of to monitor the bone remodeling and biosensor applications. Hence, high energy irradiations could be used as a tool for making biointeractive HAp with enhanced physical, chemical and biological properties and it is an approach to combine bioactivity and bioresorption of HAp.

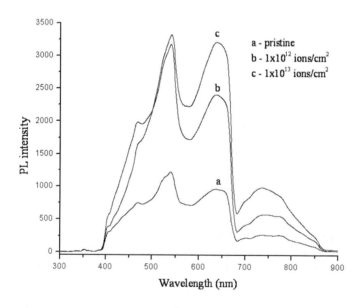

Figure 5. PL spectra of SGM showing increase in intensity with fluence.

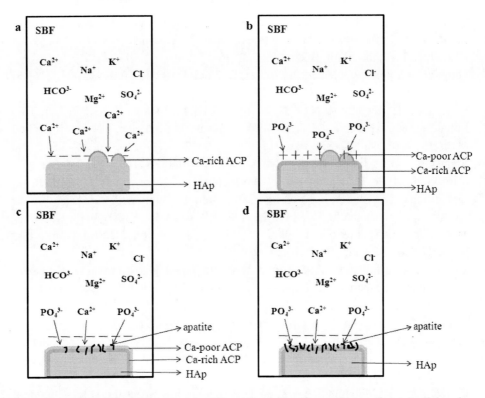

Figure 6. Schematic diagram of the process of formation of apatite on HAp surface. a) calcium ions settle on HAp surface from the SBF to form Ca-rich ACP, b) electropositive HAp surface attracts phosphate groups from SBF to form Ca-poor ACP, c) Ca-poor and Ca-rich ACP eventually crystallizes into apatite and d) ageing produces a complete layer of bone like apatite on the sample surface.

ACKNOWLEDGMENT

This study was supported by Inter University Accelerator Centre, New Delhi, India and also by Department of Science and Technology, New Delhi through Research Project No. SR/SO/HS-05/2005.

REFERENCES

[1]   Ginebra, M.P.; Traykova, T.; Planell, J.A. *J. Cont. Release* 2000, 113, 102–110.

[2]   Woodard, J. R.; Hilldore, A. J.; Lan, S. K.; Park, C.J.; Morgan, A.W.; Eurell, J. A. C.; Clark, S. G.; Wheeler, M. B.; Jamison, R. D.; Johnson, A.J.W. *Biomaterials* 2007, 28, 45–54.

[3]   Kawasaki, T. J. *Chromatography* 1991, 544, 147-184.

[4]   Suchanek, W.; Yoshimura, M. J.Mater.Res. 1998, 13, 94-117.

[5]   Lai, K.A; Shen, WJ; Chen, CH; Yang, CY; Hu, W.P. J. Bone Joint Surg. Br. 2002, 84-B, 641-646.

[6]   Hench, L.L. J.Am.Ceram.Soc. 1991,74, 1487-1510.

[7]   Sagari, A.R.A.; Rahkila, P.; Väisänen, M.; Lehto R.; Sajavaara, T.; Gorelick, S.;
       Laitinen, M.; Putkonen, M.; Sangyuenyongpipat, S.; Timonen, J.; Cheng, S.; Whitlow,
       H. J. Nucl. Instr.and Meth. B 2008, 266, 2515-2519.

[8]   Pelletier, H.; Nelea, V.; Mille, P.; Muller, D. Nucl. Instr.and Meth. B 2004, 216, 269-
       274.

[9]   Suljovrujic, E.; Ignjatovic, N.; Uskokovic, D. Rad. Phy. Chem. 2003, 67, 375–379.

[10]   Lopatin, C.M.; Alford; T.L,. Pizziconi; V.B, Kuan, M.; Laursen, T. Nucl. Instr. and
       Meth. B 1998, 145, 522-531.

[11]   Balanzat, E; Betz, N; Bouffard, S. Nucl. Instr. and Meth. B, 1995, 105, 46-54.

[12]   Miro, S.; Grebille, D.; Chateigner, D.; Pelloquin, D.; Stoquert, J.-P.; Grob, J.-J.;
       Costantini, J.-M.; Studer, F. Nucl. Instr. and Meth. B 2005, 227, 306-318.

[13]   Parthiban, S. P.; Suganthi, R.V.; Girija, E.K.; Elayaraja, K.; Kulariya, P.; Katharria,
       Y.S.; Singh, F.; Sulaniya, I.; Tripathi, A.; Asokan, K.; Kanjilal, D.; Narayana Kalkura,
       S. Nucl. Instr.and Meth. B 2008, 266, 911-917.

[14]   Girija, E.K.; Parthiban, S. P.; Suganthi, R.V.; Elayaraja, K.; Kulariya, P.; Katharria,
       Y.S.; Singh, F.; Sulaniya, I.; Tripathi, A.; Asokan, K.; Kanjilal, D.; Narayana Kalkura,
       S. J.Cer.Soc.Jp 2008, 116, 320-324.

[15]   Kokubo, T.; Takadama, H. Biomaterials 2006, 27, 2907-2915.

[16]   Suganthi, R.V.; Parthiban, S. P.; Elayaraja, K.; Girija, E.K.; Kulariya, P.; Katharria, Y.
       S.; Singh, F.; Asokan, K.; Kanjilal, D.; Narayana Kalkura, S. J. Mater. Sci. - Mater.
       Med. 2009, 20, S271-S275.

[17]   Chowdhury , S.; Mohanta, D.; Ahmed ,G.A.; Dolui, S.K.; Avasthi, D.K.; Choudhury,
       A. J. Lumin. 2005, 114, 95-100.

In: Synthesis and Engineering of Nanostructures…   ISBN 978-1-62100-261-1
Editors: Devesh Kumar Avasthi & Jean Claude Pivin   © 2012 Nova Science Publishers, Inc

Chapter 21

THERMAL SPIKES PRODUCED BY HEAVY IONS IN MEDIA CONTAINING EMBEDDED NANOPARTICLES

J.P. Stoquert
InESS; UMR 7163 CNRS-UsS; BP20; 67037 Strasbourg Cedex 2; France

ABSTRACT

One of the approaches to understand track formation, along ion trajectories relies on the thermal spike model. In slowing down, incident ions transfer progressively their energy to electrons of the irradiated material, elevating mean energy (or temperature). A thermal spike calculation consists in evaluating the evolution in space and time of two interdependent temperatures, characterizing the electronic and lattice subsystems coupled through electron-phonon interactions. Observed nanostructures, induced by the incident ions can be compared in form to calculated temperature spikes.

Until recently, mainly tracks in homogenous media have been studied. In the thermal spike model, amorphous tracks in crystalline insulators are associated with a quench of the molten phase, created around the ion trajectories. Due to the symmetry, in cylindrical space coordinates, coupled heat transfer equations in a 1D (r)-space, have to be considered. The thermodynamic parameters are those of the irradiated bulk material.

During the previous years, heterogeneous media, containing embedded nanoparticles, have been irradiated with energetic ions and unexpected new features have been observed. Trying to understand these new results in the framework of the thermal spike model, necessitates special attention on several new aspects:

1) Two media (bulk and embedded nanoparticle) have to be considered and coupled equations solved in a 2D (r,z)-space for trajectories crossing a nanoparticle.
2) For a given material, thermodynamic properties of nanoparticles can be different from bulk values (melting temperature, latent heat…).
3) Interface effects can modify electron-phonon interactions.

I will describe in detail calculations for spherical metallic nanoparticles in an insulator, illustrated by the cases of Co, Au and Ag nanoparticles in SiO_2. Nanostructures observed, after swift heavy ion irradiation, under various experimental conditions will be compared with theoretical predictions.

1. INTRODUCTION

Swift heavy ion irradiation offers the unique opportunity to investigate phenomena occurring at the nanometric level, at timescales of 10^{-15} to 10^{-9} s (fs to ns). Moreover, with the miniaturization of technologies, it becomes of great practical interest to evaluate the possibilities to fabricate nanostructures, by ion track engineering.

The thermal spike (TS) model has often been used to describe ion tracks in homogeneous media [1,2], where the ion path induces a 1D (r) nanostructure with cylindrical (θ,z) symmetry. Here, an extension of this model is described in the case of embedded nanoparticles, traversed by ion tracks, which needs to consider nanometric objects (~0D) in a 2D (r,z) space with cylindrical (θ) symmetry.

In addition to modeling of track formation and nanostructuring with ion beams or simulations in nuclear waste management, many technological applications need heat treatments of nanosystems, particularly in microelectronic device fabrication. It is therefore necessary to check the limit of applicability of heat transfer equations on nanometric objects, in order to validate their use in calculations, applied to technological systems. In this view, the extreme temperature/time conditions, prevailing during ion tracks formation, constitute an attractive borderline case.

In high energy ion-solid interactions, the nuclear energy loss is negligible compared to the electronic energy loss, and the TS is described by a two-step process: first the ion transfers its energy to electrons, in the vicinity of the ion trajectory. After thermalization by mutual interactions of electrons, an electronic temperature can be defined. In the second step, the electronic subsystem transfers progressively its energy to the atomic subsystem by electron-phonon (e-ph) interactions, generating a fast variation of the atomic temperature, which may affect the local nanostructure.

The TS model has been applied to metals [3], and insulators [4], and no explicit differences between hot electron energy transports were made in the two cases. Effective thermal parameters were used in both cases, and temperature evolution calculated as a function of time in the femtosecond to nanosecond range. A similar approach is applied here to the case of metallic nanoparticles, embedded in an insulating matrix. Numerical applications for Au, Ag and Co nanoparticles, in a silica matrix are presented. As calculated temperatures cannot directly be compared to measurements, a correlation between simulated thermal spikes and observed resulting nanostructures has to be established. The criterion generally admitted is that observed nanostrucures should correspond to calculated melted/vaporized zones.

2. MAIN EQUATIONS AND HYPOTHESIS

According to the thermal spike model, the ion-solid interaction is described by two temperatures, in a two bath system (the two temperature model). Along its rectilinear trajectory, the incident ion transfers energy to the electronic subsystem characterized by the temperature $T_e(\vec{r},t)$ where r is the radial distance from the trajectory and t the time. The electron energy is then transferred to the atomic lattice, characterized by the temperature $T_l(\vec{r},t)$. The evolution of the two subsystems is driven by the two following coupled equations:

$$\rho_e C_e \frac{\partial T_e(\vec{r},t)}{\partial t} = \text{div}\left[K_e \text{grad}(T_e(\vec{r},t))\right] - g(T_e - T_l) + A(\vec{r},t) \tag{1}$$

$$\rho_l C_l \frac{\partial T_l(\vec{r},t)}{\partial t} = \text{div}\left[K_l \text{grad}(T_l(\vec{r},t))\right] + g(T_e - T_l) \tag{2}$$

Where g is the e-ph coupling parameter and $A(\vec{r},t)$, the energy density brought into the electronic subsystem by the incident ion. Other quantities, used in the model are known macroscopic parameters for electrons and atoms: specific heats C_e and C_l, thermal conductivities K_e and K_l, and densities ρ_e and ρ_l, respectively.

Eq. (1) and (2) are valid in a 3D space without symmetry considerations. If we take cylindrical symmetry around the ion trajectory into account, computing times in cylindrical coordinates (r, θ, z) can be largely reduced in two cases:

— angular (θ) and height (z) symmetries. Eq. (1) and (2) reduce in an 1D (r) space to:

$$\rho_e C_e \frac{\partial T_e(r,t)}{\partial t} = \frac{1}{r}\frac{\partial}{\partial r}\left[rK_e(T_e)\frac{\partial T_e}{\partial r}\right] - g(T_e - T_l) + A(r,t) \tag{3}$$

$$\rho_l C_l \frac{\partial T_l(r,t)}{\partial t} = \frac{1}{r}\frac{\partial}{\partial r}\left[rK_l(T_l)\frac{\partial T_l}{\partial r}\right] + g(T_e - T_l) \tag{4}$$

— angular (θ) symmetry only. Eq. (1) and (2) can be written in an 2D (r,z) space:

$$\rho_e C_e \frac{\partial T_e(r,t)}{\partial t} = \frac{1}{r}\frac{\partial}{\partial r}\left[rK_e(T_e)\frac{\partial T_e}{\partial r}\right] + \frac{\partial}{\partial z}\left[K_e(T_e)\frac{\partial T_e}{\partial z}\right] - g(T_e - T_l) + A(r,t) \tag{5}$$

$$\rho_l C_l \frac{\partial T_l(r,t)}{\partial t} = \frac{1}{r}\frac{\partial}{\partial r}\left[rK_l(T_e)\frac{\partial T_l}{\partial r}\right] + \frac{\partial}{\partial z}\left[K_l(T_l)\frac{\partial T_l}{\partial z}\right] + g(T_e - T_l) \tag{6}$$

The first case corresponds to an ion crossing a homogeneous medium. Calculations based on eq. (3) and (4) have been developed by Toulemonde et al. in various type materials.

The second case (Eq. 5 and 6) corresponds, for example to a spherical metallic nanoparticle in an insulating matrix, crossed by an ion along a diameter. These equations will be used in our calculations involving nanoparticles.

By considering some general properties of the equations, one can define several useful parameters in TS calculation. In an uniformly (in space r) excited electronic system at a high temperature Eq. (3) reduces to $\rho_e C_e \dfrac{\partial T_e(r,t)}{\partial t} \approx -gT_e$ and the electronic subsystem relaxes

by e-ph interactions, characterized by a relaxation time $\tau_{e-ph} = \dfrac{\rho_e C_e}{g}$

This e-ph interaction time can be determined by femtosecond laser experiments and is in the range 500-1000 fs for Ag and Au nanoparticles [5], and of a few hundreds of fs in SiO_2 [6].

If one takes C and K as constants, the heat transfer equation becomes $\dfrac{\partial T_e(r,t)}{\partial t} = \dfrac{1}{r}\dfrac{\partial}{\partial r}\left[rD_e(T_e)\dfrac{\partial T_e}{\partial r}\right] - \dfrac{(T_e - T_l)}{\tau} + \dfrac{A(r,t)}{\rho_e C_e}$ which shows the similarity with a

diffusion equation, with diffusivity D_e given by $D_e = \dfrac{K_e}{\rho_e C_e}$. The mean free path λ for e-ph

interaction is $\lambda = \sqrt{D_e \tau}$. Taking electron diffusivities in the range 1-5 $cm^2.s^{-1}$, one deduces e-ph interaction distances of the order of 1-20 nm, depending on the material properties. Meftah et al. [7] obtained a phenomenological relation for several crystalline oxides between λ and the band gap energy: $\lambda = 5.24 + 7.96\exp(-0.782\,E_g)$, where Eg is in eV and λ in nm, corresponding to values from $\lambda \sim 13$ nm for conductors to $\lambda \sim 5$ nm for insulators (3.8 nm for amorphous SiO_2). These considerations on the time and space dimensions of the region involved in the calculation justify, trying to use a thermal spike approach. To this end, the concept of temperature has to be clarified, with respect to the interaction times involved in the energy transfers. The primary scattering interaction between the ion and the electrons is much faster than the femtosecond, but the resulting non thermal energy distribution of the electrons takes a time τ_{therm} to become a Fermi distribution by mutual e-e interactions. Resolution of the general Boltzmann equation, including e-e and e-ph interactions show that τ_{therm} varies from femtoseconds to hundreds of femtoseconds, depending on the energy density of the primary distribution. Interestingly, the thermalization time decreases with increasing primary density [8]. This argument is generally used to justify the application of the two temperature model, by considering electron thermalization times of the order of tens of femtoseconds. However, this point remains somewhat controversial. Moreover, non-thermal energy dissipation has also been described in some cases [5, 9].

We will apply the thermal spike model with the assumptions that:

[91] non-thermal effects can be neglected.
[92] all the incident energy lost by the ion is transferred into the electron Fermi-distribution as described in [2] for 1D spikes, with the same initial energy deposition distribution.

2.1 CALCULATION PARAMETERS

2.1.1 Atomic Subsystem

Lattice specific heat and thermal conductivity depend on the temperature T_l. Data for Ag and Co have been taken from [3] and from [10] for Au and recapitulated in table 1 and 2.

Table 1. Lattice specific heat and thermal conductivity as a function of temperature T_l.

Metal	T_l (K)	C_l (Jg^{-1}K^{-1}) and K$_l$ (W cm^{-1} K^{-1})
Co	300 <T<1500	$C_l = 0.3050 + 3.846e\text{-}4*T_e$
	T>1500	$C_l = 0.88$
	300 <T<T$_m$	$K_l = 2.3\text{-}0.0055*T+6.5e\text{-}6*T^2$ $-3.6e\text{-}9*T^3+7.5e\text{-}13*T^4$
	T>T$_m$	$K_l = 0.42$
Ag	300 <T<T$_m$	$C_l = 0.25\text{-}6.8e\text{-}05*T+5.2e\text{-}08*T^2$
	T>T$_m$	$C_l = 0.28$
	300 <T<T$_m$	$K_l = 3.5+0.0034*T\text{-}3.9e\text{-}06*T^2$
	T$_m$<T<T$_b$	$K_l=1.2+0.00043*T$
	T>T$_m$	$K_l = 2.3$
Au	T>300	$C_l = 0.14$
	300<T<T$_m$	$K_l = \text{-}6.81e\text{-}4*T+3.38$
	T>T$_m$	$K_l=\text{-}1.17e\text{-}4*T+1.45$
SiO$_2$	300<T<T$_m$	$C_l = 0.65 + 3.297e\text{-}04*T$
	T>T$_m$	$C_l = 1.3+\text{-}3.006e\text{-}07*T$
	T>300	$K_l = 1e\text{-}03$

Table 2. Phase transition parameters used in the calculations

	Co	Ag	Au	SiO$_2$
Melting temperature T$_m$ (K)	1768	1235	1337	1950
Boiling temperature T$_b$ (K)	3143	2485	3080	3223
Latent melting heat (J.g-1)	272.5	104.6	64.6	142
Latent boiling heat ($J.g^{-1}$)	6490	2096.8	1675	4715

2.1.2 Electronic Subsystem

For metallic particles, in a first time the bulk values of electronic specific heat and thermal conductivity in metals, are determined as described by Dufour [11].

2.1.3 Electronic Specific Heat ρ_{Ece}:

for $T_e<T_0$: $\rho_{Ece} = \gamma*Te$ with $\gamma = \dfrac{\pi^2 k_B^2}{2E_F}$ where k_B is the Boltzman constant, and E_F the

Fermi energy

for $T_e > T_0$ $$\rho_e C_e = \frac{3}{2} n_e k_B$$

The temperature T_0 is determined by $\gamma T_0 = \frac{3}{2} n_e k_B$.

2.1.4 Electronic Diffusivity De:

at 300 K, the electronic diffusivity and conductivity are related by $D_e = \dfrac{1}{3} \dfrac{v_F^2 m_e}{n_e e^2 \rho}$ where ρ

is the resistivity, m_e the electron mass, n_e the electronic density and e the electron charge . From this relation we deduce $D_e(300)$.

In the second step, we determine D_{emin} from the D_e curve calculated as follows

$$D_e = D_{e0} \phi (\xi)$$

where $\xi = \dfrac{k_B T_e}{E_F}$ and $\Phi(\xi) = \dfrac{z^2}{\xi^2} (\xi^2 + 0.16)^{1/4} \left[\ln(1+z) - \dfrac{z}{1+z} \right]^{-1}$

with $z = \dfrac{2}{3} \left(\dfrac{9\pi}{4} \right)^{4/3} \dfrac{1}{r_s} \sqrt{\left(\xi^2 + 0.16 \right)\left(\xi^2 + \dfrac{4}{9} \right)}$ and $D_{e0} = \dfrac{8}{9\pi} \dfrac{h}{m} = 0.328$ cm^{2}s^{-1}

r_s is the radius of the mean volume around a free electron in Bohr units (a_B=0.529 Å) :

$$\frac{1}{n_e} = \frac{4}{3} \pi (a_B r_s)^3$$

A temperature T_{lim} and a constant k are introduced as:

$T_{lim} = 300 \dfrac{D_e(300)}{D_{emin}}$; $k = 300 D_e(300)$. The variations of the electronic

gas parameter are given in table 3 and 4, where the relation $K_e = \rho_e C_e De$ is used.

Table 3. Variation of electronic parameters with temperature

T_e	300 K - T_{lim}	$T_{lim} - T_0$	$T_0 - 100000$ K
D_e	k/T_e	D_{emin}	D_{emin}
$\rho_e C_e$	γT_e	γT_e	$3/2 n_e k_B$
K_e	γk	$\gamma D_{emin} T_e$	$3/2 n_e k_B D_{emin}$

T

Table 4. Characteristic temperatures (°K), diffusivity (cm^{2}s^{-1}), parameters γ (Jcm^{-3}K^{-2}) and e-ph coupling constant g (W.cm^{-3}.K^{-1}) used in the calculations

	Co	Ag	Au
T_{lim}	2655	20200	15371
T_0	41300	21516	18500
γ	9.1e-5	6.5e-5	6.6e-5
D_{emin}	4.64	3.35	3.36
$D_e(300)$	41.06	240.5	172.2
g	3.3e12	3.5e10	3.0e10

The electron phonon coupling constant can be evaluated as given in ref. [3]. For Au and Ag we have used the same values as Hodak et al. [12] for γ and g.

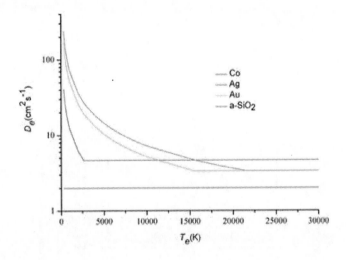

Figure 1. Variation of electronic diffusivity with temperature for metallic nanoparticles of Co, Ag and Au in insulating a-SiO$_2$ matrix.

3. SIMULATION RESULTS FOR THERMAL SPIKE IN Au-SILICA COMPOSITE

The general behaviour is depicted on the case of Au nanoparticles irradiated with 100 MeV Au ions.

3.1 ELECTRONIC SUBSYSTEM

The electronic temperature evolution is illustrated in Figure 2 for diameters of 2 and 8 nm. Isothermal curves correspond to times ranging between 10 fs and 1 ps. We observe that the hottest electrons are in or around the metallic nanoparticles and their lifetime is ~20 ns. The maximum electronic temperature increases with diameter from ~30000K to 60000K.

d=2 nm

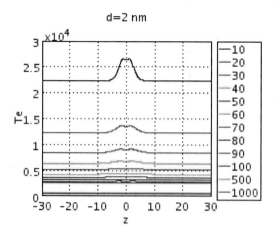

d=8 nm

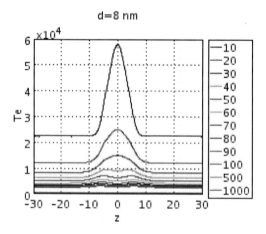

Figure 2. Electronic temperature along the symmetry axis z (ion trajectory) at times between 10 and 1000 fs for Au particles (at z=0) in SiO$_2$. Nanoparticle diameters are 2 and 8 nm, respectively.

3.2 ATOMIC SUBSYSTEM

The general behaviour is illustrated for the case of Au nanoparticles, irradiated with 100 MeV Au ions in Figure 3 for diameter 2 nm and in Figure 4 for 8 nm, respectively. Pictures correspond to snapshots at 0.1, 0.5, 1 and 2 ps, respectively. We observe that the hottest lattice temperature in the insulator is reached after 100 ps, and after 1 ps in the metallic nanoparticle.

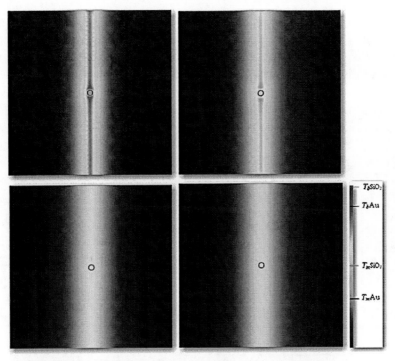

Figure 3. Atomic spike for 100 MeV Au ions in a Au nanoparticle of diameter 2 nm (center of figure) at times 0.1, 0.5, 1 and 2 ps. The temperature scale is 300K (blue) to 3500 K(brown).

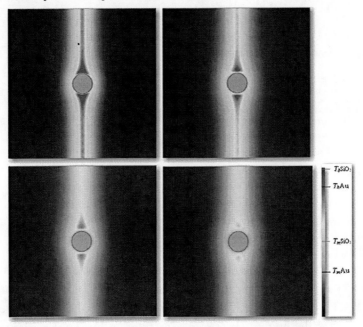

Figure 4. Similar to Figure 3 for nanoparticles of diameter 8 nm. The temperature scale is 300K (blue) to 3500 K(brown).

To follow, in detail, the lattice temperature evolution, we show in Figure 5 the temperature profile along z-axis (ion trajectory), from 1 to 10 ps for nanoparticles with diameters up to 8 nm, in a time-interval corresponding to the beginning of the cooling phase.

We observe that along the beam direction both gold and silica are in molten state for nanoparticles, with diameters smaller than ~6 nm. This corresponds experimentally to nanoparticles, which disappear under ion beam irradiations. So, it is assumed that these nanoparticles are "dissolved" or explode in small strings or atoms. The liberated atoms can contribute to the growth of particles with diameters greater than 6 nm. This ripening phenomena with constant mean metallic fraction is experimentally observed in Au, Ag [||13] or Co [14].

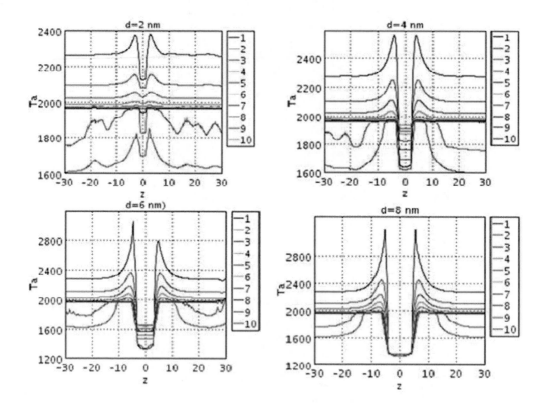

Figure 5. Atomic temperature evolution along the z-axis (ion trajectory) for Au nanoparticles (at z=0) in SiO₂ at times between 1 to 10 ps. Diameters vary from 2 to 8 nm. Oscillations appearing in some cases (9-10 ps for d = 2-4 nm) are attributable to imprecision in numerical calculation.

In Figure 6, we follow the temperature profile along z-axis (ion trajectory), from 10 ps to 1 ns, corresponding to the end of the cooling phase, for particles with diameters greater than 8 nm.

We observe that both gold and silica are in the solid state. Gold remains at its melting temperature from 10 to 30 ps for 8 nm particles, but it cools down faster when the diameter increases. At the beginning (10 ps), the temperature in the silica track is larger than in the nanoparticle, but it cools down faster than the nanoparticle.

For diameters of the order of 10 nm, elongated nanoparticles have been observed for various metallic nanoparticles embedded in silica, as illustrated in Figure 7, by two examples of Ag and Co. This range typically corresponds to diameters for which the nanoparticle remains near the melting time for tens of picoseconds, whereas silica cools down faster. For larger diameters, silica and gold cool down more similarly. It can therefore be suggested that the observed deformations are correlated to differences in volume expansions and/or viscosities which depend strongly on temperature.

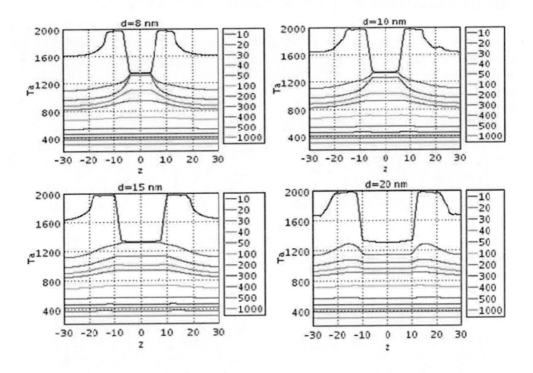

Figure 6. Atomic temperature evolution along the z-axis (ion trajectory) for Au nanoparticles between 10 to 1000 ps. Diameters vary from 8 to 20 nm.

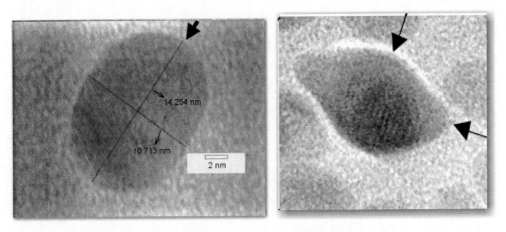

Figure 7. HRTEM micrographs of 120 MeV 3×10^{13} Au ions/cm^2 irradiated Ag nanoparticle. (Thesis F. Singh) and 100 MeV 1×10^{13} I ions/cm^2 irradiated Co nanoparticle (Thesis C.d'Orléans).

3.3 PARTICLE SIZE DEPENDENCE OF THERMAL PARAMETERS

It is well-known that many physical parameters vary from their bulk values when the surface to volume ratio increases. In particular, superheating or supercooling (variation of the melting temperature) or changes in the e-ph coupling have been related. A systematic study of this aspect for all parameters, used in our calculations is beyond the scope of this chapter, and we will limit our discussion to the melting temperature and e-ph coupling for which some data exist for embedded nanoparticles. Our aim is to estimate the influence of the size for small nanoparticles.

3.4 ELECTRON-PHONON COUPLING

Following Hodak et al. [15], the relaxation in Au nanoparticles can be assumed to occur through two different channels: bulk e-ph interaction and electron-surface interactions. The surface e-ph interaction occurs by two different type of surface modes: acoustic and capillary surface modes. The acoustic mode changes the nanoparticle volume, whereas the capillary modes modify the shape, without changing the volume.

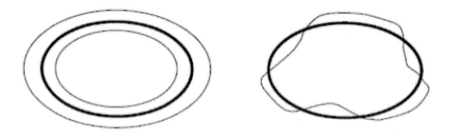

Figure 8. Acoustic (left) and capillary (right) surface modes.

The effective e-ph coupling constant in the nanoparticle is given by:

$$g_{eff} = g_{bulk} + g_C + g_A \tag{7}$$

where the two last terms stand for capillary and acoustic mode coupling terms, respectively. These terms are given by:

$$g_{bulk} = \frac{\pi^4}{18} \frac{(k_B n_e v)^2}{K_e} \tag{8}$$

$$g_C = \frac{3}{16\pi} k_B \frac{v_F}{R} n_e \frac{m_e \omega_l^2}{\sigma} \left(\frac{E_F}{\varphi_0}\right)^2 \tag{9}$$

$$g_A = \frac{1}{16\pi} k_B \frac{v_F}{R^2} n_e \frac{m_e}{\rho_l} \left(\frac{\omega_D}{c_l}\right)^2 \left(\frac{E_F}{\varphi_0}\right)^2 \qquad (10)$$

where v is the speed of sound in the metal given by $v = k_B T_D / \hbar / (6\pi n_a)^{1/3}$ with n_a the atomic number density and T_D the Debye temperature, v_F is the Fermi velocity, R the nanoparticule radius, σ the surface tension, E_F the Femi energy, φ_0 the metal work function and ω_D the Debye frequency. ω_l is given by $\omega_l = \sqrt{\frac{\sigma}{\rho_l} l(l-1)(l+2)}$ and l is the integer part

of $\pi R / d$ where d is the lattice parameter.

The results of the calculations are shown in Figure 9. It can be seen that there is only an effect on the smallest particles (R<2 nm). We have seen that these nanoparticles are in the molten phase and the (small) change of coupling does not affect this result.

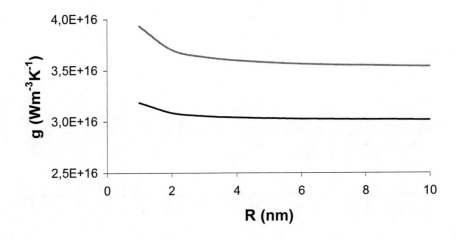

Figure 9. Electron-phonon coupling dependence on the nanoparticule radius for Au and Ag.

3.5 MELTING TEMPERATURE

Anderson and Johnson [16] made a systematic study of metallic nanoparticles of diameters between 1 and 15 nm obtained by ion implantation in Al. All the inclusions showed a melting/solidification hysteresis around the bulk melting temperature, with temperature excursion of the order of +/- 50 K. Castro et al. [17] studied free Ag and Au nanoparticles and observed significant deviations for nanoparticles smaller than 3 nm. For greater particles the variation is linearly deceasing (~10% for 3 nm). As previously, these results indicate that the melting is easier for the smallest radii, but this will not affect the conclusions concerning "dissolution" of the small particles (R<3nm), which are found to be in a molten phase in calculations, with uncorrected bulk parameters.

Comparisons are made in Figure 10, to show the influence of variation of parameters on the calculations with:

bulk parameters (reference)

e-ph coupling constant $g = 4$ Wcm^{-3}K^{-1} instead of 3 Wcm^{-3}K^{-1}. No visible effect is observed

$T_m = 1200$ K instead of 1337 K. At t = 10 ns, the nanoparticle is always in molten phase. As expected, decrease of the melting temperature allows larger particles to be molten.

Electronic energy loss of 52 keV/nm instead of 34.6 keV/nm. Here an increase of temperature allows also melting of larger nanoparticles. If one admits that shape deformation is related to melting, this could be a way to check TS calculations.

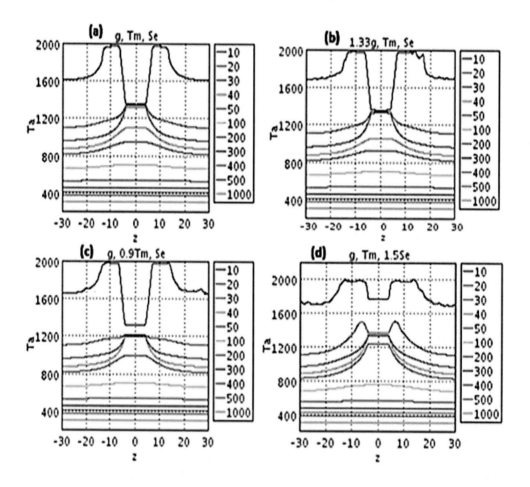

Figure 10. Atomic temperature evolution along the z-axis (ion trajectory) for Au nanoparticles (at z=0) of diameter 8 nm in SiO$_2$, at times between 10 ps to 1 ns: a) bulk parameter, b) e-ph coupling constant multiplied by 1.33, c) melting temperature multiplied by 0.9, d) electronic energy deposition multiplied by 1.5.

CONCLUSION

We have detailed general aspects of 2D TS calculations for metallic nanoparticles embedded in SiO_2. The case of gold nanoparticles has been chosen to illustrate the results, but similar data have been obtained for Ag and Co. Some specific effects related to low dimensional aspects of the problem have also been investigated. Results permit to conclude that such calculations can be applied to nanoparticles, with limitations inherent to the TS model, which are the same in 2D and 1D calculations.

REFERENCES

[1]   Lifshits, I. M.; Kaganov, M. I.; Tanatov, L. V. *J. Nucl. Energy Part A: Reactor Science* 1960, *vol 12*, 69-78.

[2]   Toulemonde, M.; Dufour, C.; Paumier, E. *Phys. Rev. B* 1992, *vol 46*, 14362-14369

[3]   Wang, Z. G.; Dufour, C.; Paumier, E.; Toulemonde, M. *J. Phys. Condens. Matter* 1994, *vol 6*, 6733-6750.

[4]   Toulemonde, M.; Costantini, J. M.; Dufour, C.; Meftah, A.; Paumier, E. ; Studer, F. *Nucl Instr Meth Phys Res B* 1996, *vol 116*, 37-42.

[5]   Groeneveld, R. H. M.; Sprik, R.; Lagendijk, A *Phys. Rev B* 1995, *vol 51,* 11433-11445.

[6]   Toulemonde, M.; Assmann, W.; Dufour, C.; Meftah, A.; Studer, F.; Trautmann, C. *Mat. Fys. Medd. Dan Vid. Selsk.* 2006, *vol 52,* 263-292.

[7]   Meftah, A.; Costantini, J. M.; Khalfaoui, N.; Boudjadar, S.; Stoquert, J. P.; Studer, F. ; Toulemonde, M. *Nucl Instr Meth Phys Res B* 2005, *vol 237,* 563-574.

[8]   Rethfeld, B; Kaiser, A.; Vicanek, M.; Simon, G. *Phys. Rev. B* 2002, *vol 65,* 214303(11p).

[9]   Klaumunzer, S. *Mat. Fys. Medd. Dan Vid. Selsk.* 2006, vol 52, 293-327.

[10]   Awazu, K.; Wang, X.; Fijimaki, M.; Tominaga, J.; Aiba, H.; Ohki, Y. *Phys. Rev. B* 2008, *vol 78*, 54102(8p).

[11]   Dufour, C. *Thesis*; Univ. Caen 1992; Report CEA-R-5638; C. E. A.: Saclay, 1993; 86p.

[12]   Hodak, J. H.; Martini, I.; Hartland, G. V. *J. Phys. Chem. B* 1998, *vol 102*, 6958-6967.

[13]   Singh, F. *Thesis*; Univ. Paris XI Orsay 2007. Fouran Singh; Mohapatra, S.; Stoquert, J. P.; Avasthi, D. K.; Pivin, J. C. *Nucl Instr Meth Phys Res B* 2009, *vol 267*, 936-940.

[14]   D'Orleans, C.; Cerruti, C.; Estournes, C.; Grob, J. J.; Guille, J. L.; Haas, F.; Muller, D.; Richard-Plouet, M.; Stoquert, J. P. *Nucl Instr Meth Phys Res B* 2003, vol 209, 316-322. D'Orleans, C. ; Stoquert, J. P.; Estournes, C.; Cerruti, C.; Grob, J. J.; Guille, J. L.; Haas, F.; Muller, D.; Richard-Plouet, M. *Phys. Rev. B* 2003, *vol 67*, 220101(4p). D'Orleans, C.; Stoquert, J. P.; Estournes, C.; Cerruti, C.; Grob, J. J.; Guille, J. L.; Haas, F.; Muller, D.; Richard-Plouet, M. *Nucl Instr Meth Phys Res B*. 2004, *vol 216,* 372-378.

[15]   Hodak, J. H.; Henglein, A.; Hartland, G. V. *J Chem Phys* 2000, *vol 112*, 5942-5947.

[16]   Anderson, H. H.; Johnson, E. *Nucl Instr Meth Phys Res B* 1995, *vol 106*,480-491.

[17]   Castro, T.; Reifenberger, R.; Choi, E.; Andres, R. P. *Phys.Rev. B* 1990, *vol 42*, 8548-8556.

In: Synthesis and Engineering of Nanostructures…   ISBN 978-1-62100-261-1
Editors: Devesh Kumar Avasthi & Jean Claude Pivin   © 2012 Nova Science Publishers, Inc

Chapter 22

HIGH PERFORMANCE COMPUTING AND SIMULATIONS OF MEV ION-MATTER INTERACTIONS

Sumit Mookerjee

Inter University Accelerator Centre, New Delhi-110067, India

ABSTRACT

Major progress has been made in the understanding of swift ion interactions in matter because of the wide-ranging experiments, the refinement of model frameworks like the thermal spike model and the use of molecular dynamic simulations in the last two decades. There is, however, much to be done to attain the goal of a consistent, comprehensive and predictive computational technique for all kinds of targets at all projectile energies. A major constraint in attaining this goal has been the prohibitively large computing power required to tackle all but the simplest of problems, and even then with simplifying assumptions. This constraint is disappearing with the spread of powerful and much less expensive high performance parallel computing systems, now widely available for research everywhere. One may hope that harnessing these systems to the goal of an all-encompassing description of ion-matter interactions will lead to exciting insights over the next few years.

In the following sections, we explore some of the areas in MeV ion-matter interactions where HPC systems may be put to productive use, and some of the physics and computing challenges to be overcome before we can expect satisfying results. Examples are the processes and systematics of the transfer of projectile electronic energy loss to the bulk material, the study of phase changes, track formation, sputtering, mixing and interface modification for different kinds of ion-target systems, and also the formation of nano-scale features, and the response of nano-materials to MeV ion bombardment.

We also survey the HPC facilities available in India, and discuss the prospect of ion-matter simulations at the upcoming terascale computing facility at IUAC, which will be accessible to research groups across the country.

1. INTRODUCTION

The interaction of swift heavy ions with matter is governed almost entirely by the transfer of the projectile energy to target electrons, and the subsequent transfer of the electronic energy to the target atoms. Unlike at lower incident ion energies in the so-called nuclear collision regime, there are no direct atomic displacements resulting from elastic collisions. This more complex interaction gives rise to many phenomena of interest not observed in low energy ion interactions with matter; it also makes it more difficult to quantitatively model the interaction. Unlike in the nuclear stopping regime, where many approaches including molecular dynamics and binary collision Monte Carlo codes have been highly effective in simulating the effects of the ion-target interaction, a comprehensive, predictive code for swift ion interactions with matter has proved elusive.

The difficulties in precisely modeling MeV ion interactions with matter can be divided into three broad categories. The first is the number and complexity of the processes involved in the energy transfer from projectile to target atoms. Atomic excitation and ionization, electron mobility, screening of atomic charges by electrons, recombination of electrons and ionized atoms, atomic transport mechanisms, and changes in phase and bonding in solid targets, all have a role to play in determining the final observables. A second difficulty arises from the need to appropriately handle the multiple time scales involved. Initial excitation and ionization processes take place at the femtosecond time scale. Interactions between affected target ions and atoms, and the movement and recombination of electrons, occur in the period of tens of femtoseconds to close to a picosecond. Phase changes, sputtering, the formation and movement of shock fronts, and other large-scale changes occur over tens of picoseconds to nanoseconds [1,2]. Experimental measurements are made at times of the order of thousands of seconds after the passage of the ion. And finally, there are multiple length scales to consider as well, from the atomic lengths involved in the first interactions of projectile ions with the target atoms to the micrometer lengths over which the effect of the ion impact finally spreads.

Not surprisingly, full first principle calculations of the interaction of swift ions with solid targets have never been implemented, even though *ab initio* methods have been demonstrated for individual processes, at least for some combinations of projectile and target species. There exists no single framework which includes in a consistent manner *ab initio* calculation methods for all physical processes involved. Even if there were, it is clear that a complete modeling of a single swift ion-target interaction for targets comprising hundreds of thousands of atoms, and for tens or hundreds of picoseconds, would be well beyond the capability of the most powerful computers that exist today.

The most successful calculations of swift ion-matter interactions have instead sought to distribute the projectile energy lost among the electrons of the target along the trajectory of the projectile ion, and then modeled the transfer of energy from these electrons to the atoms of the target. The ionic spike model considers the charges of atoms ionized by the passage of the projectile ion, and seeks to calculate the Coulomb repulsion between these target atoms [3,4]. The transfer of projectile energy to the target atoms is mediated by the electrostatic force generated between these ionized atoms. The screening of the ionic charge by returning electrons is a key parameter in these calculations. The inelastic thermal spike model (referred to in the rest of this work as the i-TS model) assumes the energy lost by the projectile is distributed among the target electrons in a manner that mimics the energy distribution of an electron gas in thermal equilibrium, and focuses on the role of the electron-phonon coupling as the mechanism of energy transfer from the electrons to the atoms of the lattice [5,6]. The electron-lattice energy transfer can then be calculated from heat diffusion equations for the electron gas and the target atoms, coupled by a parameter derived from the electron-phonon coupling. The mobility of the electrons in the target is a critical input.

Once the distribution of energies received by the target atoms from the projectile ion has been established, it is possible to proceed to calculate observable effects of the ion-matter interaction. In the framework of the thermal spike model, the heat diffusion equation for the atomic lattice itself leads to conclusions about temperatures reached. For many systems, observables like track radii and sputtering yields may then be deduced. The track size may be defined [6,7] as the radial zone containing enough energy for melting, and track formation attributed to a rapid quench of the molten phase. Sputtering yields may be determined from the number of particles evaporated from the surface, using the local temperature profiles [8,9]. In the next section, we review some of the results of the thermal spike model for different projectile-target combinations. An alternative and more general approach is that of classical molecular dynamics (MD), which follows the motion of all atoms in the target using Newtonian dynamics and an inter-atomic potential. MD methods have long been used with much success to simulate low energy ion-matter collisions, and more recently to explore various phenomena in the electronic energy loss regime as well. In Section III, we discuss some of the results of MD calculation of swift heavy ion impacts in matter. In these calculations, an assumption has to be made regarding the positions and velocities of target atoms at the start of the MD simulation (the "initial" configuration). This configuration is a function of the target lattice structure or positions of atoms in an amorphous network, and of the energy deposited on the atoms following the passage of the projectile ion. In Section IV, we describe some results from a methodology which combines the i-TS model to obtain the initial configuration, and MD calculations for the subsequent atomic transport. In Section V, we explore some of the gaps in our ability to simulate MeV ion-matter interactions, look at possible directions, and the computing requirement for various computational scenarios. The last section looks at emerging supercomputing trends, and describes the teraflop computing facility coming up at the Inter University Accelerator Centre.

2. THE I-TS MODEL

The inelastic thermal spike model (I-TS) [5,6] has been widely used as a framework to understand the effects of swift ion radiation on matter, especially track formation and sputtering in metals and insulators. Starting from the premise that the electron mobility is a key factor in the transfer of projectile energy to the lattice in the electronic stopping regime, as evidenced by the differing response of metals and insulators to swift ion impact, it includes the electronic and lattice subsystems in the target as two separate but coupled systems. The projectile kinetic energy lost is initially assumed to be dumped entirely on the electronic system, which heats up as a consequence and is expected to thermalize in a time scale of the order of 10^{-15} seconds. The subsequent transfer to the lattice is calculated using coupled classical heat diffusion equations with the electron system as the heat source, and the lattice equilibrium temperature is expected to be reached in about 10^{-13} seconds. The coupling of the equations is related to the strength of the electron-phonon coupling for the target material. The radial spread of the electronic system during the transfer of energy to the lattice is factored in, using results of Monte Carlo simulations of Katz, Waligorski and co-workers [10]. The so-called "velocity effect" is implicitly folded into the calculations through this formalism for radial spread of the electronic system. Key parameters for the i-TS calculations are the electron mobility, thermal conductivity, specific heat and electron-phonon coupling strength.

The thermal parameters of the electronic system for insulators required for this model are an issue, as there are no free electrons. However, following the arguments of Baranov [11] that hot electrons in the conduction band of insulators behave like hot free electrons in metals, these parameters may be derived. The thermal parameters for the lattice system are extracted from experiments. With these provisions, track formation or sputtering have been explored by applying the model to metals (Zr, Ti, Au, Ag, Zn, Fe), oxides (SiO_2, $Y_3Fe_5O_{12}$, $BaFe_{12}O_9$, $Gd_3Ga_5O_{12}$, $LiNbO_3$), and other inorganic insulators (LiF, CaF_2).

After the deposition of energy and the temperature at different regions in the lattice is calculated, further prescriptions are required in the i-TS framework to arrive at observables of interest. The track radius, for instance, is deduced from the radial dimension of the zone in which the temperature exceeds the temperature required for melting. Track radii calculated in this manner for a number of amorphisable insulators show a strong dependence on the value of the electron-phonon coupling used. In most cases, it is possible to find a suitable value of this parameter which fits experimental results over a large range of electronic energy losses and beam velocities. Electronic sputtering yields may be derived from the surface temperatures by calculating local evaporation rates and integrating over time and space. Good agreement with experimental results is found for a number of ion-target combinations. In particular, in the case of SiO_2 for which experimental results for both the track radius and the sputtering yield are available, i-TS calculations of track radius and sputtering yield with the same electron-phonon coupling value match well with experiment [12].

3. CLASSICAL MOLECULAR DYNAMICS

Molecular dynamics (MD) has evolved over the last two decades as a powerful technique to study ion-matter interactions. Recent applications for swift heavy ions include calculations of sputtering in Lennard-Jones solids [13] and in Si [14], defect formation in Si [15], and amorphisation and recrystallization in semiconductor materials [16]. The main input into MD calculations is the inter-atomic potential, which offers the chance to keep the model as close as possible to first principles. The calculation follows the motion of all atoms in the target, and the atom-level information available at all times enables extraction of a wide range of observables with few further assumptions, and offers a predictive power few other approaches can match. The MD framework is also easily extensible; for instance, developments in the prescriptions for force calculations are easy to incorporate, and MD calculations which include electronic forces or DFT-based force calculations are now widely used. With the explosion in available computing power and the development of potentials for a wide range of ion-target combinations, classical molecular dynamics has become a very attractive tool, especially in the nuclear stopping regime.

In the electronic stopping regime, however, the transfer of projectile energy loss to the target atoms is mediated by the target electrons, and a prescription for this in a classical molecular dynamics framework is not obvious. MD calculations therefore often start with an "initial" target configuration in which target atoms close to the projectile ion path are assigned energies derived in some way from the electronic energy loss. One possibility is to define a radial distance around the projectile trajectory which is expected to be affected by the passage of the ion, perhaps from a knowledge or estimate of the track radius. All atoms in this affected zone may then be assigned a fraction of the projectile energy loss; a popular choice has been to calculate an "effective" S_e, and equally distribute this amongst all atoms in the track core. It must be noted, however, that some results are extremely sensitive to the prescription for initial energy deposition, and some caution in choosing the initial configuration is called for.

4. COMBINING I-TS AND MD APPROACHES

The need for more or less arbitrary choices of the distribution of energy deposited on the lattice by the passage of a swift projectile is related to the one major constraint facing all classical MD calculations: that of available computing power. The impact of the projectile ion is seen by target atoms over a large radial distance, extending to several or even tens of nanometers; realistic target sizes for the MD calculation must therefore be of the order of a few hundred thousand atoms, even after using constructs like periodic boundary conditions. The calculations must span several orders of magnitude in time, from the femto-second deposition of energy on the lattice to the tens to hundreds of picoseconds for subsequent atomic transport and observable signals. Inter-atomic potentials are often many body potentials with significant cut-off distances. Coulomb forces add greatly to computing requirements, and are rarely included in this energy regime.

In this scenario, it is clear that first principles calculations of projectile energy loss to target excitation and ionization, the inclusion of electrons in subsequent atomic rearrangements, and finally an *ab initio* calculation of the energy deposition on the lattice in the electronic stopping regime, would be impossible to tackle with the computing power expected to be available even many years in the future. A reasonable prescription for calculating the energy deposition distribution, is, however, necessary: it has been shown that simply changing the radial distribution of deposited energies can change the sputtering yield from a Lennard-Jones solid by more than an order of magnitude. For metals and insulators, such a prescription is provided by the inelastic thermal spike model. The model allows a consistent calculation of the spatial and temporal distribution of the energy deposited on the lattice atoms, and offers the closest agreement so far with experimentally determined track radii for a number of systems. Finally, the i-TS model provides a method to calculate the initial transfer of energy from the electronic system to the lattice, while classical MD calculations detail the subsequent atomic transport; this separation in the time scales addressed is useful in combining the two approaches in one consistent prescription.

In such a prescription, the atoms in the target would receive energy from the electronic system, as well as move in the field of the inter-atomic potential. One implementation of this [17,18], is to calculate the temperatures of the electronic and lattice systems at every radial distance from the projectile trajectory, calculate the transfer of energy to the lattice atoms, and add this energy to the atoms as an isotropic "kick". Other than this addition, a standard classical molecular dynamics calculation is followed. In practice, the "kick" to the lattice atoms because of transfer of energy from the electrons is short-lived, of the order of a few femtoseconds. Significant atomic motion because of the inter-atomic potential appears at a later time, at least a few tens of femtoseconds. An example of a calculation using this prescription is presented in Figure 1. The sputtering yield from a Lennard-Jones solid is seen to change dramatically with a change in the distribution of energy deposition in the lattice. As with a standard MD ion-target calculation, it is possible to extract information on a large number of observables, including track radii and internal track structure [19], sputtering yields and angular distributions, amorphisation and recrystallisation, radial flow and shock fronts, defect production and surface modifications.

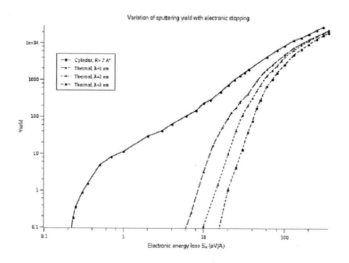

Figure 1. Variation of sputtering yield with electronic stopping power for different distributions of energy deposited on lattice [from ref. 18, Figure 1 in S. Mookerjee, M. Beuve, S. A. Khan, M. Toulemonde, and A. Roy, Phys. Rev. B 78, 045435 (2008). Copyright (2008) American Physical Society].

5. OPEN QUESTIONS AND POSSIBLE DIRECTIONS

Combining the i-TS and MD approaches works around problems associated with the distribution of deposited energies in MD calculations, and the lack of a comprehensive description of atomic transport in i-TS calculations. However, all other theoretical and computational constraints in these approaches remain. For example, the difference in response of amorphisable and non-amorphisable insulators to swift ion irradiation is still not fully understood in the i-TS framework. Neither are anomalous sputtering yields and sputter angular distributions in ionic crystals. The calculation of the energy deposition distribution in inhomogeneous media, or across interfaces in embedded systems, is not obvious in the present i-TS model. For amorphous materials, calculating the initial microscopic atomic structure required by MD calculations is not trivial, and no general prescription exists. Finding the right inter-atomic potential is also non-trivial, especially for compound systems and targets with embedded clusters, and restricts the number of systems for which MD calculations can be performed. Descriptions of electronic structure are currently out of bounds, and no models exist in this energy domain which can describe or predict changes in bonding, valence or magnetism on swift ion irradiation. These are severe constraints, and modeling efforts require to address them.

Promising approaches to deal with some of these problems have been demonstrated in recent work. Efforts are under way to extend the i-TS energy deposition formalism to three dimensions, a requirement to properly deal with interfaces and embedded systems. As calculations for more ion-target combinations become possible, comparisons with experiments are expected to enable fine tuning of the track formation prescriptions to correctly describe both amorphisable and non-amorphisable insulators. Methods to deal with interfaces and embedded systems in classical MD simulations have been proposed [20]. More rigorous force calculations using DFT techniques have been demonstrated in an application to simulate Frenkel defects in Si [15]. A method to fix a realistic initial configuration for amorphous targets has been shown for SiO_2 [21]. Further work along these lines should be expected to result in significant improvement in the scope and accuracy of swift ion-matter simulations.

More work is still required to explore computable potentials for ionic crystals, and to find general methods to generate relaxed initial configurations for amorphous targets. From both applied and fundamental physics standpoints, it is necessary to find a general method, within the i-TS formalism or otherwise, to generate deposited energy distributions, for instance for semiconductors. Given the sensitivity of final results to the radial distribution of energies initially deposited on the lattice, a closer look at the applicability of the Katz-Waligorski formulation for various targets and ion energies is warranted. And finally, a way to include electronic structure and bonding in the simulations is required to be able to simulate creation and response of embedded clusters, and changes in bonding and electronic properties, which constitute some of the most interesting experimental results in swift ion-matter interaction physics. The difficulties, both theoretical and computational, in achieving this last goal appear forbidding at present, but any progress here also promises the most exciting breakthroughs. A possible first goal is to perform *ab initio* runs including excitation, ionization, diffusion and recombination of electrons for very small samples, and scaling the results up for full-sample runs. There are, however, severe computational constraints in achieving even this goal.

6. High Performance Computing in Ion-Matter Simulations

One of the more frustrating aspects of swift ion-matter simulations is the impossibility of trying out some promising theoretical approaches simply because they demand too much computer time. This situation has been mitigated somewhat in recent years with the development of message passing software and fast network hardware, enabling the clustering of relatively cheap general purpose servers to make powerful parallel supercomputers. As a result, price-performance ratios have dropped by more than an order of magnitude compared to traditional shared memory supercomputers, and access to super-computing resources has become easier in many places.

The example of a typical i-TS / MD simulation may be used to demonstrate the scale of the computing requirement for swift ion-matter simulations. The key parameters in determining the computing requirement for a problem are the system size, the nature of the potential, and the number of time steps for which the calculation is run. The required target size is in turn determined by the radial spread of the initial energy deposition on the lattice, and on the farthest atom affected by subsequent atomic transport. In the i-TS formalism, the radial spread of the initial deposition is determined by the S_e, the beam velocity, the electron numbers and mobility, and is typically of the order of a few nanometers. The farthest atom affected by the transport also depends on the S_e, and is of the order of tens of nanometers for an S_e of 1 keV/nm. For larger S_e values, this figure is much higher. Typical target sizes for an i-TS / MD run therefore would be a few hundred thousand to a million atoms.

In an MD calculation where forces on every atom because of every other need to be calculated at every time step, the target size has a dramatic impact on the compute time. The quickest calculations would be for pair potentials, especially if the force drops off sharply enough with distance that only a few neighbouring atoms need to be considered for each force calculation. In practice, though, potentials for real target materials are seldom pair potentials; the Stillinger-Weber and Tersoff potentials and their variants used for a range of materials are cases in point. Cut-off distances too cannot always be kept low without sacrificing accuracy. An especially important instance of this is the Coulomb potential, for which more sophisticated methods like Ewald sums would normally need to be used. Interfaces in the target system add to computational costs, with special care required to be taken to ensure a correct description of potentials across the interface.

Finally, a reasonable description of the energy deposition on the lattice in the i-TS framework requires force calculations at very small time steps for at least about 100 fs. At the other end of the time scale, extraction of observables like sputtering yield requires runs to last for many tens of picoseconds. Studies of the full development of shock fronts at high S_e values require significantly longer runs. The use of adaptive time steps helps to keep the number of force calculations to within the order of 100000.

With properly chosen cut-off distances for the force calculation and adaptive time steps, the wall clock time for a single run for a 400000 atom target, a Lennard-Jones potential, and a S_e of 1 keV/nm is about 3 days on a single 3 GHz Xeon processor. For a Stillinger-Weber potential, the time reaches 20 days. Of the order of 100 runs are required for a calculation of sputtering yield, and of the order of 10000 runs for an angular distribution of sputtered atoms. The computing power of a few thousand processors running efficiently in parallel would therefore be appropriate for a typical i-TS/MD simulation. This works out to about 10 teraflops of compute power. Including Coulomb forces, or DFT force calculations, would increase the compute power required manifold. Clearly, a high performance computing system is a minimum requirement for swift heavy ion simulations.

In the Indian context, a few systems capable of 10-100 teraflops are currently in operation. However, only a 9 TF system at the University of Hyderabad is accessible to users in the general university and research institute system, and the primary mandate for even this system is to support computation for the university's own research programs. A new HPC system is now being set up at the Inter University Accelerator Centre, the purpose of which is to support the ion-matter simulation program of the Centre, and also to serve as an inter-university supercomputing facility to support research in all universities across the country in the areas of materials science, nuclear physics, radiation biology, and atomic and nuclear physics.

In the first phase, the system will consist of a 80-core, 600 gigaflops SMP system with 256 GB of RAM for shared memory applications, and a 96-node, 768-core 9 teraflops Xeon-based MPI cluster with Infiniband interconnect for distributed memory applications. Assuming the very high parallel efficiencies already achieved by some MD codes, the single 400000-atom Lennard-Jones run that takes 3 days on a 3 Ghz PC would take six minutes on the new MPI cluster, and a typical full sputtering yield calculation for a Si target using a Stillinger-Weber potential would take a little more than two days. Reducing statistical errors for angular distribution calculations, though, would still take months! The cluster is expected to be upgraded to a 3200-core system capable of 40 TF peak performance by the end of 2010. With the installation of these systems, it is expected that the immediate computing bottlenecks would to a large extent be removed.

CONCLUSIONS

We review progress made in simulating interactions of MeV ions with a variety of targets, focusing particularly on the inelastic thermal spike model, classical molecular dynamics simulations, and a method combining the two which works around some of the problems associated with either method. We also list some of the major constraints of the existing methods, and recent approaches to tackle them. While the computing power needed to implement these methods for realistic systems remains staggering, the advent of affordable parallel high performance computing clusters would make it possible to calculate at least some observables for realistic ion-target systems. We may therefore expect major progress in the effort to provide more precise and comprehensive calculations of swift ion-matter interactions over the next few years, even though a full *ab initio* calculation would almost certainly stay out of reach.

REFERENCES

[1]   Toulemonde, M.; Assmann, W.; Trautmann, C.; Grüner, F.; Mieskes, H. D.; Kucal, H.; Wang, Z. G. *Nucl. Instrum. Methods Phys. Res. B* 2003, *212*, 346 (2003).

[2]   Jakas, M. M.; Bringa, E. M.; Johnson, R. E. *Phys. Rev. B* 2002, *65*, 165425.

[3]   Fleischer, R. L.; Price, P. B.; Walker R. M. *J. App. Phys.* 1965, *36*, 3645.

[4]   Trautmann, C.; Klaumunzer, S.; Trinkaus, H. *Phys. Rev. Lett.* 2000, *85*, 3648.

[5]   Meftah, A.; Brisard, F.; Costantini, J. M.; Dooryhee, E.; Hage-Ali, M.; Hervieu, M.; Stoquert, J. P.; Studer, F.; Toulemonde, M. *Phys Rev B* 1994, *49*, 12457.

[6]   Wang, Z. G.; Dufour, Ch.; Paumier, E.; Toulemonde, M. *J. Phys. Condens. Matt.* 1994, 6, 6733.

[7]   Meftah, A.; Costantini, J. M.; Khalfaoui, N.; Boudjadar, S.; Stoquert, J. P.; Studer, F.; Toulemonde, M. *Nucl. Instrum. Methods Phys. Res. B,* 2005, *237*, 563.

[8]   Mieskes H. D.; Assmann, W.; Grüner, F.; Kucal, H.; Wang, Z. G.; Toulemonde, M. *Phys. Rev. B* 2003, *67*, 155404.

[9]   Toulemonde, M.; Assmann, W.; Gruner, F.; Trautmann, C. *Phys. Rev. Lett.* 2002, *88*, 057602.

[10] Waligorski, M. P. R.; Hamm, R. N.; Katz, R. *Nucl. Track Radiat. Meas.* 1986 *11*, 309.

[11] Baranov, I. A.; Martynenko, Yu. V.; Tsepelevich, S. O.; Yavlinskii, Yu. N. *Sov. Phys. Usp.* 1988, *31*, *1015*.

[12] Toulemonde, M.; Assmann, W.; Dufour, C.; Meftah, A.; Studer, F.; Trautmann, C. *Matematisk-fysiske Meddelelser* 2006, *52*, 263.

[13] Bringa, E. M.; Johnson, R. E.; Dutkiewitz, L. *Nucl. Instrum. Methods Phys. Res. B* 1999, *152*, 267.

[14] Schwen, D.; Bringa, E. M. *Nucl. Instrum. Methods Phys. Res. B* 2007, *256*, 187.

[15] Holmström, E.; Kuronen, A.; Nordlund, K. *Phys. Rev. B* 2008, *78*, 045202.

[16] Gartner, K.; Weber, B. *Nucl. Instrum. Methods Phys. Res. B* 2001, *180*, 274.

[17] Beuve, M.; Stolterfoht, N.; Toulemonde, M.; Trautmann, C.; Urbassek, H. M. *Phys. Rev. B* 2003, *68*, 125423.

[18] Mookerjee, S.; Beuve, M.; Khan, S. A.; Toulemonde, M.; Roy, A. *Phys. Rev. B* 2008, *78*, 045435.

[19] Kluth, P.; Schnohr, C. S.; Pakarinen, O. H.; Djurabekova, F.; Sprouster, D. J.; Giulian, R.; Ridgway, M. C.; Byrne, A. P.; Trautmann, C.; Cookson, D. J.; Nordlund, K.; Toulemonde, M. *Phys. Rev. Lett.* 2008, *101*, 175503.

[20] Djurabekova, F.; Nordlund, K. *Phys. Rev. B* 2008, *77*, 115325.

[21] von Alfthan, S.; Kuronen, A. and Kaski, K. *Phys. Rev. B* 2003, *68*, 073203.

INDEX

K

L

M

Q

R

T

U

V